AGGRESSIVE
BASKETBALL

AGGRESSIVE BASKETBALL

Robert M. Davis

PARKER PUBLISHING COMPANY, INC.   WEST NYACK, N.Y.

Library of Congress
Catalog Card Number: 69-16925

PRINTED IN THE UNITED STATES OF AMERICA
(BC)

WHAT THIS BOOK OFFERS YOU

This book contains the basis for aggressive basketball boiled down to workable lists of pointers. It contains unique drills for improving team and individual aggressiveness. And it contains a futuristic approach to defenses by condensing defense down to three basic attacks.

Coaches who do not have a carefully organized approach to tournament play will learn one from this book. Those looking for a simplified system to activate pressing defenses will find the answers here. Coaches who often wonder about how hard to drive their teams will find one solution to their problem.

My purpose in these pages is to provoke thought and to present my conception of aggressive basketball.

I recall when my team participated in the Hapoel International Games. Only at the opening ceremonies, as we marched in the stadium at Tel-Aviv, Israel, displaying the Stars and Stripes before 50,000 persons, did I realize that overseas my team was *the* United States Basketball Team. Were they properly prepared, I wondered, and did they have the toughness and pride to best represent our country?

In the final championship game, we had pulled ahead by a small margin. In an effort to dominate the rebounds, the opponent sent in three huge substitutes. The going became progressively rougher under both baskets; the action was aggressive and our rivals were strong and tough. Fortunately, my squad had been prepared by aggressive drills and they were mentally and physically hardened. Their pride and training took charge, they played more aggressively than their opponents, and the United States basketball representative brought home another trophy.

Aggressive basketball means winning basketball. Coaches interested in improving the aggressiveness of their team will profit by studying a basketball program founded on an aggressive philosophy and extended through aggressive drills and play.

Bob Davis

ACKNOWLEDGEMENTS

DR. ROBERT L. MILLS, President of Georgetown College, for his sincere encouragement and continuous support.

MRS. CAROL RAMEY for her guidance, suggestions, and advice.

Special thanks to the great coaches who have contributed so much to my career: ADOLPH F. RUPP, University of Kentucky, for the help and inspiration that he has rendered; HARRY LANCASTER, University of Kentucky, for his many hours of counseling; CAM HENDERSON, Marshall College, for introducing me to basketball; BERNARD "PECK" HICKMAN, University of Louisville, for his helping hands through the years; HOMER "KID" McCOY, Vinson High School, Huntington, West Virginia, my first coach; C. Q. SMITH, Georgetown College, my college coach and close friend; TONY SIMEON, High Point High School, High Point, North Carolina, a real friend who helped me during my first year of coaching; JOHN BILL "BULL" TRIVETT, Pikeville High School, Pikeville, Kentucky, who gave me encouragement and advice when I needed it most, and whose coaching philosophy has helped me through the years; ROBERT LUECKE, Highlands High School, Fort Thomas, Kentucky, for his loyalty and many suggestions; DR. BILLY O. WIREMAN, DAVID "STICK" COTTRELL, HARRY "GIPPY" GRAHAM, and BOBBY JONES, my former assistant coaches who contributed immeasurably to the success of my teams of the past; and LARRY PHILLIPS, my assistant; a man never had a better friend or helper.

My most grateful appreciation goes to the wonderful young men who have played for me during the past 17 years. Without their loyalty, hard work, and undying devotion, I would not have anything to write about.

It is true that behind every man stands a great woman. I have been especially fortunate in this department and have been blessed by having two marvelous women in my life. DOLLY MARTHA WILSON DAVIS, my mother; she inspired my life. JOYCE HUDDLESTON DAVIS, my wife; she has shared my life, the long hours, the hard work, the critical times, the losses, and the joys.

CONTENTS

SYMBOLS USED FOR ILLUSTRATIONS

○   Offensive Player

⊙   Offensive player with ball

X   Defensive player

○———⊣   Offensive screen

○----➤   Air pass

○--↘➤   Bounce pass

○——➤   Offensive player running

○∿∿➤   Offensive player dribbling

○---2--➤   Numbers used to indicate sequence of passes

1

Aggressive Play Wins

Winning coaches are aggressive. Their very nature and their every action depict this attitude. They attack every task in their daily living as if this were the last day on earth. They conduct their basketball practices as if it all had to be done within the next hours. They believe that playing to win is the only way to play basketball.

AGGRESSIVENESS NECESSARY

Unparalleled coaching success has always necessitated aggression. The meek shall not inherit the championship trophies of the basketball world. This does not imply that unfair practices are followed by coaches of championship teams. It does mean that those men who teach rugged, aggressive basketball, where no quarter is asked or given, will generally win more games and more fully develop their players than coaches who do not drive their squad members.

Referring to an aggressive coach now requires a definition of the term *aggressive*—the word defies a simple interpretation. It is also reasonable to assume that everyone will probably use different terms to define the word. Aggressiveness connotes enthusiasm, desire, a strong will to win, confidence, and a special lust for life. An aggressive person is one who will go to any limit to achieve a goal he has set for himself. He possesses an unquenchable thirst for achievement and success. Several outstanding authorities have stated that no one has completely satisfied them on this point: how much heritage will affect aggressiveness and how much it can be changed by altering the physical, social, emotional, and intellectual environment of growing boys. There is room for argument here, I suppose, but not for me. I know that through the years, I have taken some "lambs" and turned them into "tigers." I am thoroughly convinced that my coaching techniques have made many of my players become aggressive men with a passion for success.

3

TWELVE TRAITS WHICH MARK THE
AGGRESSIVE BASKETBALL PLAYER

The best way to define the word *aggressive* as it applies to coaching basketball is to list the personal traits of aggressive players. Through the years, in order to be successful in recruiting high school players, I have developed a checklist for a potentially aggressive player. These traits must be present if a player is to be classified as an aggressive competitor.

He must: (1) be quick and fast, (2) possess a burning desire to win, (3) be rough and tough and have a love for physical contact, (4) be strong in regard to his physical build, (5) possess confidence enough to show, and sometimes even be "cocky," (6) be able to sustain a minor physical injury and continue to play, (7) be reckless and anxious to take chances, (8) be capable of temper explosion, (9) be anxious to go on the floor after loose balls, or make desperation dives into the bleachers after the ball, (10) play his best under pressure situations, (11) possess self-pride, and lastly, (12) be capable of producing results for his action.

TWELVE TRAITS WHICH AGGRESSIVE COACHES POSSESS

There are different traits used to judge aggressive coaches. In an effort to more clearly define aggressiveness, these traits are listed and a coach can check himself. Before listing the characteristics of an aggressive coach, it should be an established fact that *all coaches* possess the following qualities. A coach must be honest, truthful, live by ethical truths, have compassion for all people, and most of all, have a deep belief in the young men who play for him. *Every move he makes must be for the good of his players.* He drives them with only one thing in mind—to make them better men. The aggressive coach (1) is a hard worker (many times working 16 and 18 hours per day), (2) is a stern disciplinarian: one man runs his program and practice schedule, and *he* is the one, (3) is demanding, and will require more physical exertion from every boy on his squad than any normal human being can give, (4) is never satisfied with the technical results obtained and constantly demands improvement, (5) is an avid reader and devotes many hours to clinics and to the study of film, and is not afraid to change with the times, (6) is a fairly hard man in all business dealings, (7) is not worried about public opinion—he never tries to win popularity contests—his players have great respect for him, but do not like him as a pal, (9) does not like weakness and shows little sympathy for chronic injuries, (10) never brags about any of his players until they graduate and then talks about them constantly and has a deep affection for all of them, (11) must despise losers or losing, and (12) is emotional and thrives on action. He must respond to an unusual situation with a tremendous show of action of some nature.

Sometimes the action takes an unusual turn. My team was playing a very important conference game away from home several years ago and had played a miserable first half. As we first entered the visitors' dressing room before the game, I had attempted to hang my overcoat in a locker, and the entire row of lockers had almost fallen over because they were not fastened to the floor. When we went to the dressing room at the half, and after the team was settled, I began raging at a high pitch over their sickening first half play. While stomping by a row of lockers that I though was loose, I decided to kick them over to convince the team of my anger at their miserable performance. I turned and with a great burst of energy kicked the lockers. Much to my sorrow, I had kicked a row of lockers which was sunk in concrete. While I hopped around the locker room nursing a badly broken toe, my squad members turned their heads so I would not see them snicker. This broke the tension, and my very relaxed team returned to the floor, overcame a fifteen point deficit, and went on to win with ease.

Regardless of the action taken by the coach, the squad must know that he is deeply concerned with how they perform. If the coach has made a mistake in his selection of strategy, he must not blame someone else. He should always pay close attention to the game and statistics in order to place blame where it properly belongs.

The aggressive coach must always maintain his sense of humor. He must be capable of laughing at funny things even if they happen to him. He should even create humorous situations whenever possible. Every now and then it is good for the squad to completely break up laughing. The wise coach will select this time to call off practice for the day.

Several years ago I was conducting a rugged practice and was fussing about everything because the practice was not going well. We began to work on a drill which requires the squad to run the full length of the court until they hit twenty shots in a row. They had reached eighteen three times and had missed. On the fourth try, when all squad members were tired and mad, a player missed on shot number twenty, meaning the drill would continue for another five minutes. The center on the squad lost his temper and slammed the ball down on the floor. Just as the ball started to bounce toward the ceiling I yelled, "If that ball comes down, the entire squad will run fifty laps after practice." The ball was thrown so hard that it knocked a piece out of the ceiling and lodged in the attic of the gym. When it did not come down, the squad began to shout and yell for joy. I laughed with them and told them to go on home. Practice was over for the day.

AGGRESSIVE PHILOSOPHY

By reading my philosophy on aggressiveness, the reader can better understand my treatment of this topic. Before trying to understand a technique or a drill used by another coach, it is wise to know why he employs the drill or technique. My experience over the years leads me to this conclusion: *"Winning basketball requires aggressive action."*

Wishing won't make it so. There is no easy road for an aggressive basketball coach to follow. Hard work, tension, long hours, sweat and tears are descriptive terms which consistently characterize aggressive coaches. The logical question might be, "Why should players and coaches be aggressive?" The answer to this question is much more than just to win games. One reason that players and coaches must possess aggressiveness is that if they aspire to be champions, sooner or later they will run into the rugged powerful team that will smash them into the floor unless they are aggressive and have the will to cope with the situation. There will always come the time when the stakes are high and a team is expected to represent its school by winning the big game.

Aggressive basketball means playing to win at all cost within the rules of the game. The basic American philosophy of life is striving for excellence. Excellence in basketball means winning, being the best sport, executing fundamentals with perfection, hustling and out-scrapping the opponent. When a team plays with winning as their ultimate goal, they will always display that extra hustle which causes them consistently to make the big play. It is not luck when a team continues to grab the big rebound, recover the "must" loose ball, and successfully executes a last second play that wins the game. Luck is the culmination of well-formulated plans which each player has aggressively committed himself to carrying out, even at the expense of personal hardship.

It has been said that it takes a big man to be a good loser. This may be true, but I feel that it takes a much *bigger* man to be a good winner. Aggressive coaches have often been condemned by other coaches for placing too much emphasis on winning. The condemners claim that it is not in keeping with the principles of basketball to teach young men to go after loose balls with a reckless attitude, and to rebound and play defense as if it were a case of life and death. These same complainers contend that aggressive coaches have taken the fun out of the game. As far as I am concerned, the real fun in basketball is more nearly realized when winning occurs.

It is difficult for coaches who have never consistently received the championship trophy at the end of a grueling year to understand the thrill that comes to young men when they realize that they have paid an extreme price but have achieved an important goal in their lives. The joy and satisfaction that comes to members of a championship team should be enough to inspire any coach to want this for his players.

Aggressive coaches and players should place the game of basketball first in their *business life* and then devote all of their energy to trying to improve the game by improving themselves. To lose while working 16 hours per day means that more hours will have to be utilized until winning occurs. Several years ago, my team lost a game in which I felt they had displayed an evident lack of aggressiveness. I called a practice the following morning from 4:30 A.M. until 7:30 A.M., from 3:00 P.M. until 6:00 P.M., and again from 8:00 P.M. until 9:30 P.M. This routine continued until the team began to win. They won seven out of the next eight games.

CONTACT BASKETBALL

If non-contact basketball will not produce a winning team, I am for as much contact as the rules will allow. No unfair advantage should be taken of anyone, nor should anything be done which is underhanded or contrary to the basic rules of basketball. However, *a coach must have a thorough knowledge of the rules and take advantage of everything that the rules will allow.* No player should hold, strike, run under a player or commit an act with the expressed intention of hurting another player. There are situations when players will get hurt as a normal phase of the game. When a great offensive player is driving to the basket for a sure crip shot, he should keep his eyes on the basket and drive only with intention to score. If a defensive player is standing in his path and gets hurt, this is one of the hazards of the game. However, if the offensive man runs over the defensive player only with intentions of hurting him, it is foul play and does not belong in the game of basketball. Basketball is not a soft game. Aggressive basketball infers contact and requires a *special breed of man to play it successfully*, one willing to assume the responsibility of receiving physical punishment.

Aggressive contact play is sometimes misunderstood by fans and will often bring down the wrath of passive people who like to see basketball teams stroll out on the court for some nice light exercise. In teaching young boys how to become men willing to stand the stress and tension of winning in adult life, they must be instructed how to win in play.

One night while my team was in Israel participating in the Hapoel International Games, we were practicing on an outdoor court with about 100 people watching us. We started working on our full court press and loose ball drill. The longer we worked, the more aggressive my players became. The crowd murmured on many plays and at one point when a loose ball, which would decide who ran ten laps around the stadium, rolled into the stands, my entire squad went into the stands and ended up in a pile of kicking, thrashing, flailing bodies. It was obvious that the people watching did not agree with our enthusiasm to win. After practice was over, several fans asked me why we played with such toughness and determination. They felt it was not worth the effort to be so reckless. I told them that we worked this hard so we could carry their beautiful trophy back to the United States and put it in our trophy case. I also told them that if a job was worth doing, it was worth doing right. We won the tournament. We had to play some great basketball and work harder than we had worked the entire year. The competition was keen and we had to fight for our lives to beat those scrappy Israeli teams. Some of their fans might have been passive, but their players had not read the same book.

HOW AGGRESSIVE PLAYERS USE THEIR FOULS

Aggressive players will foul more than average players. In order to play aggressively, players *must* foul occasionally. Each player is allowed five fouls which should be used intelligently. They are as much a part of the strategy of the game as any other phase. If an offensive player is scoring consistently, intelligent use of personal fouls may tell the defensive player how to stop the offensive player. Let me hasten to repeat that nothing should be done to deliberately hurt the offensive man, but he must be stopped and if using three or four fouls properly will stop him, then this is intelligent use of fouls. *Never kick a sleeping dog.* If the offensive man is having a bad night and is not hitting, stay away from him and do not waste personal fouls.

It takes an aggressive player to step in front of an opponent and draw a foul at the expense of being knocked down. Players should be taught to stand in front of anyone for a foul shot. In Chapter 6 about defense, there is a drill named "step-in." This is a good drill for teaching boys how to fall and not get hurt. Most boys are a lot tougher than coaches and parents think. They do not mind being knocked down as long as it will enable them to win. Players who will stand in and take physical punishment in order to win are the real champions. Each of my great players of the past has almost been willing to step in front of a "freight train" for two foul shots.

AGGRESSIVE COACHING TACTICS

Most boys are inherently lazy and need an aggressive coach to force them beyond their limits. Many years ago I heard my wise old mother say (as I was complaining about how my high school coach was driving me), "I am thankful for those men and women in my past who demanded the best of my life. I only regret that I did not come in contact with more of them because if enough men and women who cared about my future had driven me, I might have been a greater person."

If players are never taken to "outer limits," it becomes rather obvious that maximum effort has never been realized. There can be no superior growth until absolute extension has been reached. A person can never completely learn to swim in shallow water; sooner or later he must be placed in water over his head. He might sink, but a qualified life guard will pull him out, and a week later he should go back to deep water. Another truism which applies to basketball coaching: if players are not overworked occasionally, the maximum potential of each squad member cannot be uncovered.

An overwhelming desire to win *is* the American way of life, and as long as this philosophy prevails, each young American should be taught *to strive for excellence.* To do only what is expected implies that there is no such thing as progress. Almost every parent wants his child to be a valedictorian, to be president of his class, to make all A's, to play on the first team, and to respect accomplishment. The person going into the operating room for brain surgery wants the doctor with the most skill to perform the operation. The man on trial for his life wants to be defended by a lawyer who has a reputation of winning the majority of his cases. People do not hesitate to put their money in banks which are managed by presidents whose establishments show profits and pay the highest dividends.

With this American philosophy of expecting the best, it would be inconsistent to ask basketball players to settle for anything except winning. If people were not interested in winning, they would not keep score. Winning is not just an important goal in basketball—it is the only goal which should be set.

SUMMARY

In the previous pages an attempt has been made to mention some of the reasons why coaches need to develop a philosophy which embodies the need for aggressive play. The philosophy of the coach will generally dictate the type of play his team will manifest. When a coach firmly believes in aggressive basketball, his teams will display a pressure-packed, ball-hawking style of play. They will usually employ the fast break, the half and full court press, and the man-to-man defense. They will also be known for their scrappy play, their inward toughness, and their desire to do the impossible. These facets of basketball *demand* an aggressive attitude on the part of the participants if success is to be achieved.

Both established and inexperienced coaches constantly search for means of improving their players. Herein, I offer them my proven plan of attack. Make a boy bold, forceful, domineering to the point of hostility; accomplish this by persistently injecting this spirit of aggressiveness into the teaching of the most minute details. Little things are important—mean, tough little things. They develop big, hard men who win.

My way is not for pacifists or the weak of heart. But it works.

2

How to Encourage
Aggressive Play

METHODS FOR DEVELOPING BASIC AGGRESSIVENESS

Any coach can help his players develop aggressiveness if he displays the proper attitude and creates the appropriate environment during his practice sessions. Every drill, chalk talk, or mention of basketball should be described in a language which will convey aggressive ideas. Drills should be given names which encourage aggressive play. An example is naming a rebounding drill the "Blood and Guts Drill" or calling a loose ball drill the "Wampus Cat Drill." The keyhole can be called "No Man's Land." Every offensive and defensive play should be named to convey the idea that some rugged, aggressive action is desired. The aggressive coach should also utilize fear, love, devotion, or any other sound motivating force which will develop his players to their maximum, and in the process will help insure victory.

Awards should be given to squad members who display exceptionally courageous plays. When two players run together violently in an effort to recover a loose ball, the one who recovers the ball should be given a silver dollar or the day off. When a player makes an impossible play, he should be given praise and recognition. All bouquets should be directed toward exceptional efforts, and the idea of going "above and beyond" should be constantly expounded. One hundred per cent should be expected from every squad member; therefore, only one hundred and ten per cent efforts should be praised. Any player can play on a well ankle, but it takes an *aggressive champion* to play on a severely sprained one.

The coach should carry a stop watch with him during practice. All drills and patterns should be timed and these times recorded until the coach knows the exact time a player or team must obtain on each activity in order to win. The pressure of time will improve the speed and quickness essential to the aggressive player.

Players must be given certain freedom in their choice of movements. They must understand that if they take a calculated risk, the coach will not reprimand them. When a rebound falls near the foul line, the aggressive guard knows that if he has a fifty per cent chance of getting the rebound, he can neglect getting back on defense and take a chance to recover the rebound. If the opponent retrieves the rebound and scores, the guard should not be reprimanded if the risk was anywhere near sensible. Aggressive players must be given the freedom to gamble a great deal. They must also be taught the necessity of recovery. Immediate recovery is an indispensable quality of an aggressive player.

My players are always instructed to shoot when they get open in the high percentage area. They know they are at liberty to take the wide open shot regardless of the situation.

In a game against Kirksville Mo. State Teachers' College in the Quincy Tournament, we had the ball with 23 seconds to go and the score was tied. A substitute guard got open at the foul line and missed a shot. Kirksville got the ball but missed their last shot. During the time-out before the first overtime, the player who had taken the shot said, "Coach, I was open and I knew I could hit that shot." I told the boy that if possible we try to keep possession of the ball until less than ten seconds to go in the game before we took the shot. However, he was right to take the shot if he felt that he was completely open. In the last 20 seconds of the first overtime, the same player got another open shot even closer than the first one. He took the shot and missed. During the time-out, I again assured him that he had done the right thing. We were beaten in the second overtime. The boy felt badly after the game and blamed himself for the loss. I asked him if he really believed that the shots he had taken were good shots. His answer was that he felt down deep they were as good as he could possibly get. I then told him he had done the right thing, and that he would be my first substitute under pressure situations the rest of the year. He won three games for us during the remainder of the year by hitting clutch baskets in the waning minutes of the game.

When my team is freezing the ball, regardless of the score, all players are told to use good judgment, but to take open shots close to the basket. We have lost a few games as a result of taking a bad shot, but my statistics prove that we have won more of these games than we have lost. The fact that we never quit shooting also keeps the opponents from double teaming on their press as much as they would like.

A player should never be removed from the game because of a mistake, unless he has disobeyed instructions. Players must know that mistakes will not take them out of the game if they are aggressive and recover fast. Those who continually make mistakes must learn to reduce their errors in practice or "B" games. Any boy who is good enough to enter a varsity game is good enough to be allowed to make a reasonable number of mistakes. If he continues to make excessive mistakes, he should not be on the varsity team.

COMMITTED TO A COURSE OF ACTION

Before a player can develop aggressiveness, he must be completely committed to his task. There must be a burning of bridges, a going beyond the point of no return. Players must know that they cannot turn back. Either they win or lose; they get better or get out. A coach must know his limitation and never place himself in a position where he cannot completely back his play. There cannot be a consolation for a champion. Many coaches, however, will not create a desperation atmosphere in their basketball program because they are concerned about what will happen to a boy when he fails while doing his best. This is a nice comfortable argument for those who fear failure. A boy will never fail when he does his best. He might have a temporary setback, but when the going gets tough, the tough get going. If a player with an aggressive attitude fails to do something the 100th time, he will try much harder the next 100 times.

John Lykins, one of my former players, proved to me what a person can accomplish when he is completely committed to a course of action. Georgetown had wrapped up the regular season conference championship and was playing a conference school on their home court for the last regular season game before the conference tournament. John had been assigned to guard the opponent's leading scorer, an all-conference player. The boy tallied 38 points and helped his team defeat Georgetown. In the dressing room after the game, my squad was quiet and very unhappy about the defeat. John stepped into the middle of the floor and asked me if he could guard the same boy when Georgetown met this team in the first round of the conference tournament the following week. The pairings had already been announced. With tears in his eyes he said, "I want to guard this boy again, and I'll promise the entire squad that if he scores more than ten points against me, I'll walk the fifty miles back to Georgetown." I let John guard this boy when we played the next week. When John left the game late in the fourth quarter, we led by twenty-five points, and his man had scored a scant six points. *As a man believes in his heart so is he.*

INDIVIDUAL CONFIDENCE

Confidence is one of the magic words used when describing an aggressive, championship player. Coaches must develop confidence in their players. Every time one of my players takes a shot he is instructed to yell, "Two, baby." A good shooter knows that each time he shoots, the ball is going in. Sometimes the basket moves or the ball swells, but the aggressive player shoots with sureness, calls out, "Two, baby," and then follows his rebound like a longtailed nervous cat in a roomful of rocking chairs.

Many times during practice it is a good idea to stop scrimmage and ask for a volunteer to shoot two foul shots to see whether the entire squad runs five laps or not. If the volunteer hits two shots (with the entire squad earnestly pulling for him), the squad does not run. If he misses, the squad (as they run) angrily ask him why he volunteered.

In Kentucky during the past few years, there have been many All-American basketball players who were great shooters. Some of these were the members of the "Fabulous Five" of the University of Kentucky, Cliff Hagen, Frank Ramsey, Cotton Nash, Pat Riley, also of U. of K., "King" Kelly Coleman of Kentucky Wesleyan, and others. However, the state's leading and second place college career scorers played for me at Georgetown. Dick Vories had a career total of 2,968 for the first place, and second place belongs to Cecil Tuttle with 2,340 points. These two boys had as much confidence in their shooting ability as any two players could have. Another player with exceptional confidence who played for me was Charles Grote, Little All-American for two years. Charlie never said he was going to take a shot. He always said, "Give me the ball and I'll *hit* one." He used to say to the team, "If you get in any trouble, give me the ball and get back for defense."

My team was playing the University of Louisville (the year Louisville went to the semifinals in the N.C.A.A. Tournament), and Charlie missed six shots in a row. I called a time out to point this fact out to him. He came to the huddle grinning from ear to ear, and, before I had a chance to speak, said, "Hot dog, boys, I've missed six shots in a row and I'm hitting 50 per cent for the year. This means I'm due to hit the next six shots. Keep feeding me." I didn't say anything because of the confidence that Charlie had in his voice. He hit the next seven shots he took and went on to score 28 points and help us defeat the University of Louisville.

Another year we were in the semi-finals of the N.A.I.A. Tournament at Kansas City, Missouri, against undefeated Western Illinois. Charlie missed his first seven shots. I called for a time out, and not wanting to embarrass Charlie, I called him to the side and asked him to let the other squad members shoot for a while. He whispered in my ear, "I can't trust them, they might miss." Through the years I have seen other great shooters, and every one has been aggressively confident.

TEAM UNITY AND CONFIDENCE

Aggressiveness is needed by the entire team. A coach can do many things to help his team develop an aggressive attitude. In order to do this the team must be placed under conditions which demand aggressive action. It is easier to get aggressive play when pressing or fast breaking because under these conditions a player is allowed to try to outdo the other members of the squad, and this induces competition among teammates.

Shooting relays should be used during daily practices. At the beginning of each week the co-captains choose their relay teams. The last two boys chosen should be expected to stay 15 minutes after practice every day during that week to improve their shooting. When the shooting relays are finished, the winning team should be allowed to sit in the stands and tease the losing team while they work for a few minutes on a very strenuous defensive drill.

During practice sessions there should be many situations in which one group or team will win and another lose. The winners should always be given a rest while the losers perform some strenuous tasks. In order for a team to become aggressive, each player must be aggressive in regard to the task at hand. Any time one member of a team makes a mistake or fails to accomplish something, his entire team should be given the same punishment. After a while the other boys on the team will encourage the offender to become more aggressive in his efforts.

There should be two environments on the practice floor. One should be very peaceful, enjoyable, and pleasant (for winners only). The other should be obnoxious, disagreeable, and miserable (for losers only). When a boy practices and plays aggressively, he should be in the "wonderful world of winners." When he fails to be aggressive, he should be placed in the "world down under," or loser's world.

Team confidence can best be developed by selecting the first five as soon as possible and building them into a unit of "five brothers." It is wise to select the first team after two or three weeks of practice, or at least two or three weeks before the first game. Care should be taken in selecting the starting unit and the coach should stick with this unit for the remainder of the year. Occasionally an injury or some unusual event might occur to alter the first team. Once the first team is selected, they are treated with more respect than the remainder of the squad. The first unit should be given time off near the end of a rugged practice or should occasionally be allowed to skip sprints or some really hard drill. These boys are "number one" and should be treated with more kindness than the rest of the squad. The rest of the squad will soon strive to become members of this "select group." The first unit learns early that they are the best and know they have to prove it every day. Once they develop a confident attitude, they become champions.

Several years ago my team was playing Western Carolina College at Cullowhee, North Carolina. Western had a fine club and had won their last five games, scoring over 100 points per contest. My team was having a bad night and couldn't get going. I called a time out with ten minutes left in the game. Western was ahead of us by 19 points, 87–68, and three of my first five had four fouls. During the time out I was informing my team of the odor of the gym which had been caused by their rotten play and was pointing out some of their other shortcomings. The opposing crowd began to stomp on the bleachers and chant, "We want 100." Kent Mosley, a fiery little guard on my squad, had been playing a very nonchalant and uninspired game. All of a sudden, he broke from our huddle, charged out in front of the stands, and yelled to the crowd, "OK, you want to see 100 points, get your pencils and pads ready and we'll give you one to write in your memoirs." He returned to our huddle with tears in his eyes and screamed, "Come on, champs! Let's show them what we're really made of!" The team broke from the huddle in a full court press, and before Western had advanced the ball across mid-court, my team had scored ten points and were within nine of them. We went on to beat Western 106 to 97. A superior team spirit, with confidence in their ability to win, turned the tide.

One of my teams posted a 27–3 win-loss record and became the winningest team that I have ever coached. They did not believe that anyone could beat them and were aggressive enough to fight to the last second. We were playing our last regular season game against David-Lipscomb of Nashville, Tennessee. David-Lipscomb was experiencing the best year in the history of the school. They had already won 19 games, a school record, and needed only their last game to become a 20 game winner. This was their last home game, and the school had sponsored a huge pep rally during the day. When tip-off time came, the gym was filled with the largest crowd ever to attend a basketball game on their campus. Their team was inspired and was playing flawless basketball. They were rebounding, shooting, and executing their fundamentals in a spotless manner that was bringing many accolades from the crowd.

When we went to the dressing room at the half, we were behind by six points. As soon as the team was settled in the dressing room and before I had started my half-time rundown, David Lee, the captain of my team said, "Don't worry about this team, coach. They're playing far above their heads and can't keep up this pace. When they get back to normal and make a couple of errors, we'll convert them into baskets and go on to win." When he spoke, he seemed to be saying what the entire team was thinking. These players felt their confidence and knew their capacity. We went on to win the game after a hard fought second half in which several of David-Lipscomb's mistakes were converted into winning baskets by a team that believed in their hearts that they were going to win.

Naturally, all of my teams have not developed this confidence because they have been composed of different individuals and have been harder to reach. However, these examples have given me encouragement, and I constantly search for the right combination of players and drills to reproduce the attitude that these champions had. *The one constant that appears in the practice schedules of the past is that the first team remained intact for the entire year during each of these great years.*

By selecting the first unit early and allowing them to work together, they develop a unity and a "sense of feel" which allows them to make unusual plays. They also develop a balance which gives them the edge on their opponents. They know where their teammates are on the fast break and on defense. They recognize voices quicker, and understand timing and characteristics of individual team members. Having this advantage of unity over the opponent is good therapy, as it breeds confidence and aggressiveness. Players who know where their teammates are never have to hesitate. They can commit themselves immediately to a task because they know they are covered. Before a player can become extremely aggressive, he has to remove all fears from his mind.

FEAR AS A COACHING FACTOR

Fear as a psychological and emotional human characteristic can affect a person in many ways. Those fears that affect basketball players are the ones that coaches need to recognize. Fear of making a mistake, of being out of position, of contact or chance of personal injury, and of diving on the floor can become deterrent factors which will prevent players from developing an aggressive attitude if not properly dealt with. Many years ago, I read a Latin phrase, "Arripe jugulo timorem priusquam te strangulat." The translation of this phrase into English is, "Grasp fear by the throat before it strangles you." The message here is quite clear. Face up to your fears and learn by practice to overcome them. Everyone has probably heard the old adage about riding a horse. If a horse throws you, get back on the horse immediately and prove that this fear can be overcome. The same thing is true in basketball.

The best way to remove personal fear from basketball players is to create an environment where they must face their fears, learning to understand them enough to either completely overcome them or discover how to live with them. Secondly, form an atmosphere that will tend to remove the prospect of fear. Team unity and confidence in one's ability are two tremendous factors for removing fear from players.

An example of how fear will affect a player occurs when he is shooting and his coach reprimands him. I was scouting a basketball game several years ago, and every time a player on that team started to take a shot that his coach didn't want, the coach yelled, "No!" Without exception, the player froze and it seemed impossible for him to get the ball out of his fingers. Of course, when we played this team we yelled "No!" on all of their long shots. Maybe it was our defense, but their team hit a miserable 29 per cent against us, and we beat a good team rather handily.

SUMMARY

Coaches are charged with the responsibility of creating practice and playing environments which encourage and develop aggressiveness. Anything which creates pressure and requires overextension by players will generally develop an aggressive attitude. Winning depends on the frame of mind of the players, and *practice* (under the proper conditions) makes *perfect*.

3

Conditioning

INCREASING PHYSICAL FITNESS

The heights of winning can only be reached by climbing an intelligently organized ladder. *The first rung of this ladder must be physical conditioning.* The second should be fundamental movements and skills, the third offensive and defensive skills, etc., all the way up to high level game strategy. A basketball player must walk before he runs, and run, and run, and run before he competes for the championship. *The hallmark of an aggressive team is its always superior physical condition.* These are the teams whose players dash onto the court before the game, scrap and hustle during the game, and sprint off the court after the game.

Recent research concerning the development of power by various isotonic and isometric techniques has focused a new emphasis back on the need of strength for athletic excellence. Volumes of written material and many research programs conducted during the past few years deal with increasing physical fitness. *Condition* may be defined as the physical ability to expend energy over an extended period of time. A person in superb condition can delay muscular fatigue and has the ability to recuperate rapidly following strenuous exercise. Proper physical conditioning for basketball players requires a high level of physical fitness, which implies increased muscular strength and endurance. There are other aspects of condition which must be improved, such as general motor ability and mental, emotional, and psychological conditioning. However, before each of these can be improved, an advanced degree of physical fitness must be present as a firm foundation.

Most coaches do not have an opportunity to select their players and, therefore, have very little control over the size, speed, jumping ability, and natural aptitude of their squad members. However, a coach can offer no acceptable excuse when his team is not in superior physical condition. Many inexperienced coaches do not understand the limits to which players must be driven if they are to reach peak physical condition. *"If a player is physically sound, it is impossible to run him to death or cause him any cardiovascular damage."*[1] Many winning coaches I

---

[1]H. C. Carlson, "Basketball Research in Fatigue," 1956. (Mimeographed)

have observed conduct long, hard practice periods. I have, myself, held four hour practices and at the conclusion of these sessions had the squad alternate running steps and sprints for half an hour. Practice periods of this intensity cannot be executed sequentially, but they can be conducted much more often than many coaches realize.

TRAINING RULES

Conditioning off the playing court depends primarily on the personal training habits of squad members. *Moderation in living* and the problem of training for basketball is practically solved. The sensible coach will not burden himself with a multitude of training rules. Regulations should be simple and realistic. Squad members should accept this principle: *All players have individual freedoms, but are not free to commit acts which are detrimental to the well-being of other squad members.* This simply means that bad training habits will affect other players on the squad, and this should not be tolerated.

There is no foolproof way to handle the headache of training rules. The most logical approach to this problem is to establish some basic concepts and stick with them. Two general principles regarding the administration of training rules are: (1) establish rules and use a graduated punishment system. The first time an offender is caught, the penalty should be 50 laps. The second offense carries with it 100 laps and no play for one week. The third time means suspension from the squad. Some coaches allow the squad members to vote on the punishment and suspension period; however, I do not follow this practice. (2) Another method of enforcement is simply to suspend the offenders as caught.

The enforcement used must remain fair and realistic. A coach should not make a rule prohibiting smoking and then turn his head when he sees a star smoking. No one will be deceived except the coach. There is also an adage which is very apropos—don't cut off your nose to spite your face. The meaning here is simply do not make insignificant rules which might be easily broken. It could cost a team a winning season by carelessly expelling a player who might have changed his attitude and helped the team. Following are the training rules I use for *College players*:

(1) Absolutely no drinking.

(2) Reduce smoking during the season and never smoke in public.
    If a boy has already acquired the habit, he should only smoke

in his room. If he is seen smoking in public places, public opinion will hurt the school, the coach, the squad members, and the athlete.

(3) Get from eight to ten hours of sleep per night.

(4) Do not overeat, and refrain from eating greasy foods during the season.

(5) Each boy should check with the coach or trainers at the first sign of sickness. This will protect the player and the other squad members.

(6) Report all injuries immediately.

(7) Think like a winner. Small goals do not challenge champions.

A team cannot win the championship unless all players are well conditioned. The most important prerequisite to conditioning is that squad members live by the established training rules. Every boy on the squad represents a different problem, but it is important to remember that the welfare of the team is larger than the individual whims of one member. The coach is in charge, he runs the squad, he is the ultimate recipient of the blame when the squad fails.

PHASES OF CONDITIONING

Basketball conditioning readily divides itself into three phases: preseason, early season, and late season. Preseason conditioning programs can be organized in various ways. Several preliminary activities are: weight training, cross country running, running steps with and without weight belts, and individual work such as one-on-one, two-on-two, and three-on-three. Early season conditioning deals with the exercises, agility drills, and basic fundamental drills, specifically designed to contribute greatly to conditioning. Once the season is well under way, conditioning should become a by-product of a technical improvement with the exception of post practice sprints, the Bunn Technique or step running. Late season conditioning should involve the basic phases of the game such as the fast break, offense, defense, and pressing and freezing to improve physical conditioning. The remainder of this chapter will be devoted to elaborating upon preseason, early season, and late season conditioning.

PRESEASON CONDITIONING

Preseason conditioning programs should start in March as soon as the State Basketball Tournament has been completed. This is the time to begin long range programs for increasing muscular strength and weight. Before any boy begins a program to improve weight or strength, the team physician must examine the boy and advise the coach as to the most effective program. Once the program has been approved by the coach and the team physician, the work can begin. Players are not able to see immediate improvement and tend to lose interest unless a rigid schedule is imposed at first, and maintained until the program becomes routine.

Preseason or off-season work should not require a great deal of time. Four hourly workouts per week are sufficient. Monday and Friday should involve intense weight work utilizing isometric and isotonic exercises. Tuesday and Thursday should include agility drills, rope jumping, reaction drills, karate, wresting, handball, boxing (each participant should be completely protected by head gear and mouth piece, and should use 16 ounce gloves with the emphasis on defensive boxing), gymnastics, trampoline, and running.

Players should be encouraged to continue as much of the off-season program as possible throughout the summer months. My players are allowed to substitute summer vacation activities for any of the Tuesday and Thursday workouts. Bicycle riding, hiking, swimming, water skiing, tennis, and similar activities are very beneficial.

During the last week of the regular school year, all squad members should be weighed. Their pulse rate should also be taken after a prescribed step test. This same procedure should be repeated the day they return to school in the fall, and again during the first day of the regular season practice.

The overweight boys should be expected to report to fall practice lighter, and the underweight ones should report heavier. There will be a marked difference in the conditioning of the boys who report to fall practice with a decreased pulse rate over that of the spring testing. Squad members who have a low pulse rate will be in better physical condition, and their endurance will be much greater than the squad members with the high pulse rates.

The reporting weights established for the overweight squad members should either be reached before the first early season practice, or the overweights should be expected to continue dieting and running steps or sprints after practice until the established minimums have been reached.

Available research concerning nutrition and the value of certain dietary supplements can be helpful in determining which products are best for given individuals. Boys needing weight should be advised to eat one portion per day of a food supplement (Nutriment, Metrecal, Knox-Gelatin, and similar products). They should also be encouraged to eat extra helpings of food and to drink milk shakes at a time when it will not affect their appetites for regular meals.

EARLY SEASON CONDITIONING

Early season conditioning must be started at a rather slow pace. The first accomplishments should be the toughening of the feet and the removal of muscular soreness. This generally takes a week or ten days. Blisters and muscle soreness can be reduced by using properly fitted shoes and socks. Tuf-Skin and powder will also help control blisters. If blisters do occur, they should be opened and the area cleaned thoroughly and covered with a lubricant. A gauze pad should be placed over the lubricant and the entire area taped. This will hold the coating of lubricant over the blister to reduce the friction *during practice that day*. No player should be excused from regular practice periods because of blisters.

The Exer-Genie[2] exerciser or (similar aid) should be used for a series of exercises, then shooting practice begins. Following shooting drill, a full court fast break or similar drill which requires ample running should be used. Early drills are designed to have rather long lines. This way a player does not have to run the drill too often. As the season progresses, drills involving more and more men are used, and the time in line is reduced. All early season conditioning drills are found in the last portion of this chapter.

The main point to remember concerning early season conditioning is to begin slowly and gradually work up to an overextension. At the conclusion of early season conditioning, the squad should be looking forward to games as a day of rest. Games are only 40 minutes long, and the squad should be capable of playing two continuous games under regulation conditions before they open the season, or at least by the 10th of December. The progress of the squad will vary due to experience, injury, etc.

The past several years I have scheduled two scrimmages for the same day during the week preceding our opening game. The first scrimmage is started at 6:00 P.M. and the second one at 8:00 P.M. Both opponents are either equivalent or superior to my team. These are regulation games

[2] Exer-Genie, Inc., Fullerton, California. Copyright, 1964.

with a clock, scorekeeper, and officials. Just to keep things honest, there are sprints and step running assigned if we happen to lose either of these scrimmage games!

LATE SEASON CONDITIONING

Late season refers to the "stretch drive" and the tournament. The time of year when late season begins varies, but it is usually around the 15th of January. At this time of year, squad members tend to become weary, and many innovations must be made in the practice schedule to revive competitiveness. The type of season a team is having will affect the attitude of the squad members. Regardless of the attitude, there are still procedures that must be followed in order to maintain and improve conditioning. If the team is winning and spirit and aggressiveness is running high, only drills which will maintain status quo should be used. The losing team's pace must be increased, and the squad pressed into intense drills aimed at winning the post-season tournament.

Staleness is only a state of mind and should never deter or reduce practice time. I have been faced with staleness only once in my coaching career, and that was during my third year as a head coach. My team was having a better than average year and was in second place in the conference standings. They began to show signs of disinterest. Shooting percentages took a dip, and mistakes began to mount. I reduced practice periods and removed strenuous drills from the practice schedule, but this did not solve the problem and the team became progressively hapless. Finally, I decided to correct the situation by doubling practice periods. For a week we practiced from 3:15 P.M. until 6:00 P.M. and again from 7:30 P.M. until 9:30 P.M. Our aggressiveness picked up considerably, and we began to win by comfortable margins.

CONDITIONING DRILLS

Bunn Technique

One of the best pre and early season conditioning drills is the Bunn Technique.[3] This method is recommended as a means of increasing the

[3]John W. Bunn, *The Basketball Coach*, (Englewood Cliffs: Prentice-Hall, 1961), pp. 75–78; cf. Robert M. Davis, "A Comparison of Three Approaches to Increasing Physical Fitness in Students of Low Fitness," unpublished D.ED Dissertation, George Peabody College for Teachers, 1963, for a statistical study of the effectiveness of this technique.

physical fitness of basketball players. It must be conducted after practice because it is extremely fatiguing. The technique consists of pushups, situps, and the Carlson Spot Run Technique.[4] The distinguishing feature of the Bunn Technique is that the exercises are not done in cadence but at maximum physical exertion for a definite period, completing a prescribed number in a given time.

For the pushups and situps, the squad is divided into pairs and each partner aids and counts for the other. Pushups are performed on the fingertips for a period of thirty seconds. The chin has to touch and the elbows lock on each pushup. A standard of 25 in 30 seconds is established. Situps are performed in the usual manner with hands clasped behind the head. Legs are kept straight and feet are held by a partner. The elbows are extended to knees in an alternated pattern. This exercise is executed for two minutes at maximum exertion. A standard of 90 situps is the goal.

The Carlson Spot Run Technique consists of running in place for ten seconds with a ten-second rest. This is repeated ten times. Feet are raised just high enough to clear the floor. The cadence is as rapid as the subjects can move. A standard of 80 steps per ten seconds should be sustained for the duration of the ten repetitions. The only way to count the number of steps is to count the number of times the right foot hits the floor and then multiply by two.

Isotonic Exercises

The most effective exercises to use in athletics are isotonic exercises. *Isotonic* means muscular action with the muscle under tension. Stress or tension will develop muscular strength much faster than exercising without tension. The Exer-Genie exerciser is a convenient, inexpensive coaching aid for developing muscle strength. Below are the Exer-Genie exercises I use:

THE BIG FOUR

Here are some of the best combination isometric and isotonic exercises. These four important weight training exercises would involve a great deal of weight changing and approximately seven minutes of time. The Exer-Genie method enables one to complete these vital exercises with maximum resistance in approximately thirty seconds.

[4]H. C. Carlson, "Basktball Research in Fatigue," National Association of Basketball Coaches, 1956. (Mimeographed)

PHOTO 3-1   **PHOTO 3-2**

Photo 3-1—Control resistance with finger around trailing rope and set muscles of the entire body and hold isometrically for 10 seconds. At beginning of exercise, weight is on balls of feet.

Photo 3-2—Straighten back, keeping arms down and legs bent, duplicating the dead lift.

PHOTO 3-3   PHOTO 3-4

Photo 3-3—Straighten legs duplicating the squat, and bring the hands up with the elbows in completing the forearm curl.

Photo 3-4—After the handle has been curled to the chest, reverse the hand grip, drop the trailing line, and complete the military press against the preset resistance.

Bicycle Against Resistance (Photo 3-5)

This exercise is designed to strengthen the calves, thighs, and hip areas. By bringing the leg through high, the calf, hamstring area, and buttocks are isolated. If the legs are lowered and pushed out rather than down, the front of the thigh is isolated. Five repetitions with each leg is suggested for maximum results.

PHOTO 3-5

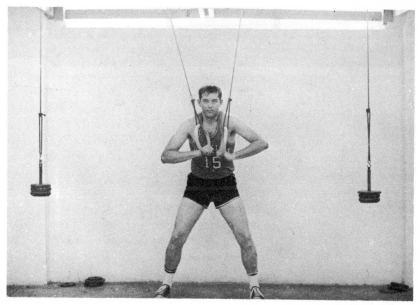

PHOTO 3-6

Exer-Genie Rebounding

The Exer-Genie provides excellent basketball development for strength, control, and technique in lieu of extensive equipment. The Exer-Genie exerciser with "long line" can be looped over an overhead fixture and the coach or fellow player can control both the height and amount of resistance of the rebounds as the player grasps the ball and pulls it down.

Arm and Shoulder Exercises (Photo 3-6)

Developing the extensor of the arms and shoulders is very important. Photo 3-6 is a picture of a specially designed gymnastic exercise machine which is very beneficial to basketball players.

Rope Climbing (Photo 3-7)

Rope climbing is another means of increasing finger and wrist strength without extensively tightening the shoulder muscles.

PHOTO 3-7

Run on the High Ground

When players become extremely tired, they will not extend themselves while running laps or performing any other type of running done on level ground. Climbing steps are the best means of increasing the physical condition of a squad that is very near the point of fatigue. It is impossible to loaf while running up steps. When my squad is near the point of fatigue, I tell them that all of our opponents have terminated their practices and are walking home hand-in-hand with their girl friends. Now is when we will beat them. This will be accomplished by running for ten minutes up and down the 100 steps that are in the balcony of the gym. Running steps is the best means of extending squad members beyond the point of normal conditioning procedures. This drill should be used at least three times per week.

Agility Drills

Running and agility are basic conditioning factors. Both may be improved by using the following drills.

1. *Backing up*—Have two lines of players, one on each foul line and behind the end line. Players stay in a low, crouched fundamental position and back up to the opposite end line as fast as possible and jog back to the end of their line.

2. *Backing and cutting*—Have the same two lines of players start by backing up and then cut and run in the direction the coach indicates. Squad members must learn to change direction without taking their eyes off the ball.

3. *Wave drill*—Have four men situated along the mid-court line in a crouched fundamental position—watching the hands of the coach. Use all four directions: up, back, left, and right.

Handball

Handball is an excellent conditioning activity. It is also very beneficial for developing hand and eye coordination which will improve quick hand action for defense. Single wall handball is not as fast and physically taxing as double or four wall, but facilities are less expensive.

Ring the Bell Jumping Drill (Photo 3-8)

Jumping drills used near the end of practice are excellent means of improving timing on rebounding, tipping, and conditioning.

PHOTO 3-8

Several years ago, I found an old bell which had been used to indicate rounds in boxing. I fastened the bell to the wall ten feet and one inch from the floor. After all running has been completed, all of the forwards and pivots must ring the bell ten times before they can take a shower.

ABOVE AND BEYOND NORMAL CONDITIONING

An aggressive coach should realize that every other coach works hard on conditioning drills. The only way to get the edge on opponents is to overextend or drive beyond normal procedures. This cannot be accomplished unless squad members can be convinced of the need for superior conditioning. Good habits are marvelous, but very hard to acquire. Therefore, players must be driven until they acquire the habit of going beyond the point of normality.

Diagram 3-1—shows the entire squad lining up with both feet on the outside of one end line and sprinting until both feet are beyond the other end line—then they return to the starting point. The last man to complete the round trip should be timed and if he does not make the trip in the established time (eight seconds or less), the entire squad runs again. Five to ten round trips should be satisfactorily completed. After two round trips have been executed, it is wise to allow the winner of each sprint thereafter to either sit down or go in for the day.

PRO SPRINTS

Diagram 3-2—The squad should be divided according to positions or speed, or both. Players start with one foot behind the end lines. On a signal from the coach they sprint to the first foul line—return to end line, sprint to mid-court—return to end line, sprint to mid court—return to end line, sprint to other foul line—return to end line, sprint to end line and finish at end line. Guards should make the full trip (singles in 24 to 26 seconds; forwards in 26 to 28; pivots (and big forwards) in 30 to 32. Guards should run doubles (two times in a row without stopping) in 58 to 60 seconds; forwards in 62 to 64; pivots in 65 to 70.

FAST BREAK CONDITIONING DRILL

Diagram 3-3—Many drills which are used to teach fast break basketball are very useful for improving conditioning. This is an excellent

DIAGRAM 3-1

DIAGRAM 3-2

DIAGRAM 3-3

warm up drill which should be used later in the season to end regular practice. The drill should be run until an established number of crip shots are made consecutively. Players change lines each time they complete a trip.

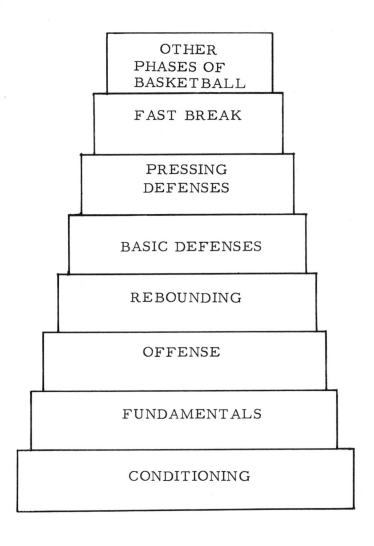

An aggressive basketball program must be established upon a sound foundation. The most dependable asset a coach can claim is proper squad conditioning. It is one phase of basketball that will never vary.

Aggressive teams will naturally have to hustle, scrap and physically extend themselves more than normal teams. This being the case, it follows that a coach interested in producing aggressive teams must be sure that squad members are physically capable of withstanding the pace.

SUMMARY

In spring, the School Board's fancy turns to the basketball coach's efforts; he should wisely arrange to be rolling out a string of victories then, even if he did not fare as well earlier. The Board and the fans have amazingly short memories. They look with pleasure on the coach who overcomes a disastrous start and goes on to a grand finish; he will get a pat on the back for "developing poor material." But for the coach whose team went down the hill at the end of the season, there are no smiles—and very likely, no contract either.

Purely and simply—conditioning of the finest degree will keep a coach free from this embrarrassing predicament. A squad proprely and thoroughly conditioned is the team whose superb stamina and sheer doggedness will win late season laurels and tournament acclaim.

4

Fast Break

AGGRESSIVE TEAMS MUST EMPLOY THE FAST BREAK

The fast break is an offensive weapon that an aggressive team must possess. The primary point emphasized in this chapter is that *the fast break is imperative to success.* Whether this system of using the fast break is unique is actually not as pertinent a question as the philosophical beliefs which accompany fast break basketball.

I firmly advocate the profits of this particular style of play. It has proved not only advantageous but usually decisive in game outcome. First, it affords the offense an excellent opportunity to gain a "cheap basket." Secondly, the threat of the fast break forces the opponent to keep at least two men back for defense and this, in turn, reduces the number of offensive rebounders.

Utilizing the fast break is extremely demanding on every player on the squad. Each must be well conditioned, *aggressive,* alert, and quick of foot. By emphasizing scoring in a minimum of time, players concentrate on getting the ball to the offensive end of the floor before the defensive team has had sufficient time to get completely set; therefore, speed is at a premium.

The fast break is a colorful style of play and appeals to the supporting public. Most fans like to see fast, alert, snappy ball handling and speedy, graceful body movements. Disregarding the fan appeal, a balanced offensive attack should present every known threat to the defense. The opposing rebounders and defensive men have a distinct advantage when the competition fails to include the fast break in its repertory of "goal-getters."

Using the fast break successfully demands an aggressive attitude on the part of each player. Aggressive players can enjoy an intense tempo, reckless play, and the opportunity to take daring chances. They must be constantly challenged in order to develop sufficient confidence in their ability to beat the opponent at every opportunity. This improves each man's toughness. When the demand for execution of high speed maneuvers is removed from the game, the opportunity to sharpen the mental keenness of squad members is greatly reduced.

A team must possess a speedy method of erasing a large score deficit. Many times during the season a team will "go cold" or attempt an experimental strategy during the early stages of a game and fall far behind the opponent. If a team has an explosive fast break and a sticky pressure defense, it can overcome a huge lead in a minimum of time. The following is a case in point.

Georgetown had reached the consolation round of the N.A.I.A Tournament. We were playing Texas Southern for the fifth game in a row. Texas Southern had Bennie Swain, a seven foot pivot, plus several other tall men. Our game plan was to switch from our usual fast break style of play to a controlled game and take only high percentage shots. We felt that Texas Southern would control the rebounds.

With ten minutes remaining in the game, and Georgetown hitting close to 50 per cent of their field goal attempts, Texas Southern was leading 102–82. We took a time-out and decided to go to a half court pressure defense and an all out fast break. With about three minutes left in the game, the score was 104 to 96. Texas Southern called for a time-out and decided to stop controlling the ball and employ their fast break. The game ended, Texas Southern 121, Georgetown 109, and several scoring records were set that are still on the N.A.I.A. record books at Kansas City.

For three minutes that ball moved as if it were a ping-pong ball in a hurricane. At the conclusion of the game, the crowd of close to 10,000 people applauded for two minutes as Texas Southern and Georgetown sprinted off the court still "raring" to run. This was fast break basketball as it should be played. Every pass known to the game had been used and shots had been taken from almost every spot in front court. The pace had been devastating. Ten players who had played five games in as many consecutive nights still had the stamina and the aggressiveness to "dog fight" down to the wire.

SEQUENCE OF EVENTS NECESSARY FOR
THE EXECUTION OF THE FAST BREAK

The fast break style of play requires precise organization and demands many hours of practice. Every minute detail must be anticipated and a plan devised to control the situation. Correct timing for the successful fast break reduces to fractions of a second. Most teams can set their defense in less than five seconds; therefore, the fast break can triumph only if it is executed in less than five seconds. Outstanding defensive

DIAGRAM 4-1

teams, on the other hand, can set their defense in less than four seconds, which means the successful fast break must now be completed in less than four seconds. All things being equal, the success of the fast break requires a numerical offensive advantage over the defense. Pressurized aggressive action by all squad members is the only means whereby a team can achieve this advantage.

Starting the Fast Break

The fast break must be initiated the *instant* a team obtains the ball. Pressure defense, blocking-out and rebounding techniques are very important prerequisites to the fast break and will be discussed in later chapters. The starting point for the fast break is floor position the instant a team gains possession of the ball. This requires an instantaneous mental switch from defensive to offensive thinking. The mental alertness to analyze the situation quickly and move to the proper floor position must be an automatic reflex action. If a player must take time to think about his own placement to start the fast break, he will be too late. He must know in advance his responsibilities and carry them out the instant the ball is recovered by a teammate.

The primary problem encountered in using the fast break is getting it started. There are two general methods popularly used to initiate it. Some teams employ the (1) quick pass-out, while others like to have the (2) rebounder bring the ball out by use of the dribble. I utilize both of these methods. If the ball is recovered near the basket, the rebounder is expected to pass the ball out (preferably with a baseball pass). In the event the ball is recovered near the foul line, the rebounder, whoever he is, should dribble the ball down the middle of the floor.

Diagram 4-1 shows the floor coverage that I use to get the fast break organized. The problem of floor position is critical for the effective fast break. The two pass-out lanes must be filled quickly, and the other players must know in advance who is to fill the third lane. The three lanes will be filled by different personnel depending on the situation. The lane assignment will be discussed under each fast break situation. If the fast breaking team uses a zone defense, the lane assignments are much simpler. Some fast break teams do utilize the zone defense solely because of this fact.

Advancing the Ball

I have previously stated that the first pass-out is the key to the successful fast break. When the ball is obtained by a player, he must know what outlet areas are open and quickly manuever into position to throw a snappy pass to either the primary or secondary outlet man. The baseball pass is the most effective and the safest pass to use, because it can be thrown faster and is harder for the defense to intercept.

There are many differences of opinion concerning the proper lane in which to advance the ball. Many coaches believe that the ball should be advanced in the middle lane, because the ball handler can pressure the defense and have the option to pass or drive to either side of the floor. The other school of thought contends that the ball should be advanced up the sideline out of the congestion of players, taking the shortest distance to the basket for offense or defense. Both methods have their merits and must be understood. The long pass up the sideline will advance the ball quickly; however, it is harder to get proper lane coverage. Without lane coverage, it is more difficult to obtain the floor balance which insures rebound strength and defensive balance.

Advancing the ball up the middle requires a great amount of dribbling skill on the part of the middle man of the fast break. The reason I prefer the middle lane for advancing the ball is that, as the ball is advanced up the middle of the floor, each pass or dribble brings the ball closer to the basket, and will eventually result in an easy lay-up shot. If the ball is advanced up the side lane, it will never become a lay-up until it makes a sharp angle turn.

TAKING THE SHOT

The middle man dribbles the ball to his foul line where the defense must commit themselves to stopping the ball before it penetrates inside the foul line. The middle man must not let himself be stopped easily. He should drive to the basket one out of three times for a crip shot. The two side-lane men should have maneuvered to a position about one yard in from the out-of-bounds line by the time they reach their foul line extended. As the middle man stops with the ball, the side-lane men should make a banana pattern cut to the basket. The middle ball handler should face the basket and pass to the open side-lane man and go to the end of the foul line nearest the ball. He establishes a shooting position and awaits a feedback if the defense over-shifts to stop the side-lane man. The fourth man on the fast break is considered the trailer and should break to the basket through the foul line opposite the middle lane man. The fifth man on the break stays back for defense in case of an intercepted pass or loose ball.

UTILIZING THE FAST BREAK IN GAME SITUATIONS

There are several opportunities during a game when the fast break can be operated most effectively. It is generally used following (1) a loose ball, (2) a recovered rebound, (3) a made field goal, (4) a made free throw, (5) a missed free throw, and (6) a jump-ball play. The aggressive team should occasionally employ the fast break after each of the above situations in order to keep the opponent's defense off balance. However, a majority of the practice time should be devoted to perfecting the fast break following the loose ball and recovered rebound. These are the situations in which the opponent cannot anticipate consistently enough to establish an effective defense without handicapping his offensive attack and rebound strength.

RECOVERY OF LOOSE BALL

Probably the most effective time to employ the fast break is when the

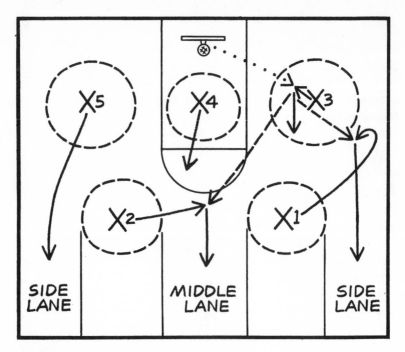

DIAGRAM 4-2

defensive team recovers a loose ball. The opponent is not prepared to switch from offense to defense and their off-balance mental alertness will reduce the effectiveness of their defense. Also, it is much easier to get an offensive numerical advantage over the defensive team because they are usually advancing toward their goal and must shift body weight and overcome momentum.

Aggressive teams should be prepared to anticipate the recovery of a loose ball and to immediately obtain a numerical advantage over the opponent. This mental readiness to switch from defense to offense in a fraction of time will keep the opponent from "crashing the boards" or "hanging" a fourth man inside of the foul line to secure the long rebound.

RECOVERED REBOUND

This is the usual game condition when a majority of the fast breaks materialize. The aggressive team will capture a large share of the rebounds. Therefore, they should be capable of converting many of them into points obtained with the least amount of effort. This situation is so common to basektball that it should be relatively easy for squad members to be exposed to sufficient practice.

RECOVERED REBOUND OR LOOSE BALL
FAST BREAK POSITIONS

Diagram 4-2—The circles on the floor represent zones. Any player in these zones when the ball is recovered carries out the assignment which is indicated. Zoning the floor is necessary when the team employing the fast break uses the man-to-man defense. The offensive team, by using intricately designed patterns, will force the players of the fast break team out of normal fast break position.

The player in zone 3 rebounds the ball and passes it out to either the player who was in zone 1 or 2 and then stays back for the defense in case of an interception. The player in zone 1 moves to the sideline as the primary outlet man. The player in zone 2 comes to the middle of the floor as the secondary outlet man. If the man in either zone 1 or 2 receives the ball, he brings it up the floor on the dribble and as soon as possible passes the ball out or dribbles to the middle of the floor. The player in the middle of the floor should advance the ball down the court in order to have either of the two side-lane players as targets when the defense stops him. The player in zone 5 comes out in a hurry and fills the third lane. The player in zone 4 becomes the trailer. The player in zone 3 (the pass-out man) becomes the defensive trail man.

If the ball is rebounded on the opposite side of the basket, the above procedure is reversed. If rebounded in the middle of the floor, the players in zone 1 and 2 "fan out" and cover the two sideline lanes and either the rebounder brings the ball on the dribble or the nearest forward takes the middle. If the ball rebounds deep out on the court, the player who recovers the ball dribbles it down the floor, and the two closest men fill the other lanes. The first man in a lane keeps that lane; the second man into a lane, when he sees his lane filled, starts maneuvering to an open lane or into "trailer" position.

MADE FIELD GOAL

It is very difficult to execute a fast break following a successful field goal. The opponent should be able to organize and completely set the defense before a fast break can be put into action. However, many teams will loaf back to their defensive position and this allows the aggressive team to make the long pass, thus cutting off defensive players. I do not use the fast break a great deal under these circumstances, but I like to use it occasionally as an aid to keep the opponent off balance.

DIAGRAM 4-3

DIAGRAM 4-4

Diagram 4-3—The fast break after the made field goal depends on the long first pass. If a team is blessed with a pivot or forward who can throw the long baseball pass accurately, the fast break from the made field goal is very effective. The most successful fast break I have had from this situation was when I had a left-handed pivot who could throw the baseball pass the length of the court almost on a line.

The pivot grabs the ball out while it is still partially in the bottom of the nets and maneuvers to a throwing position immediately. The player in zone 1 hurries down court to a position one yard in from the out-of-bounds line and approximately two yards from the top of his own foul circle. The player in zone 3 breaks to a side outlet position and moves down court. He should receive the ball near the mid-court line. The player in zone 2 "fans out" and breaks up the court in the side lane opposite the ball. He moves at a rapid pace and tries to get behind the defensive men. If time permits, he continues down his lane and across the foul lane to the opposite side of the floor. (This maneuver causes the defensive men great concern because it takes place behind them.) The player in zone 5 breaks up the middle lane of the floor in the event that the outlet man (zone 3) passes to the zone 1 man or dribbles the ball up the floor in the side lane. If the zone 3 man dribbles to the middle of the floor and tries to reach the foul line, the zone 5 man will "fan out" and trail the zone 2 man to the basket. The pivot or pass-out man becomes the defensive trailer.

MADE FREE THROW

Diagram 4-4—This is an excellent time to execute the fast break. The fast break team has sufficient time to organize their personnel since definite floor position can be assigned. There are many advantages to running the fast break at this time. If personnel are properly deployed, the fast break is advantageous in placing pressure on the foul shooter and in reducing his shooting percentage. It will also prevent the team shooting the foul shot from crashing the boards for the rebound.

MISSED FREE THROW

Using the fast break following the missed free throw is very similar to the made free throw situation. The two circumstances are usually included in the same plan with consideration for the timing element of the made free throw. These two circumstances have approximately the same advantage.

Either X1 or X2, the inside position rebounders, catches the ball as it comes through the nets and moves to a predetermined position. He throws a snappy baseball pass to X3 who either throws directly to X1 or dribbles the ball up the floor as rapidly as possible. Position X5 "fans out" and moves up the floor in the side lane opposite the ball. Position X4, who set the screen for X1, becomes the "trailer," and the "throw-in" player becomes the defensive trailer.

If the free throw shot is missed, X4 and X5 carry out the same assignments and as soon as X3 sees whether X1 or X2 has the ball, he moves to an outlet position on the side of the ball. The rebounder will pass the ball to X3 and the same procedure is carried out as in the made free throw situation.

In the missed free throw situation, taking X4 and X5 out of rebound position sacrifices some rebound strength. However, if the opponent fails to compensate his defense, he leaves himself vulnerable for a cheap score.

JUMP BALL SITUATION

Employing the fast break following the jump ball depends upon the caliber of the team's jumpers. It is a waste of time to plan for a fast break at this time unless squad members can be expected to control a majority of the tips. If a team is fortunate enough to have the personnel to control most jump balls, they should definitely use the break. It is rather simple to organize the fast break structure, but split-second timing is required to gain the proper advantage, because the opponent generally knows the ability of their jumper and can compensate rapidly.

The advantage of employing the fast break in the above mentioned situations is that it is possible to achieve a great deal of success with minimum practice. Most teams do not drill the defensive unit extensively on these situations; therefore, a minimum of practice time devoted to this phase of basketball will produce a rather large profit.

Diagram 4-5—The jumper tips to a spot and X2 breaks to catch the ball while he is moving and continues up the middle of the floor. Position X3 breaks up and tries to cut off a defensive man as he continues down the side lane. Position X4 anticipates the controlled tip and breaks as the referee tosses the ball up. He continues up the side lane and tries to become the lead man on the break. Position X5 becomes the trailer and X1, the jumper, is the defensive trail man. This fast break situation is predicted on the controlled tip. It is useless to wait until possession of the ball is determined before starting the fast break. If a fast break will

DIAGRAM 4-5

DIAGRAM 4-6

DIAGRAM 4-7

DIAGRAM 4-8

work against a team under these conditions, its use will not be needed to win anyway, so why run up the score?

The aggressive team takes advantage of the small things. Herein lies the success of utilizing the fast break on every possible occasion. Most opponents have weaknesses due to improper preparation. The aggressive team should be able to "pick" at a team's offense and defense all during the game. If they find a weakness and can capitalize on it for several "cheap" baskets, it will tend to destroy the opponent's confidence. The opposition's squad members will feel inadequately prepared and will blame their coach for not properly training them to handle all situations. Coaches: encourage some member of your squad to inform the opponents of their deficiencies if success is achieved easily. This is an excellent opportunity to destroy the morale of the opponent!

FAST BREAK DRILLS

Nets to Nets in Four Seconds

Diagram 4-6—This is a team drill. Offensive man O1 takes a shot from around the foul line area and then tries to break up the outlet pass. Offensive man O2 is a rebounder, and he tries to rebound the shot. His main task is to keep defensive men X3, X4, and X5 from leaving too soon. Offensive men O3 and O4 form a defensive tandem and try to destroy the fast break. The defensive team, or the fast break team, must score in four seconds after the ball is in their possession. They continue this drill until they score three times, with each score under the four second limit and then another team moves in for the same procedure. The emphasis of this drill is placed on instantaneous floor position and speed in execution of the fast break.

Run for Your Life

Diagram 4-7—Only six men are used at a time in this drill, and the ball is not allowed to touch the floor except when it is being dribbled by a player. The rebounder who throws the ball to the outlet man must run for his life if he is to beat the dribbler to the other end of the court. The six men must space themselves evenly over the entire floor. They are not allowed to bunch up at one basket.

Go-Go-Go

Diagram 4-8—The squad is divided into three groups and each squad

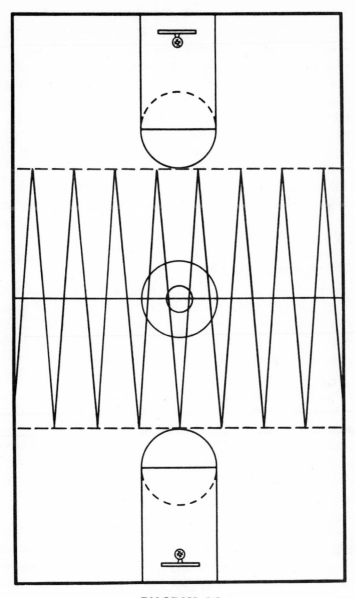

DIAGRAM 4-9

member alternates lines. The players in line one rebound the ball and pass it out to outlet man O2. O2 passes to O3 who should be at the front edge of the jump circle. O1 fills the side lane after he passes to O2. O2 passes to O3 and then fills the side lane opposite O1. O3 receives the ball and dribbles to the foul line at the other end of the floor. He then passes to either O1 or O2 and follows for the rebound. The player who shoots the ball becomes the outlet man. The middle player rebounds and throws out to the man who had just taken the shot. The player who does not shoot hustles around and receives the ball at the front edge of the jump circle and dribbles down the floor. Meanwhile, the other two players cover their regular side lanes and the shot is taken at the other end of the floor. Three players are waiting to bring the ball back.

I call this drill GO-GO-GO because we go until we hit a prescribed number of crip shots. The crip shot must be taken in less than four seconds after the pass-out player has possession of the ball.

Get Out of "Pussy-Foot" Lane

Diagram 4-9—I refer to the area of the floor which lies between the top of the two foul circles as "pussy-foot" lane. This could better be called the three-second lane. During a game, if my team has more than two men in this area for more than three seconds while we are switching from offense to defense and vice versa, we generally lose. I have kept some rather exacting statistics on this area, and it's a sore spot to me. I don't hesitate to let my squads know it.

It is a known fact that very little offense and defense is played out in this portion of the floor. A good fast breaking team will get their offense inside this area to begin their offensive attack, and most defensive teams realize that the largest percentage of the defense must also be played inside of the top of the circle. In other words, there is no reason to loaf around in "pussy-foot" lane. If a player needs to rest, he should come out of the game and go home and go to bed.

I mark this area off with yellow tape early in the season, and all of our drills are timed to keep players from pitching a tent in this area. If players are going camping, this would be a fine deserted area. Otherwise, they need to move through this lane and get down to business playing offense on one end and defense on the other.

Eleven Man "Gut Buster"

Diagram 4-10—Offensive player O1 starts the drill by dribbling the ball down the floor. Players O2 and O3 fill the side lanes. As the three

DIAGRAM 4-10

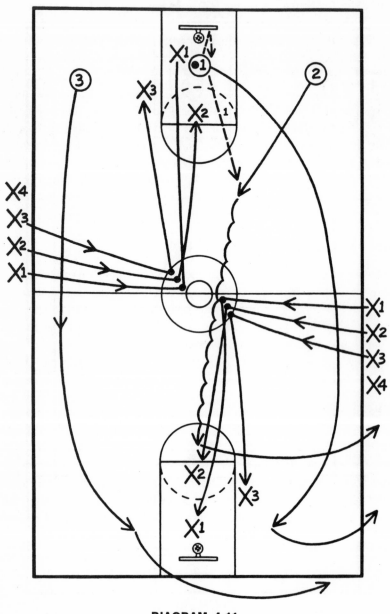

DIAGRAM 4-11

offensive players who start the drill come down the floor and pass the top of the foul circle, X3 and X4 jump into outlet pass position and wait for the pass out. Defensive players X1 and X2 form a tandem and try to keep the three offensive players from scoring. They keep working until either X1 or X2 gets the ball. If the three offensive players score, either X1 or X2, depending on who gets the ball first, throws the ball out to X3 or X4 and fills the side lane to the side the ball was thrown.

As soon as X1 or X2 throws the balls to X3 or X4, the player who does not get the ball fans out and fills the side lane opposite the ball. These three players advance the ball, and X5 and X6 form the defensive tandem as X7 and X8 become the outlet pass players.

Only players who are hustling are removed from the drill. Any player who doesn't "bust" his "guts" remains in the drill. If he is still there when the drill ends, he receives 25 laps on the steps after practice.

Hustle Back and Stop the Flood

Diagram 4-11—The squad is divided into two lines on either side of the court at the center line. Offensive player O1 has the ball to start the drill. He throws the ball on the backboard and as the ball touches his hands, players X1 and X2 dash to the jump circle and put one foot in the circle and fall back to form the defensive tandem. As offensive man O2 crosses the center line with the ball, X3 dashes to the jump circle, places one foot in the circle, and hustles to defensive position. It is now three-on-three, and the drill continues until the three defensive men get the ball. If the offensive team scores, the closest defensive man grabs the ball and throws it out and fills the side lane to the side the ball was thrown. The instant the three defensive men get the ball, the first two defensive men on the other side of the court dash to the jump circle and then fall back to form the defensive tandem. As the ball crosses mid-court, X3 joins the drill and the procedure is continued. After the three players who are running the fast break have either scored or lost the ball, they always go to the end of the line to their left.

This is a good drill to teach the third defensive man whom to cover when he gets back on defense to help his defensive tandem.

SUMMARY

I cannot repeat enough my belief that it is impossible to play aggressive basketball without using the fast break. It is the weapon with which aggressive players destroy their opponents. When a truly aggressive team gets ahead, they "smell blood" and go in for the "kill." The aggressive team never lets up until the game is over. There should be no such thing as running up scores on opponents. If a team can beat an opponent by a large score, scheduling is faulty and competition dull. A razor-sharp squad will remain so only by meeting teams who relinquish victory at the very highest cost—blood, sweat, and high gear extension for a full forty minutes of basketball.

The fast break is the portion of basketball where the truly conditioned team can crush the opponent by running them until they wilt under the physical strain. Fast break basketball will separate the "sheep" from the "goats" in a hurry. If a coach has a superior well-conditioned team, he should use the fast break to take advantage of a rival who is evidently in poor physical condition.

Never let up when a competitor shows a weakness. Hit them where they are hurting, and pour on the steam. The devastating fast break will cause the opponent grave concern. If running isn't your adversary's cup of tea, and he plans to control the ball, defensively force him with the press, and make him run. Now he's playing *your* game, and his preplanned strategy is shot! Run, and let the opponent worry about stopping you. Don't show mercy on the basketball court. If you have an urge to be kind to your fellow man, join the Peace Corps.

In closing, I must mention the element of gambling involved when using the fast break. This, and only this, is the foundation on which to base judgment as to whether or not a coach should employ the fast break. Actually, the coaching of basketball has always relied heavily on the intelligent choice of gambles. The sensible approach is to employ the method or technique that involves the least risk. However, there are situations when a greater risk taken will produce more dividends than losses, and this is the time to buy *bull stock*! And the fast break is generally *Blue Chip* in my market.

5

Aggressive Rebounding

CONTROL THE BOARDS AT ALL COST

The team in control of the boards controls the game. Dominating the boards simply means that one must get the rebound from the offensive and defensive boards. Obtaining a majority of the rebounds is a very difficult task, and the aggressive team must necessarily be very mean under the boards at both ends.

Rebounding divides itself into two easily discernible phases—offensive rebounding, and naturally, defensive rebounding. The techniques necessary for either offensive or defensive rebounding remain the same. However, the maneuvers used by the offensive player to obtain the rebound are much different from those used by the defensive player. The defensive rebounder is in a more advantageous position because he has the inside position. The offensive rebounder must be capable of fighting around the defensive player and beating him to the ball.

The most important prerequisites for the aggressive rebounder are hustle and heart. Of course, in order to be an outstanding rebounder, a player must have, in addition, jumping ability. But there have been many cases in which a player who could not jump had the competence to hustle into position and the knack of intelligently using his body to grab the rebound. I have had players who couldn't jump and who were not extremely tall; yet, they were excellent rebounders simply because they blocked out and scrapped for the ball. They also never gave up on a rebound. Many times when two tall, excellent rebounders are fighting for a ball, they will knock it loose and a shorter or less agile jumper can obtain an easy rebound if he is "Johnny on the spot." The man who doesn't possess the talents of a great jumper can and must learn to extend his body and to use his weight and strength in order to take advantage of an opponent who can jump.

POSITION IS THE KEY

Body position is the key to good rebounding, The extended spread-out—knees bent, hips back, head back, and arm slightly out— position

71

is the ideal one for rebounders to assume. On page *74* is a drill called "Body Extension." In this drill, players are taught to extend the body to a position where the hips are down, the knees bent, the elbows are out, and the arms are ready to swing up after the ball. The body position will be affected by the block-out method used and other factors.

The ideal body position and rebound action can best be described by the following characterization. A good rebounder should *spread out like an eagle*, leap high into the air, *tear* the rebound off the board, and *shake like a wet dog*.

BLOCK-OUT

Blocking out is generally considered a defensive method of preventing the offensive rebounder from obtaining the second shot. However, an offensive man may block the defensive man if he is in good position.

There are many methods of blocking out. The defensive rebounder must first block his man and go for the ball. If a player is close enough to the man he is guarding to get contact on his first move, he should pivot into his man while the shot is in the air. If players are away from their men and cannot get contact on the first pivot or move, they should use a jump spin, take one look at their man, and move for the rebound. The sequence is something like this: defensive position, shot, block, look at the man being blocked, move to basket and rebound.

Some coaches instruct their players to move to the rebounding position the instant the shot is taken, and then block their man before they attempt to rebound the ball. I have found that the run-in rebounder will jump over the back of the block-out player if he can gather momentum. The rebounder who crashes the board and leaps on top of the block-out player standing under the basket generally learns to do this without the penalty of a foul. I instruct my players to block and then move to the basket for position. This keeps the run-in rebounder from getting his normal run at the rebound.

Diagram 5-1: Rebounding Jump Spin. The "jump spin" block-out maneuver is used when the defensive player is away from the man he has been assigned to guard and cannot get contact with his man by employing a pivot. The instant the shot is taken all away defensive men use a jump spin to place their backs to their assigned men. They must, however, keep their eyes on their men until the offensive players make their first move. The defensive men then step in front of their offensive men and block them away from the ball as they go for the rebound.

OFFENSIVE REBOUNDING

As was stated earlier, the defensive block-out man has a better opportunity to keep the offensive rebounder away from the boards. However, most coaches design their offensive plays to facilitate offensive rebounding. My offensive plays are designed to have three and one-half men on the offensive board. Both forwards and the pivot cover the rebounding triangle under the basket, and one guard hangs on the foul line for the long rebound. As soon as the play starts and before it culminates, the rebounders begin making their move to beat the defensive player to the boards. If, however, they are met by a well-disciplined defensive block-out, they must use several methods to outmaneuver their defensive man.

Players should use the simple "step beside the defensive man and jump as he jumps" method hoping to at least interfere with the block-out

DIAGRAM 5-1

player's jumping ability. The second course open to the offensive rebounders is the pivot-out or the "spin in front" of the block-out man.
This is a maneuver where the offensive rebounder must gamble and
choose one side of the defensive block-out man and spin out and in
front of the defensive player. This is a very difficult maneuver, and it
requires extensive practice until it becomes a reflex action.

Offensive rebounding is a phase of basketball that all big men must
perfect. The most important aspect of offensive rebounding is for coaches
to use offensive plays which will permit the offensive rebounder to have
at least a 50-50 chance of obtaining the rebound.

The offensive rebounder must develop movements to free himself from
the block-out before the shot, during the shot, and after the shot is
taken. These factors, plus peripheral vision and judgment, will place the
offensive rebounder in a position to control the defensive player.

Reading the boards or judging the spot where the rebound will fall
depends on experience. Rebounders should spend their practice time
studying the flight of rebounded balls following shots taken by players
from certain areas of the floor. When a team uses spot shots for all
players, it is much easier for rebounders to spend their free time reading
the rebounds. Rebounders should be required to make a chart of these
spots and the areas into which they fall. This procedure will make them
conscious of the necessity for reading the boards.

REBOUNDING DRILLS

Body Extension

In Photo 5-1, the rebounder has assumed a "broken knee" or a body
balanced position which will permit him to jump and extend his body
completely. The coach stands to the side and bounces the ball off the
backboard. The rebounder leaps high into the air, extends his hips and
head backwards, and spreads his feet as he squeezes the ball with his
fingers and *tears* it off the board, returning to the floor in a spread position which will occupy space and prevent the pile-on rebounders from
tying the ball up. His elbows should be extended, and the ball squeezed
firmly at all times. The main point to emphasize in the body extension
drill is the assumption of a crouched position with the arms down and
the elbows out. As the ball nears the position to be rebounded, the
rebounder leaps high into the air extending his hips backwards and
throwing his head back allowing his arms to reach up and out.

PHOTO 5-1

This drill can be done to either side. Of course, the offensive rebounder will later be asked to slide from side to side as if he is blocking out, to jump for the ball as he extends himself, to protect the ball, and to throw it to the outlet man.

Body Extension Drill

Photo 5-1—The player is in a ready-to-rebound position. The coach throws the ball on the backboard and has the rebounder go through form rebounding.

Tear Off the Rebound and Throw It Out

Photo 5-2 (A, B, C)—This drill is very similar to the body extension drill. The throw-out which is used here can be added to the body extension drill. However, I like to use a McCall Rebounder and have the player tear the ball off the rebounder and throw it out. This helps the player develop finger strength while working on form.

It Takes a Tiger to Shoot Twice

Diagram 5-2—Two men are in a defensive position, and the two offensive men are passing the ball between themselves. As one of the

PHOTO 5-2A

PHOTO 5-2B

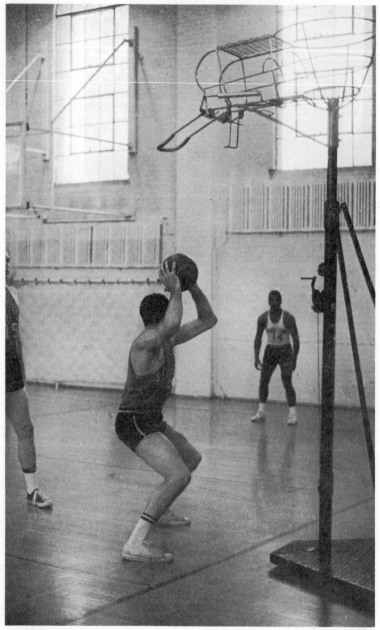

PHOTO 5-2C

offensive players takes the shot, the two defensive players block the offensive players away from the basket. The defensive player guarding the shooter will pivot into his man and block him immediately. The offside defensive player must use the "jump spin" block-out. Anyone can take the first shot, but it takes a tiger to get the second shot. The two offensive men will smash the board and try to get the second shot— either a tip in or a "muscle-up" type of shot.

"Muscle-Up" Drill

Photo 5-3—The player with the ball must use muscle to knock the arms of the other players back and continue up for a shot. Each forward and pivot does this five to ten times in a row. The players holding their arms out create normal fouling pressure as the shooter starts up.

Pink "Pantie" Drill

Diagram 5-3—The entire squad is allowed to choose a position under the basket. The assistant coach or manager will shoot the ball to insure no prejudice. As each player gets two or three rebounds, he sits down. The last player left standing is asked to wear the pink ladies' bloomers for the entire day. This drill is run early in the practice schedule. It should be discontinued before the first regular season game.

PHOTO 5-3

DIAGRAM 5-2

One-Two-Three And In

Photo 5-4—The idea in this drill is to have each player tip the ball on the board three times and then score. He should repeat this ten times with the left hand and ten times with the right hand. Players can do this during a rest break or any free time, utilizing all baskets in the gym.

Team Rebounding Drill

Diagram 5-4—The offensive team should run a weave or any type of movement that does not put them under the basket in a position where the defensive block-out man does not have a chance to block out and hold the offensive rebounder away from the ball. After the shot is taken, the defensive team cannot touch the ball but must hold their men away from the ball. A stop watch is used to see for how many seconds the defensive team can keep the offensive team away from the ball. Each team is given ten attempts and the time cumulated. The losing team will run laps on the steps after practice.

DIAGRAM 5-3

SUMMARY

Rebounding starts and ends with one human quality—a strong desire to "get the ball." When a player has a firm belief that his team must have the ball to win, he will generally figure out a way to get it. A player who wants the ball badly enough never gives up a chance to grab it. Once the initial desire is implanted in a player, he can be taught offensive and defensive rebounding techniques which will aid him in the successful recovering of the ball.

There is considerable physical contact involved in rebounding. The great rebounder cannot be a player weak of heart or one who shuns physical contact. Rebounders need constant drilling in situations where the going is rugged. Within a given period of time, players will learn to protect themselves from the normal number of elbows as simple reflex action. They also learn to maintain balance and adjust their timing to the normal contact under the baskets.

The great rebounders develop a love for physical contact and enthusi-

DIAGRAM 5-4

astically face the challenge that exists under the baskets. The stronger
the player is, the easier he will rebound. This is another good reason to
stress development of strength in the taller player.

Modern day basketball has seen its greatest change under the baskets.
Players today are bigger and stronger than ever before. If coaches want
to compete on a contending basis with the champions, they must develop
strength under the baskets. This is undoubtedly one phase of the sport
of basketball where a "boy" cannot be sent to do a *man's job*.

PHOTO 5-4

6

A Constant-Attack
Aggressive Defense

Aggressive basketball and pressure defense are synonymous with winning basketball coaches. The distinguishing feature of aggressive defense is the constant attack psychology. Aggressive defensive players will make the first move and *never* allow the offense the same privilege. This phase of the game should be a distinct challenge to an aggressive player. He should consider a basket scored against him as a personal insult to his ability as a basketball player.

The manner in which a coach organizes and utilizes his defense contributes more to aggressive basketball than does any other aspect of the game. Most boys learn to play offense adequately, because of the very nature of this portion of the sport. However, defensive basketball requires a special "hardnosed" type of boy. In these days of the high percentage shooters, the jump shot and unorthodox shots, the defensive man starts the game at a decisive disadvantage.

The defensive star is generally a man who possesses an unusual inner toughness, tremendous self-pride, and an extraordinary desire to sacrifice. He is not driven with the ambition to score and receive public acclaim, but instead, counts it an honor to be considered by his teammates as a loyal devotee to the team. In a manner of speaking, good defensive players are the "insides" or pillars of the team.

The physical prerequisites for defensive players are speed, split-second reaction, quickness, strength, and toughness. However, without *self-pride* and *desire*, even players with superior physical equipment never become proficient in defensive play.

Aggressive players who have no fear of hard knocks are generally the ones who excel in defense. Therefore, the drills which are used to teach defense must inculcate maneuvers involving physical contact, quick movements, recovery situations, and goal seeking opportunities. The man on defense must become *over*-aggressive and develop the "killer" instinct. When a team is behind and victory depends upon getting the ball, defensive players willing to *completely* extend themselves are a comfort to have around.

87

There are several reasons why sound defensive basketball is difficult to teach: (1) Defensive play demands great physical exertion and receives very little recognition from the press and the spectators. Most players feel that the best way to make the All-American squad is to own a high offensive average; (2) good defensive play requires continuous concentration, and the average player does not report to practice mentally disciplined to the point where he can enjoy defensive pressure; (3) there is very little thrill to defensive play, and (4) practice on defense is grueling and monotonous.

DEFENSIVE POSITION

The starting point for considering defensive play is the basic position. It is simply between the player being guarded and the basket. We also must consider the fundamental body position which each squad member assumes while maintaining his basic floor position. Each player must maintain a position which allows him to contain *his* man.

When a player is in the proper fundamental defensive position, he can move in any direction adroitly and with the least expenditure of energy. The best body position for basketball players to assume, as their fundamental position, is the one used by boxers. This position is sometimes called the "broken knee" or "triple threat" position. Basketball players, like boxers, must maintain near perfect balance and be capable of moving in all directions at any time.

Photo 6-1—Photo 6-1 shows the fundamental defensive position. The player has his feet spread until they are approximately under his shoulders. His lead foot is from 6 to 12 inches ahead of his back foot. *The forehead is perpendicular* to the floor and the hands are carried high with the elbows out and the palms down. Until the jump shot became so prominent, the hands were carried much lower. It is still advisable to carry the hands low and in a palms-up position when guarding near the mid-court line. This helps to hold the hips down, and makes it possible for the defensive man to stab up at the dribbled ball.

A defensive player must look serious and as mean as possible. Pointing the fingers in a stiff, clawlike manner and looking stern causes the offensive man grave concern. A happy player should not play defense. An offensive man is happy; the defensive man is worried and in a very nasty mood and should show it in his stance and facial expressions.

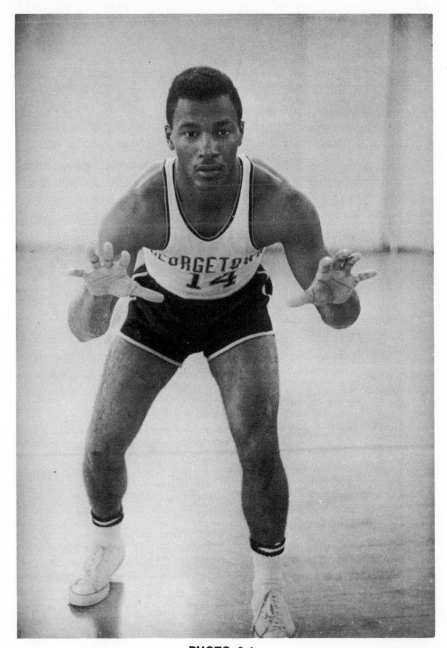

PHOTO 6-1

BASIC POSITION

The basic position for defense is always maintained when the man to be guarded moves through the different areas of the floor. Diagram 6-1 shows how defensive position varies according to the areas of the court.

From the end line to half-court is called "aggravation" area. Here the defensive man worries the offensive player by stabbing at the ball and trying to drive the offensive player out of his normal path. In this area, it is not wise for the man on defense to overplay and allow the offensive player to get by him. After the offensive player has reached the mid-court line, he must be pressured and prevented from taking straight paths to the ball or to screen for a teammate.

When guarding in the scoring area, or "skintight" area, there is only one way to play aggressive defense. The defensive man should almost crawl into the uniform with the man he is assigned to guard. Toe to toe and knee to knee, he should practically breathe the same air as the offensive man.

The most obnoxious player on the basketball court should be the man playing defense. Defensive basketball is rough and demands tenacious, aggressive contact. In some quarters, there exists a false impression concerning the game of basketball. Many high school coaches, fans, and players feel that basketball is a non-contact game. They consider football players as the boys who love contact. In some schools, there is even a belief that only "sissies" play basketball. This belief would be removed in a hurry if those people who believe that basketball is a "sissie's" game would practice with my team for about a week.

Winning basketball teams are composed of aggressive players who will legally manhandle their opponent when on defense. The recovery of loose balls and rebounds are also phases of defense which demand a great deal of physical contact. Needless to say, all contact must take place within the confines of the rules.

GUARDING THE MAN ON THE SIDELINES OR BASELINE

A. Each defensive man should assume a sound fundamental stance.
B. His feet should be open to the sideline and baseline.
C. He must protect the baseline. An offensive man should never be allowed to drive the baseline. (This is a cardinal sin which always carries with it a severe penalty.)

D. The defensive man should learn to retreat straight back on fakes and not lunge up on the recovery step.

E. He must learn to use his hands. (Karate Hand Action.)

GUARDING CLOSE TO THE BASKET

A. When the offensive man is in a position close to the basket, the defensive man should always play in front or halfway around and prevent the ball from coming to the offensive man.

B. When the offensive man is in a high position, play to the side of strength of movement or to the side of the ball. When the ball is in the middle of the floor, play behind and as close to the offensive man as possible and be ready to go to either side for an interception.

C. The defensive man should be in a position to pivot and block the offensive man away from the basket when a field goal is attempted.

D. The defensive man should always force the offensive man to run in banana patterns when going to screen or to receive a pass. A great defensive player never allows his man to run in straight lines.

GUARDING THE OUTSIDE MAN

A. Keep feet open to strong side of the opponent.

B. Stay in front of opponent when he attempts a cut. Never allow an offensive man, with or without the ball, to take the path which he prefers.

INDIVIDUAL DEFENSIVE RESPONSIBILITIES

1. Assume and maintain good body position with karate hand jabs at the ball.

2. Hands up on all shots as the shot is being taken. Do not try to block the shot. Just force the shooter to raise his aim.

3. Block the offensive man away from the board while the shot is in the air.

4. Move to the board and assume rebound extension position.

5. Tear the rebound off and protect it.

6. Get into a balanced passing position and fire the ball out to the outlet player to start the fast break.

All of these responsibilities must be executed instantaneously and must, therefore, be repeated in practice until they are done as reflex action. Another way of stating the above sequences of action in practice is defense, hands up, block out, rebound, and pass out. (All five actions must occur within less than two seconds.)

DRILLS FOR IMPROVING FUNDAMENTAL BODY POSITION

Slide Drill

Diagram 6-2—Players go around the gym floor. They must keep their heads up, hips down, and touch the floor with the palms of their hands on each slide step. They change direction at each corner.

"Boxer's" Drill

Diagram 6-3—Boxer's approach step. Start forward with right foot first, back up with right foot forward at half-court, go back to forward position but use left foot first, etc. Change directions at all corners.

"Pussy Cat" Drill

Diagram 6-4—A1 uses a boxer's stance to creep up on Line B. B1 chases A1 back to first of Line A. A2 then jumps out and chases B1 back to Line B and B2 chases A2 back, etc.

Fight-Through Drill

Diagram 6-5—Defensive men must fight through the screen and never allow more than one man to get between their man and themselves. O1 dribbles to O2 and either goes in front of or behind O2. O2 takes the ball and dribbles over to O3 and either goes in front of or behind O3. This routine is continued very rapidly until defensive men learn to allow only one man between their men and themselves.

Wave Drill

Diagram 6-6—The coach directs these slides. The entire squad faces the coach, and assumes a fundamental defensive position which is crouched, hips down, and head and eyes up. Hands should be above the shoulders and the elbows should be below the waist. Coach uses hand to indicate left, right, backing up, and forward. This drill should last about ten to fifteen minutes per day.

DIAGRAM 6-1

FACE OUT

FACE IN

FACE IN

FACE OUT

FACE OUT

FACE IN

DIAGRAM 6-2

DIAGRAM 6-3

DIAGRAM 6-4

DIAGRAM 6-5

DIAGRAM 6-6

DIAGRAM 6-7

DIAGRAM 6-8

DIAGRAM 6-9

DIAGRAM 6-10

Diagonal Slide Drill

Diagram 6-7—Players must slide diagonally from corner to top of foul circle and switch directions and slide diagonally to center corner. They must face the coach until the other end is reached and then face the assistant coach while coming back.

Recovery Drill

Diagram 6-8—O1 dribbles the ball up the court and allows X1 to steal it. O1 recovers and tries to beat X1 to the basket.

Step-In Drill

Diagram 6-9—X1 steps in front of offensive man O2 and draws fall-down foul. X1 must give with the lick of O2 and fall clear of traffic in order to avoid being stepped on.

5 WAYS TO DEFENSE THE SCREEN

1. Switch: (Diagram 6-10, Photos 6-2A & B) X1 guards O1, and O1 dribbles until he forces X1 into O2 creating a switch situation. X2 calls switch and takes O1, and X1 takes O2.
2. Over the top: (Photos 6-3A & B) Same screen situation, but X1 must go between O1 and O2 with no switch. X2 must force O1 wide enough for X1 to go over the top.
3. Slide Through (Photos 6-4 A & B) Same screen situation, but X1 must slide between O2 and his man, allowing one man to come between him and his man.
4. Fake switch: (Photo 6-5) X2 calls switch and jumps O2, the offensive guard. O2 will roll to the basket and X2 will hurry back and guard O2. X1 will ignore the switch call and keep after his man—O1. X1 and X2 must plan this maneuver and know in advance that no switch will occur.
5. Switch over the top: (Photo 6-6) X2 calls the switch and X1 comes on over the top and switches in front of X2. He then fronts X2

PHOTO 6-2A

PHOTO 6-2B

PHOTO 6-3A

PHOTO 6-3B

PHOTO 6-4A

PHOTO 6-4B

PHOTO 6-5A

PHOTO 6-5B

PHOTO 6-5C

PHOTO 6-5D

PHOTO 6-6A

PHOTO 6-6B

PHOTO 6-6C

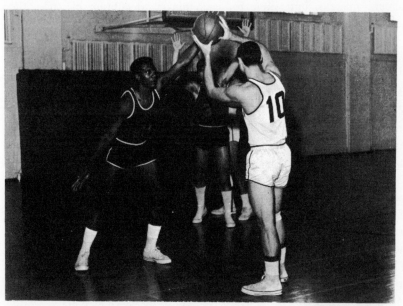

PHOTO 6-6D

until the switch back can occur. This is a good maneuver to employ when a 5'10" guard is forced to switch on a 6'9" pivot. The guard should front the pivot and force the high pass which should be intercepted by offside defensive help.

Three-on-Three

Diagram 6-11—Use the screen and roll formation. All phases of the screen can be covered. O1 dribbles past O2, and O2 breaks to the basket for a possible feedback. If O2 does not get a pass, O3 fakes to baseline and comes to foul line for outlet pass. O3 is then the outside dribbler, and O1 is on the right and O2 is on the left side. The move is then repeated. The defensive players X1, X2, and X3 make the appropriate defensive adjustment utilizing the switch, fight through, over the top, etc.

TEAM DEFENSE

There are situations when defensive players cannot prevent their men from obtaining an advantageous offensive position without help from their teammates. When personnel weaknesses and complicated offensive screens make it impossible for each player to contain his man, then team defense becomes necessary.

The various agencies which publish and exploit basketball statistics consider the teams which have the least number of points scored against them as the leading defensive teams. Yet, the best measure of defense is not just how few points are scored against a team. The final N.A.I.A. statistics one year listed Colorado Mines as the leading defensive team in the N.A.I.A. Colorado Mines had a poor won-lost record of 11 wins and 14 losses; yet, their opponents scored only 54.6 points per game against them.

The real tests of defense are: (1) The number of victories, and (2) point-spread rather than number points scored against a given team. The team that wins 120–118 has a better defense than a team that loses 30–31. A team which scores 100 points per game gives the opponent the ball twice as much as the team that scores 50 points per game. The more times the opponent has the ball, the tougher the defense has to be. An average point spread of 15 to 20 will produce a championship team. Therefore, this is the defensive goal to be set each year.

In the final analysis, the game of basketball reduces to one man shooting and one man assigned to guard the shooter. Regardless of the

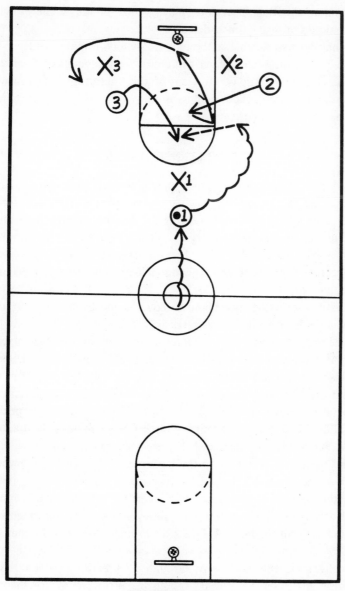

DIAGRAM 6-11

defensive structure or strategy, eventually all offensive plays culminate with one man shooting. Therefore, players must be taught the principles and techniques of man-to-man defense.

The man-to-man defense is the only one which remains 100 per cent aggressive at all times and which will cover troublesome situations without necessitating variations. In view of this factor, plus a desire for aggressive, pressure-packed defensive play, the man-to-man defense should be the basic defense.

TEAM DEFENSE DRILLS

Effective team defense demands player coordination and balanced floor coverage responsibilities. Each squad member should be placed in the floor area where he will be playing most of his defense, and taught the techniques necessary for carrying out the following responsibilities:

1. Primary responsibility (guarding his assigned man).
2. Secondary responsibility (giving half-man help to his closest teammate).
3. Tertiary responsibility (how to cover a loose offensive player when a defensive breakdown occurs).
4. The procedure to follow when more than one switch takes place.

The offensive team assumes a basic single pivot alignment. Diagram 6-12 illustrates this normal position. O1 has the ball. X1 plays him very tight and prevents him from easily passing the ball to a teammate. X2 sinks baseline and inward toward the ball. X2 then faces in a position which allows him to see his man with his left eye and the ball and offensive pivot with his right eye. He uses feinting motions toward his man and the pivot. X3 plays to the ball side of the pivot and prevents the pass to the pivot. X5, the offside forward, sinks baseline and inward toward the foul lane, then faces in a direction which permits him to keep his left eye on his man and his right eye on the ball, and then steps in front of O5, cutting him off if O5 tries to break to the ball either high or low.

The offensive team will walk through all situations which require defensive help. Defensive players should be instructed to use the most effective method to cover all possible defensive breakdowns.

Diagram 6-13 illustrates the defensive adjustments required to handle a simple defensive breakdown. X1 falls to the floor, allowing O1 to drive to the basket unguarded. X4 loosens from O4 and assumes a zone

DIAGRAM 6-12

DIAGRAM 6-13

attitude concerning the foul line area. X3 jumps in front of O1 and yells, "I have your man, take mine." X1, who must always quickly recover, dashes after O1 and takes O3. In some instances, X3 will merely jump out and stop O1 and then go back to his man. In this event, X3 yells, "Take your man," indicating to X1 that X3 is only using delay tactics to detain O1. There are many other defensive breakdown situations which must be covered from this basic defensive alignment.

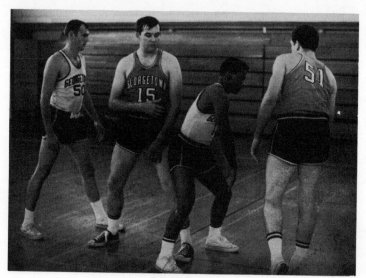

PHOTO 6-7

TYPES OF MAN-TO-MAN DEFENSE

Photo 6-7—Strict man-to-man (no switching) defense simply means that each man is assigned a member of the opposing team and he must stop him from scoring. There are two ways to play strict man-to-man defense. Photo 6-7 shows the first method called over the top. The defensive man goes over the top of the screen with help from the man guarding the screener.

Photos 6-4A & B—This shows the second method called fight-through. The defensive man is allowing one man between his man and himself.

Photos 6-2A & B—Switching when called by the back defensive player. Three methods of employing the switch. This shows the normal switch where X2 switches from O2 to O1 as the screen occurs. X1 switches from O1 to O2 as the screen takes place.

Photo 6-5—This shows the fake switch. X2 calls switch and acts as if he is going to take O1 but hurries back to cover O2. X1 ignores the called switch and stays with O1.

Photo 6-6—This shows the switch over the top. X2 calls the switch from O2 to O1. X1 continues over the top and switches to O2 in front of him.

Automatic switching when offensive men cross is the same as the normal switch above, but it is predetermined. The automatic switch is always made when offensive men cross, regardless of the situation. Many teams use this as a team defense when their players are of equal size and height.

COMBINATION DEFENSE

Diagram 6-14—The two guards, X1 and X2, are man-to-man and the three back men, X3, X4, and X5, are in a triangle zone. The only major adjustment necessary is the forward overload when both forwards move to one side—one high and the other low—and the pivot stays high. This will force a match up by one defensive forward—either X3 or X4.

This defense is very effective against a team which has one or two stars and otherwise mediocre personnel. This is an extremely effective defense against good guards.

ZONE DEFENSES

The zone defense is a very effective measure to use against the team that runs a continuity offense or a series of screens which is very difficult to handle with a man-to-man defense. There is a very definite need for zone defense, and each coach must be familiar with his personnel and their capabilities of employing the zone when it becomes necessary.

I have personally used the aggressive man-to-man and a pressure or half-court zone for a number of years. My concept of a zone defense is to apply defensive pressure or to press a majority of the time. I am opposed to a standing, shifting zone which does not attack the ball but merely moves around and places men on certain areas of the floor.

All of my zone defenses are divided into the one-man front and the two-man front. The normal one man front can be the 1-3-1, 3-2 or the 1-2-2, or the 1-1-3. The normal two man front can be the 2-3, the 2-1-2, or the 2-2-1.

DIAGRAM 6-14

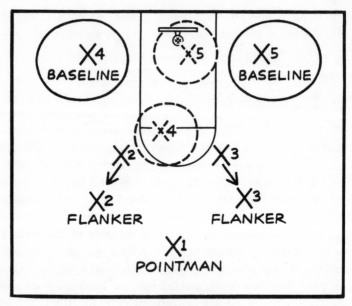

DIAGRAM 6-15

NORMAL ONE-MAN FRONT ZONE

Diagram 6-15—The one-man front such as the 1-3-1 is very effective against an offensive team that uses a one-man front. The one-man front defense is also very effective against a team that has a strong pivot or that uses baseline pivots or utilizes the forward movement in their guard play.

The point man in the one-man front should be a large guard with good movement patterns and capable of stopping the dribbler. He should also be very adept at preventing the ball from going around the horn. The basic rule for the point man on the one-man front defense is to keep the ball away from the middle and the high pivot. The one-man front point man also should be adept at piling on when the double-team occurs. The middleman or pivot play in the one-man front defense is no different than the man-to-man or the two-man front coverage. It is simply a matter of preventing the ball from penetrating the middle area and also guarding whoever is in the middle area man to man. The flankers must play higher and be ready to pick the ball up faster in the one-man front than in the two-man front. Both flankers must stay out on the floor and be capable of helping the point man. The baseline man is simply a rebounder or an addition to the baseline defense.

There is very little difference between the normal one-man front zone defense and the half-court pressing defense. The half-court press starts at the midcourt line and double-team traps are used more frequently than in the normal defensive alignment. The pointman X1 has the responsibility of forcing the ball out of the middle, which requires that the defensive flankers X2 and X3 stop the dribbler. By playing back near the top of the foul circle, the point man is in a better position to keep the ball from going to the pivot in the high position. The flankers X2 and X3 pick the dribbler up deeper and more "inside-out" which prevents inside penetration. The baseline men X4 and X5 have more outside help and can concentrate on protecting the basket area and covering the rebound triangle. The baseline men X4 and X5 must apply a reasonable amount of match-up in order to be in the needed area of the floor. (The dotted lines indicate coverage against an offensive high-low alignment.)

NORMAL TWO-MAN FRONT ZONE

Diagram 6-16—The two-man front defense is necessary when an offensive team has two excellent outside players who can get open and hit the high percentage shot from 20 to 25 feet in the areas on both sides of the top of the key. The major difference in this normal two-man front and half-court pressing two-man front is the area and stunts. In the normal defense, there is a concentrated effort to protect the basket area and position the defense to control the rebounds and initiate the fast break. There is very little double-teaming and generally the outside and corner shots are allowed without too much pressure. Adjustments can be made to pressure the outside and corner shots and still maintain normal defensive structure.

The two outside men X1 and X2 are generally the guards who are used to defense the long shot. The middleman X4 acts as a normal defensive pivot and takes the offensive men in the middle almost man to man. When a team uses two deep pivots, the middle men protect deep, and the offside guard and the offside flanker cover the middle area. The two flankers X3 and X5 start high and cover deep as the ball penetrates front court. Or flankers will go to the corner with the ball, and the offside flanker shifts over and protects high or low depending upon the position of the middleman X4.

The two-man front defense is used when an offensive team uses an attack where the two guards or two players out front try to station themselves in the good shooting area and take the shot the instant they are open. When the two-man front attack is effective, then the zone that is being used that night must return to a two-man front coverage. This can be done in many ways and with many alignments, but it is necessary that the shooting spots out front have two men in order to cover the two potential scorers.

Another reason for utilizing the zone defense is to station the defensive men in a position to utilize the fast break immediately. Several coaches throughout the country use what is called a fast break defense. Fast break defense simply means a defense which will allow the fast break to be started the instant the ball is recovered. The best fast break defense is the 2-3 or the 2-1-2. This permits the two guards or the ball handlers to be in an ideal position to become an outlet and lead man on the break. The three big men deploy themselves in a triangle around the basket and grab a majority of the rebounds.

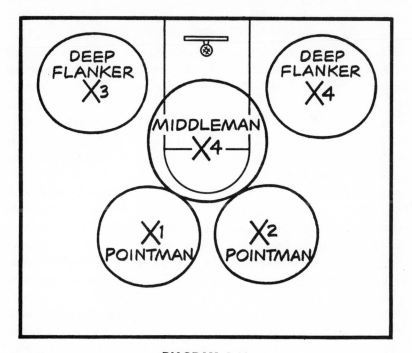

DIAGRAM 6-16

It is good strategy to use a zone defense in order to initiate the fast break. A good fast break team can get all players organized into an efficient pattern and get down the floor much faster if the defensive players play in the same areas at all times.

MATCH-UP ZONE

Match-up zone defenses are very similar to combination defenses, automatic switching defenses, and modified zones. However, the match-up is a very effective defense to use when an offensive team shifts to a zone offense from a man-to-man offense; in other words, to an offense which is more effective against a man-to-man defense than a zone.

When an offensive team changes offenses, the defensive man can confuse the offensive team by switching, not back to a man-to-man defense, but to a match-up which looks very much like a man-to-man.

In the match-up defense, players are playing man to man within an area, and wherever the offensive man goes, the defense will match up a man and move with him. This prevents the offensive team from obtaining an overload of the zone. Of course, the overload is one of the most effective ways to attack the zone. The defensive team, by switching to a match-up, can prevent the overload simply by overloading the defense to the side of the offensive overload.

DISADVANTAGES OF THE MATCH-UP ZONE

The major disadvantage of the match-up defense is the difficulty in establishing basic rules. The assignment of men requires rules, and these rules are very hard to formulate. Each coach who deals with the match-up defense must become aware of the necessity for basic rules which will cover whole situations. As an example, the player on the point or the player out front must have certain assignments. The flankers must have certain assignments. Then, as the offensive team moves through specific areas, the match-up will take place and create a man-to-man situation against any type of offensive overload or double or triple screens.

Regardless of the structure of the zone used, variations must be made to handle overloads and abnormal spacing of offensive players. In the past, I have used several numbered structures to teach the variation necessary to make each defense work. This can be very confusing to players. The simple method of using either a one-man front or a two-man front zone eliminates teaching a multitude of variations. Of course, numbered zones will probably cover the floor better against various offensive situations; however, the simplicity in instruction will outweigh the advantage gained if the defensive team will let hustle be the difference.

SUMMARY

Defensive basketball demands aggressive players who care enough to send their very best. Years ago I heard a wise old doctor give some words of wisdom to a young recruit; "Son, as you enter the Navy and head down life's long trail, keep one thing in mind. *Never roll dice on a blanket.*"

The advice sounds rather trite and simple, but it is the key to the intelligent coaching of basketball. It simply means never play the other man's game. If the opponent can control the tempo and run his patterns uninhibited, he will generally win. The ability to play superior defense will keep a team from having to play the other man's game.

In order to play aggressive individual defense, players must master the techniques of maintaining a proper balance position. They must also learn to keep the elbows out, and "flash" them occasionally. They must be prepared to put their hands in the opponent's "choppers" and dare him to score. A squad must be prepared to meet the enemy and conquer him. They must stop the opponent or be defeated, no "mugwumping."

There simply isn't any comfortable course to take when teaching defense. A team either wins or loses. Each player either prevents his man from scoring on him or he suffers defeat. Another sure thing is that there is no fast way to teach defense, and the coach who looks for one is only kidding himself. Teaching defense requires perseverance, patience, tenacity, and unbelievable repetition.

7

Pressing Defenses
for Team Aggressiveness

REASONS FOR USING PRESSING DEFENSES

Using pressing defenses will greatly enhance team aggressiveness. They cause all players to enter into the spirit of things. When one team member steals the ball, the other players respond to the challenge. There is a tremendous excitement involved when these particular stratagems are working.

The press is used to create confusion, to make a team hurry its passes and shots, and to change the tempo of the game. All coaches should have several pressing defenses in their repertory. This will force opposing coaches to use a portion of the practice time, allocated to a particular foe, to prepare their teams to cope with the press. And, of course, employing the press also permits the offensive players an opportunity to become acquainted with its techniques.

A CONCISE SIGNAL SYSTEM FOR CALLING DEFENSES

The signal system used to set each defense in motion should be simple and easy for all squad members to comprehend. When the defensive structures aren't complicated, it's easier to establish a more elementary signal system.

One proven method for activating the signal is to use colors for court position and numbers for the style of defense. Odd numbers should be used to call the one-man front defense, and even numbers for the two-man front defense. Single digits will activate the man-to-man defense. If the defense is to be full-court, red can be used, and white called for three-quarter defense. Blue signifies that a half-court defense will be put into operation. Therefore, if "13 red" is called, this would mean that a full-court one-man front press will be used.

By using a brief signal system, players do not become confused, and it is easy for the coach to communicate with his defensive unit. There are many other means of calling or sending signals. Some coaches use the last digit of the home scoreboard to activate their defense. Others have managers hold up signs from the bench.

The best time to call the defensive signal is while the team is still on offense. The guard who has been designated as defensive captain will make the defensive call as the ball is moved into offensive front court. Each coach must work out his own signal system but, above all, should strive for simplicity and ease of communication.

STRONG AND WEAK POINTS OF PRESSING DEFENSES

A better way to understand pressing defenses is to examine their strong and weak points.

STRONG POINTS OF THE PRESS

A. It utilizes individual team members who are endowed with unusual defensive abilities.
B. It reduces the effectiveness of the systematic offensive teams, because complicated play patterns cannot be run against a good press.
C. It helps to increase the effectiveness of normal defensive play by developing a more aggressive attitude toward defense.
D. It permits players in superior condition to take advantage of the opponent.

WEAK POINTS OF THE PRESS

A. The press demands a balanced effort and responsibility on the part of each player. Therefore, one weak defensive man cannot be as satisfactorily compensated for as with a normal defensive alignment.
B. When double-teaming or gambling for the ball, there is a greater risk that the offensive team can outnumber the defensive men guarding the goal.
C. Pressing defenses demand that team members possess a higher degree of physical conditioning than players using a normal defense.
D. As a general rule, pressing defenses require quicker personnel than normal zones or man-to-man defenses.

The advantages and disadvantages of the full, three-quarter, and half-court pressing defenses depend entirely upon the nature of the defense employed. The half-court press is a safer defense than the three-quarter or full-court press because the recovery area is reduced in size.

DEFENSIVE STRUCTURES

The same defensive structure should be used for full, three-quarter, and half-court pressing. It is very difficult for players to full or three-quarter press with a zone structure and then play a half-court man-to man defense. The same coverage should be employed over the entire court. As the defense is extended over the court, the floor coverage can be altered by either reducing or enlarging the zones. The idea is to have single floor coverage and insist that hustle and aggressiveness make the defense work. Players *should not* be burdened with complicated structures. They should have one or two basic structures and then cover the floor by burning the rubber on their shoes. Aggressive players will make any structure work effectively.

After several years of experimenting with various numbered structures for full, three-quarter, and half-court alignment, I have finally divided my defense into the (1) one-man front zone, (2) the two-man front zone, and (3) the man-to-man defense. In the one-man front zone one defensive player is out front on the point and the other four men are positioned as if in a 1-2-2, 1-3-1, 1-1-3, or 1-2-1-1. The alignment will depend on the opponent.

The two-man front zone will have two defensive players out front, and the other players will be positioned as if in a 2-3, 2-1-2, 2-2-1, or any alignment to coincide with the opponent's distribution of offensive players. The two-man front is needed many times to funnel the ball, to prevent the overload, or to handle an effective two-man offensive front.

The man-to-man defense can be very aggressive, double-teaming, trapping, aggravating, or normal, depending upon personnel, officials, and whether the game is at home or away.

HALF-COURT PRESSING DEFENSES

The One-Man Front Half-Court Press

The one-man front half-court defense remains the same and adjusts in structure to the offense. This defense is considered a match-up zone by many. However, a basic structure can be predetermined according to scout reports. Adjustments to shifts are then made by following the ball. In Diagram 7-1, the point man X1 must keep the ball out of the middle

DIAGRAM 7-1

and prevent the ball from going around the horn. The flankers, X2 and X3, must attack the dribbler when the ball is out beyond the top of the foul circle and prevent inside penetration. He should turn the dribbler to the outside or sidelines so the baseline man can pile on the ball. When the ball is on one side of the floor, the offside flanker must begin his slide to the basket. If one of the baseline men is deep, the flanker takes high pivot. If a baseline man is in high pivot, the flanker takes deep pivot position.

The two baseline men X4 and X5 must coordinate their action in order that one baseline man is always prepared to take the high pivot position while the other baseline man covers the corner area. Both baseline men must never leave the basket at the same time regardless of the situation.

The point man must keep the ball out of the high pivot area. As the ball is moved from side to side, the two baseline men will change position. Each will guard the high pivot depending on where the ball is. As the two baseline men protect the area close to the basket, they must receive help from the two flankers. If the offensive opponent is using two deep pivots, the flankers are responsible for the high foul line area and do not come back as far as they normally would. If the ball goes to the corner, the strong side baseline player moves to the corner.

RULE FOR THE ONE-MAN FRONT HALF-COURT ZONE:

1. Each player must know his basic area of the floor and what offensive player can come into it.
2. All players must watch the ball and adjust floor area as the ball moves.
3. All players *must look around* (baseball head-moving).
4. Always pick out the man to guard in relation to where the ball is located.
5. Always take the dribbler soft when two men are in one zone.
6. When in doubt, play soft. When sure, play tight and tough man to man.
7. The point man must stay on the point.
8. Stop the dribbler as soon as possible. (The dribbler should be stopped after the ball is two yards across midline.)
9. The first man from the point men belongs to the flankers, and the first man from the baseline man belongs to the flankers.
10. Both baseline men never go to the corner. (The flanker on the strong side gives help in case of an overload.)
11. Some defensive teammate must run the defensive player away from the man he is guarding if his man has the ball and moves into another area of the floor.

The Two-Man Front Half-Court Press

The two-man front zone defense is needed when the opponent is using a two-man front offensive attack and has good outside shooters and ball handlers.

Following are the three basic maneuvers of the two-man front half-court press, which utilizes the attack defensive philosophy:

Diagram 7-2—Go maneuver. The three men out front must change their attack on the ball handler and use fakes, etc., to rattle him. A defensive player should never allow the ball handler to guess with him. When the ball comes in deep, the baseline man X3 must act as a gap shooter, but the other baseline man X5 must watch and protect against

DIAGRAM 7-2

a player slipping in the back way. If a team is either placing or running a man into the middle, the middle anticipator X4 must not move away and leave the middle open. Point men X1 and X2 and middleman X4 must protect against a man breaking through the defense for a feedback. Someone must follow him for the interception. He should be taken man for man until the defense can regroup.

Diagram 7-3—Scatter maneuver. This is used when the middle offensive player has been throwing the ball just as the point men make their initial move. Both point men X1 and X2 should take one step toward the offensive man, then scatter to each side. If the offensive player does not throw the ball, the anticipator X4 will take him and the two will regroup. If the middle offensive player O1 passes the ball to offensive player O2, X1 will continue on over for interception. X2 will recover as soon as he sees the ball going the other way and try to regroup to the freethrow line in time to help take the middle offensive man O4. Any time a charge does not work, the defense should regroup

DIAGRAM 7-3

to the basket area and start over again. If the ball is close to the basket, the offense should be forced into throwing it back out on the court near midline.

Diagram 7-4—Corner trap. The point men X1 and X2 attempt to force the ball to either side by playing strong to one side. At the same time, the anticipator X4 takes two to three steps in the direction in which the ball will be forced. When the ball does go to the side, both point men X1 and X2 move to a position between the ball and the middle offensive man, making the corner the most likely place for the next pass. When the ball goes to the corner, the baseline man X3 and the anticipator X4 immediately pile on, followed by the strong side point man X1 who stops in position to cut off the pass out to offensive man O2. The offside point man X2 moves to a position near the top of the circle and becomes an anticipator moving to intercept the ball if it is passed out. The offside baseline man X5 moves under the basket.

These three basic attacks are supplemented with:

DIAGRAM 7-4

1. A normal man-to-man defense with an occasional double-team trap action.
2. One-man front half-court zone.
3. Combination man-to-man and match-up defense.*

The Man-to-Man Half-Court Press

Diagram 7-5—Defensive players X1 and X2 permit the ball to cross the mid-court line. They then jump the dribbler and use the midline as a half-man helper. The baseline players X3, X4 and X5 cover their men very tightly and employ prevent-and-pressure tactics. Each player involved in the half-court press or pressure defense must realize that *he has no defensive sink help.* If the player he is assigned to guard whips him on a reverse action, he will have an open shot under the basket. Also, there is no defensive player available to intercept the high pass to the deep-breaking offensive pivot.

*Davis, Bob. "Georgetown's Half-Court Zone Press," *The Athletic Journal,* Vol. XL, No. 2 (1959), p. 10.

DIAGRAM 7-5

Before a team can successfully employ the man-to-man half-court press, all five defensive players must be capable of containing their men with only normal half-man help from teammates and sidelines. There is no one available to render defensive help on a loose offensive player when a defensive breakdown occurs. The only way a half-court press or pressure defense can be successful is if the safety feature of normal defense is sacrificed in order to make possible broken patterns and interceptions. A defensive team using the half-court press cannot "have its cake and eat it, too," because the press is predicated upon the gambling element of overplay. The defensive team should keep so much pressure on the offense that they cannot successfully use offensive reverse actions or backdoor play.

When using the half-court press it is mandatory that some basic guides be established. (1) Any time a dribbler turns his back to his teammates, the nearest defensive player must try for the double-team steal. (2) When an effective double-team is taking place, the other defensive players should anticipate the primary receivers and gamble for the interception. (3) Once a defensive player starts for the interception, he continues through the act and then uses a cutoff recovery path to the basket. (4) Force the ball to the corners as much as possible and use a double-team trap action automatically in all four corners.

FULL-COURT PRESSING DEFENSES

The full-court pressing defense is similar in many details to all pressure defenses. The zone phases of the presses utilized employ the zone principle of floor coverage. The man-to-man differs from most defenses in one respect—that of gaming with offside players.

Following are several basic principles of the full-court press:

1. Set the defensive alignment in a hurry.
2. Never remain for any length of time in the same defensive alignment.
3. Know the weakness of the various defenses that will be used, and compensate in the event of a personnel breakdown.
4. Have explicit rules for floor coverage and recover routes.
5. Never charge the fast dribbler; wait and let him come to the defensive man.
6. Do not allow the offensive dribbler going up the sidelines to

continue in that direction unless a stunt has been called. Force him back to the middle of the court where help is available.

7. Watch for the floater; assign a man to cover the expectant floater.

8. Never permit one offensive pass to cut off two defensive men. (When this occurs, *call off the full and three-quarter press and use a half-court press.*)

The One-Man Front Full-Court Press

Diagram 7-6—In order for the one-man front zone to operate successfully, the point man X1 must be an alert, aggressive player who has the ability to pile on and to prevent the ball from going back around the horn. A tall player is desirable for this position, but a small, quick-handed man who can force an offensive player to pick up the dribble will suffice. Flanker X2 should be left-handed if at all possible in order to force most right-handed dribblers back toward the middle of the floor where the double-team can occur. Flanker X3 should be right-handed and capable of shooting the gap for the interception. Most teams will go to their right the majority of the time. Therefore, flanker X3 will be called upon to intercept the ball many times. Middleman X4 should be a tall rangy player who has the ability to prevent the feed to the middle area. Baseline man X5 must be very fast and capable of protecting the basket against two men. He must also be adept at intercepting long passes. His ability to set the trap, and to gamble, will many times decide the success of the defense.

Diagram 7-7—One of the basic setups which is used to initiate the one-man front zone press is the steal. X1 plays in the middle area and forces the ball to one side or the other and then helps to double-team the ball handler. Flanker X2 either waits for or charges the ball handler. Flanker X3 acts as a cutoff man to prevent the feedback to the throw-in man or any floater coming into the area. X4 prevents the long pass. X5 also prevents the long pass and guards back if the opponents place a man deep.

Diagram 7-8—Another of the basic setups which is used to initiate the one-man front zone press is the trap action. X1 forces the ball to one side and follows the throw-in man to prevent the feedback. Flanker X2 covers O2 half-man and permits O2 to dribble up the court at three-quarter speed. Flanker X3 comes up the floor in position to prevent

DIAGRAM 7-6

DIAGRAM 7-7

DIAGRAM 7-8

any cross-court pass and covers the freethrow line. Middleman X4 comes back, and as the dribbler crosses into the front court, charges him for a double-team with X2. Baseline X5 watches for a long pass and goes back deep for the shut-off pass.

These two basic structures are supplemented by using: (1) A full-court man-to-man press occasionally, and, (2) by changing the alignment of the basic zone attacks.*

The Two-Man Front Full-Court Press

The two-man front full-court press must be used against opponents who successfully employ the two-man front offensive attack. It is also necessary to funnel the ball into the middle. In Diagram 7-9 the two point men X1 and X2 are attacking the ball, and the two flankers X3 and X4 are moving toward the two primary receivers to prevent the advance pass. The baseline man X5 moves to a deep interception position and prevents the long pass.

Diagram 7-10—The inbounds pass has been made to O3 and point man X2 and flanker X4 are attacking the ball. X1 and X3 are covering primary receivers. X5 has revolved to a deep-side position. Sometimes X4 and X1 must rotate back to a deeper position and permit the ball to be easily passed back toward the inbounds position.

The advantage of the two-man front defense is that it has the point man and flankers in ideal position to pile on the ball on the sidelines. It is not as strong up the middle as the one-man front defense. However, when the offensive team is not using the middle, this poses no problem.

The Man-to-Man Full-Court Press

The man-to-man full-court press will always be a great defense and should constantly be employed by an aggressive team. Many nights the defensive players are capable of manhandling their opponents and should be afforded the opportunity. The man-to-man defense forces an offensive team to clear most of their players up the court and allows one player to advance the ball by dribbling. This offensive act, while effective against the man-to-man defense, is ineffective against the various zone defenses which capitalize on the double-team capabilities of the zone press.

The offensive team is kept off balance when the defensive squad mixes the man-to-man press with the various zone presses. By constantly

*Davis, Bob. "Full-Court Zone Press," *Athletic Journal*, Vol. XLIII, No. 4 (1962), p. 16.

DIAGRAM 7-9

DIAGRAM 7-10

changing defenses, the offensive team is not permitted time enough to stabilize its attack.

Another advantage of the man-to-man full-court press is that it is easier for the defense to place pressure on the ball while it is out of bounds. There are two proven ways to accomplish this goal. First, by placing a long-armed, frantic defensive player in position to wave his arms and prevent the inbound pass, the defensive player can cause the offensive player to panic. He is made acutely aware of the pressure of the five and ten second rules. Secondly, two defensive players can pressure the inbounds offensive player and ignore the offensive player out of bounds with the ball. This permits a double-team on the primary inbounds receiver, and forces the offensive team to make the inbounds pass to a weaker ball handler.

THREE-QUARTER PRESSING DEFENSES

The One-Man Front Three-Quarter Press

Diagram 7-11—The point man X1 waits on the dribbler O1 and forces him to the sideline. Flanker X3 retreats and guards any receiver in his area (O2) until the point man forces the dribbler to cross mid-court line. Flanker X3 attacks the dribbler O1 when he reaches the line. The point man X1 can either double-team the dribbler O1 or can cover primary receivers and allow flanker X3 to take the dribbler man for man. Flanker X2 retreats back as the ball advances and maneuvers into position for the possible interception. The middleman X4 must keep the pivot area covered to prevent the ball from being passed into this area. Baseline man X5 remains in the area of the basket and protects it until help comes, then moves to the corner if he's needed there.

Two-Man Front Three-Quarter Press

This defense is very effective against an offense employing the dribble to advance the ball. The advantage of the three-quarter press over the full-court press is that by the time the ball has reached three-quarter court, the defensive team should have been able to force the ball to one side of the court, and this permits the offside flanker to cover the middle area of the court.

Diagram 7-12—The two point men X1 and X2 are forcing the ball toward the sideline in order that flanker X3 can maintain a position which permits him to cover the middle area of the floor. The baseline

DIAGRAM 7-11

DIAGRAM 7-12

man X5 must play more cautiously because the offensive man with the ball can throw to the scoring area much more quickly than in the full-court setup. The baseline man X5 must also play more carefully in the three-quarter press and not gamble for the interception unless a defensive stunt has been called. If a stunt is on, one of the flankers X3 or X4 will cover for the baseline man X5.

Two-Man Front Three-Quarter Press

The man-to-man three quarter press should utilize the automatic switch as much as possible. This permits the jump-switch and creates more double-team situations. It also allows better coverage on unguarded offensive players when a defensive breakdown occurs.

Diagram 7-13—The two defensive players X1 and X2 will pick up any player who comes into their areas and will play them "skintight." The baseline players X3, X4, and X5 will play their men tight also and prevent them from receiving the pass. If their men move toward the baseline, they play between them and the ball and use cutoff tactics to prevent them from breaking to meet the ball.

DRILLS FOR TEACHING PRESSING TECHNIQUES

I use very few drills for teaching pressing defenses. The most effective way to teach defensive pressing is to use all five players who will be involved in the defense and allow them to work together as a unit. When rehearsing floor coverage patterns, all five men must move at the same time as if they were tied together with a string. However, individual pressing techniques can be improved by utilizing proper drills.

Initial Position Drill

Diagram 7-14— Spots are taped on the floor where each defensive player should be when the press is initiated. The team preparing to commence the press should use a half-court offense and strive to score. The instant they either score or lose the ball, all players must sprint to their basic positions and then begin the press attack. The initial positions will vary according to the nature of the defense taught.

Turn the Dribbler In

Diagram 7-15—The offensive man O1, using fakes and pivots, tries to dribble up the sideline to midcourt. The defensive player X1 turns

DIAGRAM 7-13

DIAGRAM 7-14

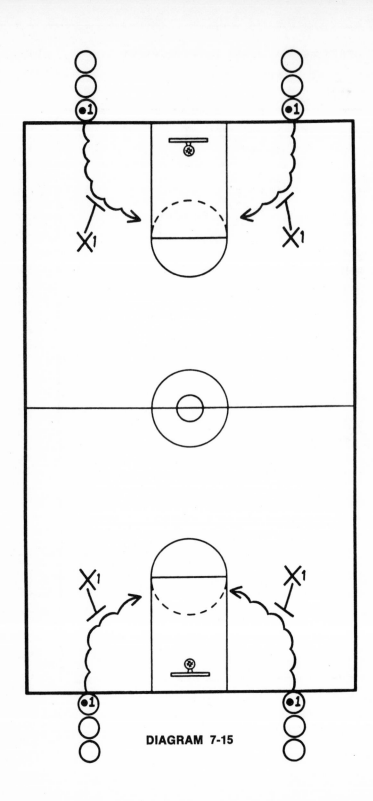

DIAGRAM 7-15

the dribbler toward the middle of the court and maintains as much pressure as possible.

Reaction Drill

Diagram 7-16—A circle two feet in diameter is drawn in the center of the foul circle. A defensive player X1 is placed in the circle facing the coach. O1 has the ball and can pass either to O4 or O2. As O1 throws the ball, X1 must move in the direction of the player receiving the pass. The number of steps that X1 takes toward the ball while it is in flight is recorded. He returns to his original position as soon as O2 has the ball in his possession. O2 waits until X1 is back in his position and then throws to either O1 or O3. When O2 or O3 has the ball, X1 must still face the coach, but he uses his peripheral vision in order to see the ball as it is thrown.

Recovery Drill

Diagram 7-17—Before starting the drill, half of the squad should be on offense (O), lined up out of bounds on the sideline. The remainder of the squad will be in equal defensive groups at both ends of the court. O1 starts the drill by rebounding the ball, running out of bounds, and throwing a baseball pass to O2 who is stationed at the point where the foul line extended would intersect the sideline. O2 dribbles the ball to the opposite basket for a crip shot. O3 follows as a rebounder. As O2 receives the ball, X1, who is behind the endline, tries to chase O2 down and prevent the clear crip shot. The same procedure is followed at the opposite end of the floor.

SUMMARY

The aggressive coach will spend considerable time perfecting his pressing defenses. The dividends received for working on the press will be multifold. Squad aggressiveness will increase as practice on pressing defenses progresses. Normal defensive play will be improved, and players will begin to show more inner toughness.

The major value of pressing defenses is their effect on the opponent. Opposing coaches have a tendency to "brainwash" their players as they prepare to meet a team with a reputation of extensively using pressing defenses. They tell their squads that the opponent's press is devastating, and they plant fears in the minds of their players. This helps the pressing

COACH WITH ⊗ STOPWATCH

DIAGRAM 7-16

team, because the offensive ball handlers will be nervous and will play cautiously.

The pressing defense is a comforting weapon to possess when normal defenses are not working and the opponent begins to build up a sizable lead. When the press is employed, the tempo of the game will quicken, and the players will start moving with renewed speed. Even the offensive tempo will improve once squad members begin to run at an increased rate.

The aggressive coach must always have some means of taking an opponent apart if the need arises. Good pressing techniques can come as close to doing this as anything in the game.

The proof of the puddin' is—how many coaches actually look forward to having their teams meet a devastating press?

DIAGRAM 7-17

8

Aggression-Plus
for Players of Limited Height

I was given the honor of being one of the coaches for the U.S.A. Team of Limited Height. This team participated in the first Intercontinental Tournament which was held in Barcelona, Spain. All participants in this tournament had to be under one meter eighty centimeters or less than 5'11".

The U.S.A. won the tournament championship by defeating teams from France, the Philippines and Spain. The only defeat suffered on the tour was a four point loss to Brazil in the opening round of the tournament. After the tournament ended, the team flew to Portugal and played in a two-game tournament plus one additional game. The small men won all three of these games. The team ended the tour with a record of six wins, one loss, and two Intercontinental Championship trophies for the U.S.A.

NEED FOR AGGRESSIVENESS

My experience with the small men emphasized beliefs I already held concerning the success of relatively short players. When a team does not have height or size, it must rely heavily on speed and aggressiveness. The U.S.A. aggregation of small men consisted of extremely aggressive boys. All the members of the squad were guards who had won berths on their college or university teams by sheer hustle and determination. Each player was fast, quick of foot and hand, agile and very clever. They also possessed the mental toughness to respond to the aggressive style of basketball very readily. The fast break and pressing defense was exactly the style of play that complemented their physical facilities. In order for the small man to survive in the game of basketball today he must be aggressive almost to the point of being vicious. He must practice and play in a more physically taxing manner than taller players. The lesson here is simple. What a player lacks in stature and power, he must make up for with split-second, devil-to-pay maneuvering.

157

PHOTO 8-1

NO SMALL FEAT. The United States team shown above recently won the "small man" world basketball championship in a Barcelona, Spain, tournament. Front row, left to right, Bobby Lewis, Mike Carson, Bill Suter, Jerry Williams and Roger Cordell. Second row: Bill Harley, Allen Eakers, John Fontanella, Ron Yates and Henry Logan. Back row: assistant coach Bob Davis of Georgetown College, Ky., and coach John McLendon, Cleveland State University.

CONDITIONING FOR THE SMALL MAN

Coach John McLendon and I decided that our only hope for victory in the Intercontinental Tournament would be insistence that the team which went overseas be in excellent condition—a team capable of obtaining and maintaining a peak of physical conditioning beyond the reach of average basketball players.

The primary demand made of the squad was that each team member report to practice in absolutely top shape. Coach McLendon wrote each player and informed him that his condition would be tested upon arrival at the training site. This would be accomplished by having him run one mile in less than six minutes. Once a player could break the six minute mark, he was permitted to leave the track. These players who had to run were timed each day before the early morning practice. As squad members broke the six minute mile, they were removed from the list for compulsory running.

Another factor that helped increase the condition of the small man squad was that they practiced three times a day. They practiced at 8:00 in the morning, 1:00 in the afternoon, and again at 6:30 in the evening. They had six days of three-a-day practices before they left the states to fly to Barcelona, Spain. In six days the squad had to perfect already faultless physical condition, master an offense, defense, fast break, and other special situations such as out-of-bounds plays, jump ball, etc.

Since conditioning was a major factor, most of the drills which were used during practice periods involved a great deal of running. We used fast break, defensive pressing, and other drills which required traveling the full length of the court.

FAST BREAK

Because of the speed and maneuverability of the players who composed the Small Man's Team, the fast break was naturally the easiest phase of the game to teach. Each player, having been a guard, understood the necessity of moving the ball rapidly to the offensive end of the floor and obtaining the numerical advantage of the defense in the least amount of time.

The only problem that existed was obtaining possession of the necessary amount of rebounds. Fortunately, three of the small men were adept at rebounding and throwing the snappy outlet pass. The fast break became the number one offensive weapon. Within a week, the team could move the ball from the defensive end of the floor to their basket in less than four seconds.

The fast break patterns used were very similar to the ones found in Chapter 4 of this book. We used only two in order to expedite matters. In addition to the normal coverage, the forwards were used to fill the center lane and to handle the ball more than they would under normal conditions. All of the forwards were experienced in advancing the ball up the middle lane, and this made the fast break even more effective.

As the tournaments progressed in Spain and Portugal, most opponents were assigning two defensive players to stop our fast break. This, of course, aided the rebounders by giving the small men the opportunity to completely control the defensive boards.

REBOUNDING

Rebounding is a major problem in planning a balanced attack when small men have the responsibility of controlling the boards. The only way that a small man can possibly rebound with players who are taller and stronger is by fast foot action, tremendous block-out and great second effort.

The offensive plays used by the small men were designed to place three rebounders on the board at the culmination of the play with a fourth player stationed on the foul line to control the long rebound. This left only one man back for defense; however, all rebounders were instructed to "pile on" the opponent who recovered the rebound and force him to delay his outlet pass. This maneuver gave the other team members time to get back to their defensive position.

The clever rebounder who could rebound the ball and pass it out swiftly did not manage to do so consistently because the opponents' fast breaks did not score with any regularity. For the seven games, the small men outrebounded their opponents by approximately ten rebounds per ball game. In one particular contest, the opponents recovered only one offensive rebound for the night. The block-out at this stage of the overseas playing was very effective, and the fast break was causing the opponent to leave the offensive rebound in order to set their defense.

There are many ways to control the boards even though a team does not have enough tall players. The main point to stress is defensive and offensive blocking out. Our small men were instructed to concentrate on preventing the opponent in their area of the floor from having a clear opportunity at the ball. They were told to attack the defensive rebounder and to block out the offensive rebounder. This helped them obtain more than an even break on the boards.

Shorter players are faster and can master block-out techniques much more easily than larger, slower players. Therefore, the wise decision for the smaller rebounder is to concentrate on block-out and to spend more time getting in position to recover the rebound than actually trying to develop his ability to jump for the ball. Some coaches brag that they don't work on block-out or fighting around the block-out because their players are tall and can jump well. Naturally, if a team has tall players, the time spent for teaching block-out will be reduced.

OFFENSE

The offense used consisted of four basic single-post plays which were simple to learn and easy to execute. All variations or options were left to the discretion of the individual players. This type of offense would need supplementing to be effective for high school players of less experience. However, we felt that the set offense would have to remain very basic and easy for the players to master since time was of the essence. The primary moves of all plays were uncomplicated, and the precise timing elements were removed. Each player was given considerable freedom of choice in the execution of all plays. Because of their ease in understanding, oral signals were used.

As a general rule, offensive basketball is very difficult to teach, and many coaches make the mistake of using too much of their practice time mastering complicated plays. By using intricately constructed patterns and devoting more than 50 per cent of the practice time to offense, the coach is depriving himself of sufficient time to teach defense. The wise coach will never allow more than half of his practice time to be spent on offense. The remaining half, out of necessity, must be spent on defense.

Following are the four basic plays used by the small man team:

Diagram 8-1—Play Number One. O1 has the ball and makes an air pass to O5 and breaks inside and all the way out to become the defensive safety man. O5 receives the pass and has several options. First, he can dribble to the basket either baseline or over the top of the pivot O4. Second, he can pass the ball to the pivot O4 and go for a score. Third, he can pass the ball to O4 and go set a screen for O2. Fourth, he can dribble the ball over and flip pass to O2 who comes around for the drive to the basket or the jump shot. O2 stays out of the play until he sees what O5 is going to do with the ball. Then he breaks to get the ball if needed. The only timing needed for the execution of this play is O2 meeting O5 at the proper time. O4 breaks to the strong side of the foul line as O1 makes the pass to O5. O3 stays out of the ball exchange area and uses the necessary movements to free himself for rebound position since he is the primary offensive rebounder.

Diagram 8-2—Play Number Two is the screen and roll maneuver. O1 calls O5 up to set a screen on his defensive man X1. O5 comes up and screens X1 and rolls to the basket looking for a feedback from O1. As this action is taking place, O4 goes over and screens X3 and rolls to the basket for the primary rebounding responsibility. O3 delays, fakes opposite, and breaks to the foul line as a safety outlet for O1. O2 remains out of the ball exchange area and becomes the defensive safety man.

DIAGRAM 8-1

Diagram 8-3—In Play Number Three, which is a pivot deep setup, O1 has the ball. O2 breaks down the middle for a possible pass and crip shot. If O2 does not receive the ball, he continues on out and becomes the defensive safety man. As O2 breaks down the middle, O3 moves to the opposite foul lane deep and becomes the primary rebounder. O4 breaks up to the edge of the foul line as O2 touches the three-second area. O4 then receives a pass from O1 and feeds O1 back on a split-the-pivot action. O5 stays out of the ball exchange area, then comes to the foul line as an outlet safety man and rebounder.

Diagram 8-4—Play Number Four. The guard O1 with the ball moves over near the sideline before he starts the play. O1 throws a bounce pass to O5 and breaks outside. O5 flips the ball back to O1 and sprints to the opposite foul lane deep and sets up as the primary rebounder. O4 comes over and screens O1's defensive man X1. O1 and O4 use a screen and roll (mismatch) for the score. O3 maneuvers into rebounding position. O2 remains out of the ball exchange area and becomes the defensive safety man. There are several options available: (1) Guard

DIAGRAM 8-2

DIAGRAM 8-3

O1 takes a return flip pass from the forward O5 and drives the baseline.
(2) Guard O1 takes the ball on the dribble and looks for a play.

DEFENSE

Once the small men were assembled, it seemed reasonable that the
most effective defense to use would be the aggressive man-to-man
defense. However, as the six days of practice time diminished, it became
evident that the ten man squad did not include ten great defensive players. The team was handicapped by having several boys who were not as
strong defensively as we had anticipated. Therefore, the obvious necessity for utilizing a zone defense became more apparent day by day.

We decided to use a full-court zone press and shift into a three-
quarter and half-court zone defense which could adjust to protect some
of the better players from foul trouble, particularly the better rebounders.
As the games progressed, the team eventually ended in a 2-1-2 and
2-3 zone defense which were utilized to launch the fast break. In other

REBOUNDS
←REBOUNDING AREA
REBOUNDS
X1
3
5
4
1
STAY OUT OF EXCHANGE AREA
2 DEFENSE
●1

DIAGRAM 8-4

words, an adjustment was made in order to facilitate employment of a fast break defense. This is a defense which will expedite the initiation of the fast break.

There were several reasons for not staying with the man-to-man defense. The major reason was the fact that fouls were called more frequently, and the team did not have the depth to afford the loss of first-string players. Secondly, a minimum of four men was needed on the boards for rebounding, and this could be achieved more effectively by utilizing the zone defense. The third factor was that the opponents were weak offensive rebounders and did not crash the board with any regularity. Thus, there was not the urgent necessity for full concentration on individual block-out, merely on position.

By using the zone defense it was comparatively easy to achieve a perfect distribution of the two forwards and the pivot around the rebound triangle. It was also easier to have one outlet player in position to start the fast break immediately following possession of the rebound. The full-court press was used frequently because the small men had very quick hands and were capable of funneling and driving their men into the trap areas. They were also adept at preventing the ball from going up the sidelines and could protect the offensive middle area by shooting the gap and intercepting long cross-court passes. Utilizing the zone defense was an adjustment necessitated because of lack of depth in various positions and because of the individual talents of the small men.

PSYCHOLOGY OF COACHING THE SMALL MAN

The small player is an enjoyable type of athlete to coach because he is usually very aggressive and capable of hustling at a faster pace than bigger, slower players. However, the limitations and handicaps of the little man are numerous. The only possible way to overcome the handicap of strength and height is to insist upon an extraordinary amount of *hustle* and *recovery*.

The little man must be capable of recovering instantaneously from a gamble and also capable of preventing costly errors. He *must* make gambling moves which take him out of sound floor position in an effort to harass the opponent into making mistakes. The small man must also risk a great deal in an effort to steal the ball. When he does either, he must be capable of recovering and preventing the gamble from becoming a disastrous blunder.

The psychology in coaching the small man is to keep constant pressure on him and insist upon recovery and the perfecting of minute details. He must use his feet more than bigger players and must constantly adjust his position. His chance of competing with taller players depends upon his burning desire to cover more area in less time than his larger contemporaries. He must also be capable of using his hands in a karate action without having the officials call fouls on him. If he is not capable of maintaining physical contact and preventing bigger players from going where they want to go, it is doubtful that he will become a great player. He must be willing to do the things that the big man will not do. He must learn how to dive on the floor for the loose ball without receiving injuries. He must be quick in getting the ball and must utilize tremendous speed in order to offset the height and strength advantage of the bigger man.

It is a pleasure to coach a small man because his desire to achieve in the face of physical limitations is inspiring. He usually has learned to eliminate false action and wasted motion. He does not expend energy uselessly, and he makes every action count by taking something away from the giants. He knows how to maintain a reserve and yet play at a pace that is much faster than his larger teammates and opponents. His physical condition and desire, as a general rule, are superior to that of other players.

There will always be an important role for the small man to play in the game of basketball. The avid interest exhibited at the recent World Small Man Tournament was a genuine testimonial to this fact.

9

Drills for Improving
Aggressiveness

The point of emphasis for coaches to remember when they teach aggressive basketball is that *every minute detail* concerning each squad member's practice habits must be scrutinized. No wasted motion or "slovenliness" can be tolerated. Another important point is that no excuse offered by a player for failing to accomplish a task can be accepted. The coach must consistently remain a stern taskmaster, capable of driving his players until they perfect every detail of the various aspects of basketball.

A stop watch should be used to time every drill, play and maneuver that is executed. A specific time requirement for each activity should be established. Some type of punishment should be meted out to players who fail to meet the required time scale. If the pressure of completing a task in a given amount of time is constantly applied, the players' aggressiveness will gradually improve. The coach should seldom be satisfied with his squad members' achievements. He should already have higher goals set when the team reaches a certain level of competency. Any show of half-effort or carelessness must receive a severe reprimand. When a player persists in not giving 100 per cent effort, the coach should get rid of him immediately. The aggressive coach *knows* that no squad member is indispensable, and the team can survive without a half-hearted performer.

The constant pressure of striving for perfection and the attitude of the coach whose demands are great will produce players capable of doing the impossible. As Browning said, "A man's reach should exceed his grasp, or what's a heaven for?"

In selecting drills to use for improving aggressiveness, the coach must exercise great care and judgment. There are probably no identical coaching environments; therefore, not all drills used under one circumstance are applicable to another. The drills which are presented here have been used predominately with college players. The coach who uses these drills must keep in mind that variations may be needed to make them usable for high school or younger players.

PHOTO 9-1A

DRILLS FOR IMPROVING AGGRESSIVENESS

Circle Loose-Ball Drill

Photos 9-1A, B & C—This is called the circle loose-ball drill. All squad members are divided according to size and ability. Three circles and three groups are use. A classified group of players faces the inside of one circle with their toes lining the outside of the circle. A signal is given by the coach or assistant coach, and all players surrounding a circle use a defensive slide drill around the circle. While the players are moving, the ball is tossed into the center of the circle, and all players go for the ball. A towel wadded into a ball and taped can be used to replace the ball. Players must snatch the ball or towel completely free. As soon as a player recovers two loose balls, he sits down. The drill is continued until there is only one player left in each classification. These three men are expected to remain after practice and run 25 laps. This additional running while their teammates are taking a warm shower will have a tendency to increase the players' aggressiveness as the weeks wear on.

PHOTO 9-1B

PHOTO 9-1C

PHOTO 9-2A

PHOTO 9-2B

Two-Line Loose-Ball Drill

Photos 9-2A & B—The drill begins with one player behind the end line on each line that borders the foul lane. Players should be matched according to speed and size. The coach or assistant coach rolls the ball toward the foul line. The instant the ball passes the foul line, both players sprint to recover the ball. As soon as a player recovers three loose balls, he sits down. The last man in each classification receives laps on the steps after practice.

Draw-the-Foul Drill

Photo 9-3—Players are lined up along the sideline in a body-balanced position with considerable weight on the toes. The coach or assistant coach gently bumps each player. At the moment of contact, the player, by pushing off with his toes, falls to the floor. He fakes the fall as if he had been violently fouled by the coach. This drill teaches players to protect themselves when they fall to the floor. Players also learn to draw fouls successfully from the opponent's star when they are trying to get him to foul out.

PHOTO 9-3A

PHOTO 9-3B

PHOTO 9-3C

Block-Out All Together Drill

Diagram 9-1—The squad is divided into two equal groups. One team is designated as the offensive team (O), and the other is the defensive team (X). The offensive team lines up across the court with their toes behind the mid-court line. They should all be facing toward the same end of the floor. The defensive men take a position on the other side of mid-court facing the players they will guard. The coach throws the ball to the defensive end of the court. Offensive players are the only ones who can retrieve the ball. The defensive team tries to block their men away and prevent anyone from recovering the ball. There is no out-of-bounds in this drill. The coach starts the stop watch the instant the ball is thrown and stops it when an offensive player has possession of the ball. Each team is given five opportunities to retrieve the ball, and each effort is timed and recorded. The team that recovers the ball five times in the least amount of time will sit down while the losing team performs a strenuous activity.

DIAGRAM 9-1

DIAGRAM 9-2

DIAGRAM 9-3

All Over the Floor Loose-Ball Drill

Diagram 9-2—The entire squad gathers around the mid-court jump circle. The coach throws the ball either (1) up, (2) to one end of the floor or the other, (3) to one side of the floor or the other, (4) or on the floor. All squad members go for the ball the instant it leaves the coach's hand. As soon as a player recovers the ball two times, he sits down. The last player left on the floor suffers the indignity of having his last name prefixed by "Miss" for the rest of the day.

One-on-One Under the Basket Drill

Diagram 9-3—Squad members are matched according to size and ability. Two players are stationed under the basket. The coach or assistant coach shoots the ball at the basket. The player who retrieves the ball is on offense, and the other is on defense. As soon as a goal is scored, the ball becomes free and either of the players can grab it and shoot. The first player to score ten goals is the winner and sits down. The loser performs some strenuous task. Fouls are not called unless a player uses his hands or fists. In other words, normal basketball contact is ignored.

All Over the Court Keep-Away Drill

The squad is divided into two equal teams. The teams gather at mid-court, and the coach or assistant coach throws the ball up. The team that gets possession of the ball becomes the offense, and the other team uses a man-to-man press to get the ball. The offensive team keeps the ball away from the defensive team by passing or dribbling. The defensive team is allowed to double-team and use pressing tactics. Gentle fouls are ignored. When deliberate fouls occur, the other team is awarded ten seconds. There is no front court; therefore, the offensive team can use the entire court to freeze the ball. The amount of time that a team maintains possession of the ball is accumulated and recorded. The length of this drill is five minutes. The team that controls the ball the longest sits down and the losers again perform a strenuous activity.

The "strenuous activity" is highly effective, for it is both additionally tiring, and above all, a smarting disgrace to the lagging men. The threat of being the loser in a drill works up a man's pride.

Three-on-Three All Over the Court Drill

At the first of each week, several captains are appointed. They choose two players to be on their teams for the week. This is the last drill conducted during daily practice periods. Four teams start the drill by playing a full-court game on the two crosscourts. The first team to score 20 points wins the contest. The winners on one court play the winners on the other court. The losers play each other. When a team wins two games, they go home for the day. Losers continue to play, and another team from the sideline comes in as winners go home.

Assistant coaches or managers officiate. All fouls are one-plus-one. Any time a defensive player gets further than eight feet away from the offensive man he is guarding, it costs his team two points. The offensive team retains possession of the ball but must take it out of bounds before starting the next offensive attack.

If two courts are not available, teams 1 and 2 will play the first game and teams 3 and 4 will play the second game. The winners of the first and second games will play the third game. The losers of the first and second games will play the fourth game. This procedure continues until all teams except one are eliminated. In order to conserve time in the event of only one court, ten points should constitute a contest.

SUMMARY

The coach, striving to improve squad aggressiveness, must exercise extreme caution in his choice of drills. The welfare of squad members must always remain foremost in the coach's mind as he selects drills to improve any phase of team play. The difference between a championship team and a good team is squad aggressiveness. Frequently, this lack of aggressiveness causes a team to lose the "make or break" game.

The question that must be resolved by the coach is whether to allow his team to be defeated by a more aggressive squad or whether to resort to harsher measures to improve his team's aggressiveness.

Coaches must come to the realization that becoming a successful coach necessarily depends upon producing winning teams. Victorious coaches, who are naturally more influential in the sports world, can contribute immeasurably to the lives of many young men. Another important reason for secondary school coaches producing winning teams is that players from winning high school teams usually receive more publicity and stand a better chance of obtaining a grant-in-aid, which insures them a college education. It would be disastrous for a coach to fail in teaching aggressiveness and consequently have several of his players denied this opportunity.

In the final analysis, a coach must decide his own course of action. There will always remain unanswered questions as to the obligation that a coach owes his squad. He can drive them into becoming champions and achieving unheard-of goals and honors, or he can cause them to fail because of his unwise choice in selecting the methods for achieving success.

The only advice that I can offer was given many years ago by Shakespeare—"To thine ownself be true." A coach must make every effort within his power to improve his squad members. It is his responsibility to the athletes and to the sport. When he recognizes a weakness, he should take the necessary measures to eliminate the cause for this deficiency. Occasionally, he must place the security of his job on the line and do the thing which he believes in his heart is for the best interest of his squad and let the wrath fall where it may!

10

Ten Steps to Tournament Triumphs

In the world of athletics it is an accepted philosophy that how you start is not so important as how you finish. Most people understand that the novice will make mistakes and will encounter difficulty in realizing success early in his career.

To make this concept applicable to the coaching of basketball, it is correct to say that most people will forgive a coach for losing during the early stages of the season, for he has not had sufficient time to expose his players to the proper instructional environment.

When a coach sincerely wants to show improvement at the end of the season, he must direct his season's plan toward this goal. In other words, he must strive to win the tournament championship. This is the ultimate mark of late season success. Every coach must have an intelligently constructed blueprint to follow if he is to build a winning squad that will come on strong at the finish.

THE MASTER PRACTICE PLAN

In March, at the climax of the basketball season, high schools, colleges, and universities crown their champions. The eyes of the state and country watch with envy and awe as the winners are awarded their gold medals. A team doesn't reach this level of attainment by wearing the same socks while on a winning streak. This type of luck is the culmination of skillfully organized plans which have been followed with great care and thoroughness.

In cases where the squad lacks experience, the coach must be patient and expect his team to appear ragged and unprepared during early season games. Frequently, my team has not received sufficient preparation until after the Christmas holidays. Most of the early season practice time is spent on conditioning, fundamentals, and perfection of basic maneuvers. Very little scrimmaging is done during the early season practice periods. This is the time to lay a firm foundation based on individual fundamentals and conditioning. Once the season opens, a majority of the practice time is devoted to scrimmaging with emphasis

187

on team unity. As the season progresses, every phase of basketball is perfected.

PROGRESSIVE CONDITIONING

As emphasized throughout this book, team conditioning becomes a progressively more important factor in deciding tournament victory or defeat. Proper team conditioning requires primary emphasis during the early stages of practice and ceaseless attention as the season continues. (A conditioning program is outlined in Chapter 3.) My point is that condition is a major contributing factor to tournament success.

During the month of February, as tournament time draws near, the squad should constantly be reminded of the importance of increasing their physical conditioning to the point where they can play three or four consecutive nights without becoming fatigued or dull. Warn against the danger of contracting colds and instruct them to increase their vitamin C intake and to avoid contact with persons or conditions which might increase their possibility of becoming ill. Urge the team to report minor injuries or infections to the trainer immediately. In some instances, it is wise to tape or wrap the ankles of all squad members during the three weeks preceding the tournament.

ADJUSTMENTS IN OFFENSE AND DEFENSE

Early in the year, the coach should alter his lineup and vary his team strategy. There should be sufficient experimentation conducted during the early stages of the season to inform the coach of the alternatives available to him under all possible conditions. Many times, a change in strategy or personnel will result in defeat. The coach should become aware of this before tournament time in order to make compensations.

The coach's philosophical belief concerning the insignificance of early season games as compared to the importance of tournament games permits him to make many changes during season games. Consequently, the gambling factor will be reduced during tournament play.

It is wise to develop an offensive series or a completely different offense during the season and hold it in reserve for tournament play. I usually have a continuity offense with three or four options available in case of dire necessity. But I do not feel that a team should use these options unless everything else has failed, or the change is being executed to aggravate the opposing team.

Several years ago, when my team was playing in a tournament, we were forced to use options. Every defensive attack that the team knew had been attempted but had failed to stop our opponent. Taking a time-out, I switched to a different offense in hopes that the opposing coach would start emphasizing his defense and cause his players to stop concentrating on offense. He began to rant and rave about defense. As his players started to concentrate on defense, their offense became less effective. This allowed our defense to start working. Preparation for offensive and defensive adjustments such as the above should be dictated by the scout reports and previous knowledge of the opponents.

DEVELOPMENT OF CONFIDENCE

From the very beginning, the coach must instill confidence in the hearts and minds of every squad member; he must encourage them to improve and stabilize their confidence with every practice and game. In the process, he will cause each player to become progressively more determined to win.

The best means of developing confidence is to prepare players to overcome all situations that might confront them. Developing team unity to a high degree will permit individuals to play in a more relaxed manner; when players can completely rely on teammates to function consistently, they perform more proficiently.

Never reprimand a first string player during the month of February. If the coach wishes to convey a message to a first team player, he should criticize a second string player when he fails in attempting the same maneuver. The varsity player will identify his own mistake in this particular situation and get the message. The first string players can do no wrong during February. They should have been corrected during the early stages of the season. The important thing at that time is team unity and individual confidence. Occasionally, allow the first unit to leave practice early and keep the second string to work longer. They need to work, and the first unit needs to know they are already good enough to win.

SCHEDULE PLANNING

A very difficult non-conference schedule should be arranged. Your squad should compete against strong teams that use a variety of offenses and defenses. This gives the team the opportunity to play under different conditions and situations. Always arrange games with teams from various sections of the state or country. This permits the team to play on a variety of courts.

A coach should schedule every opponent in his area who is expected to be a title contender. This gives him the opportunity to gather accurate scout reports and film. If it is possible to determine the location of the court on which the tournament will be held, effort should be made to play or practice on that court as much as possible throughout the year.

In order to prepare properly for tournament play, a team must constantly play under conditions similar to those encountered during actual tournament competition. Participation in an early season tournament, Christmas tournament, or a mid-season tournament is advisable. If this is impossible, arrangements should be made to play against tough opposition three nights in a row.

During February, in order that team confidence can be crystalized, it is beneficial to play weaker opponents on your home floor. There is also less danger of injury and overexertion of the squad. Following this schedule procedure reduces loss of rest due to travel. It also eliminates other stresses and strains encountered when playing either away from home or against formidable competition.

ESTABLISHMENT OF ROUTINE

Beginning the first day of practice, a rugged work schedule should be established and followed throughout the season. Every minute detail should be performed repeatedly until a habit pattern is established. Encourage all persons involved with the squad members to cooperate in every conceivable way in helping to establish a rigid routine.

Absolute game routine should be established before tournament time and should include the following items:

      (1) packing of uniforms and equipment
      (2) departure for game
      (3) travel arrangements

    (4) squad behavior while traveling

    (5) arrival at game site

    (6) conduct before game

    (7) talking with fans and well-wishers prior to game

    (8) time to begin dressing

    (9) dressing procedures

  (10) pregame procedures

  (11) warm-up procedures

  (12) return to locker room before the game

  (13) introduction of squad

  (14) first-half game procedures

  (15) half-time routine

  (16) second-half game procedures

  (17) post-game dressing schedule

  (18) trip home including eating, talking with friends, and bed time

Of course, there are numerous other details that each coach must recognize; he should tailor a routine to handle his particular problems.

CONTROL OF EMOTIONAL ATMOSPHERE

Psychological values are of utmost importance to a team aspiring to tournament success. And one of the most important is that the coach should create a playing and practicing atmosphere which will contribute to relieving tension. This helps each team member establish a good frame of mind and strive to develop more confidence as tournament time approaches. If the coach carefully creates such an atmosphere, the proper attitude toward winning will have been established. Along with it the desire to bring home the championship trophy will have been improved daily. Also, such an atmosphere subtly makes clear to the player that, although things are getting more difficult, his goals and the team's goals are about to be realized. Furthermore, establishing such a playing and practicing atmosphere helps to control the mental and emotional stress which surrounds tournament play. Naturally, tournament play is far different from that of regular season games; players feel the pressure; they know that one defeat demands subsequent expulsion from the race. Consequently, they try to play cautiously, and doing this causes increased mistakes due to the abnormality of this environment.

Controlling the emotional atmosphere as effectively as he can is largely the coach's problem—and it's a complex one. Yet he has to be the leader that the team can depend on at all times. He has to make the important decisions; he has to know what to do. Perhaps this is what I want to say: the coach has to create the atmosphere the players play in and also be a part of it. This is the ideal time to practice what you preach; it pays off, hopefully, by winning.

PREPARE FOR THE UNEXPECTED

During the month of February, the coach should set up hypothetical situations for the squad which will illustrate adjustments that might have to be made during tournament play. He should create gamelike situations and explain what offensive and defensive techniques will be used under the circumstances. These measures must be taken to prevent the team from becoming surprised during tournament play. The squad should be drilled to expect peculiar defenses, unusual offenses, changes of tempo, the press and other rare situations that might be encountered during a pressure-packed tournament game. He should continue to check the offense and defense, and drill on all special situations until the team is sure of its capability to handle all of them. Never make complicated adjustments to any phase of the game during tournament play. The element of confusion could be disastrous.

SCOUT REPORTS AND FILM

Each team that might participate in the tournament should be scouted several times during the year. You should make a complete folder on these squads and keep up to date on their progress. My assistant coach is responsible for keeping charts and writing up a report following all regular season games. The day following the game he interviews each squad member who participated in the contest. He combines their comments with his and enters them in the scouting folder. This information is used to determine the offense and defense used against this opponent if we meet them in the tournament.

Although I have a rather small budget for sports film, I take a film of six or eight games per year. We film teams that we suspect will be the strongest competition at tournament time. These films are carefully studied and all offensive and defensive maneuvers are checked against scout reports. The film of a particular team is shown to the squad the afternoon of the tournament game. This helps to refresh the player's memories concerning the peculiarities of the opponent. By the way, I seldom allow my squad to watch an opponent play before we meet them. Occasionally, when I have a senior team or one mature enough not to underestimate the opponent, I will permit them to watch for one half.

TOURNAMENT STRATEGY

During the season the coach should plan his strategy for each opponent. Each opposing coach is different; therefore, team strategy will have to be altered to fit the coach and the situation. The wise coach will study his opponents and develop a dossier of each coach. When a peculiarity is discovered, the coach should contrive a plan of attack for utilizing this information during tournament games.

It is advisable to maintain your basic offensive and defensive attacks most of the time and force the opponent to play the type of game that agrees with your game plan. *Make no pregame alteration in the basic attack when playing a team not comparable in ability to your squad.* Adjustments should be made only for superior opponents. Once the game is well under way, then, if necessary, adjustments can be made.

Never use anything in a tournament which has not been properly rehearsed in practice. This is no time to confuse a group of players. Always practice the week preceding the tournament with a new ball of the same brand used in the tournament.

All officials who will work the tournament games must be scouted during the year. The week preceding the tournament the assistant coach should mimic each official as he calls scrimmages. All of their idiosyncrasies should be explained to the squad. Understanding the officials will allow squad members to intelligently adjust their defense and use of fouls.

There are many tactics which will be effective occasionally, but the coach should be careful in using them because they can backfire if not properly executed. Never use any of these unless you are weak on material and are meeting a stronger opponent.

(1) Occasionally send several players to the court one hour before the game starts to act as "goal-getters." They will take one particular goal. Be sure they have a good chance of keeping the goal.

(2) Demand to flip a coin for the color of uniform only if it bothers the opposing coach. Plan to have this happen in front of his squad, not yours. If you win, his squad might respond to this loss in a negative manner.

(3) Insist on checking the air in the ball if it causes a delay which will worry an opposing coach.

(4) Send a telegram to the opposing coach to be delivered just before the game with this message: "Please ignore previous telegram."

There are numerous small things which are harmless and always within the rules but can cause the opposing coach to take his mind off the game and start worrying about something irrelevant. Regardless of the various tricks used, be sure of several things:

(1) To the best of your ability, make sure the team has been properly prepared.

(2) Never rely on anything except sound basketball. All extra-curricular activities are in addition to thorough preparation. (Several years ago I had a boy who crossed himself before he shot fouls. One night, as the team was walking to the dressing room following a game, a fan asked him if crossing himself helped. His answer was, "Sure, if you are a good foul shooter.")

(3) Never use unfair or unsportsmanlike tactics, only those that are within the realm of decent aggravation.

SUMMARY

Winning the tournament championship is a thrill that all players should experience. A coach should make every effort, take every chance, and leave no stone unturned to insure his players of the pleasure and excitement of standing in the winner's circle. Long range planning and persistent working habits will make any dream come true. Coaches should be dreamers with the determination to make their hopes and expectations become reality.

Many years ago, Alfred Lord Tennyson, in no particular effort to do so, outlined a philosophy which is appropriate for aggressive coaches. He said, "To strive, to seek, to find, and not to yield."

INDEX

A

A Comparison of Three Approaches to Increasing Physical Fitness in Students of Low Fitness, 30n

Adjustments and alterations in offense and defense to enable tournament wins, 188–189

Administration of training rules, 26–27

Advancing ball in fast break, 50–51

Advantages of fast break, 47
press, 128

"Aggravation" area, 90

Aggression, definition of, 3

Aggression-plus for players of limited height, 156–167
coaching, psychology of, 166–167
conditioning, 159
defense, 164–166
fast break, 159–160
offense, 161–164
rebounding, 160–161

Aggressive play, encouraging, 11–21
commitment to task, 15
fear as coaching factor, 20
individual confidence, 16–17
methods, 13–15
summary, 20–21
team unity and confidence, 17–20

Aggressiveness, drills for improving, 170–183
All Over the Court Keep-Away, 181
All Over the Floor Loose-Ball, 181
Block-Out All Together, 177
Circle Loose-Ball, 172
Draw the Foul, 175
excuses not acceptable, 171
One-on-One Under the Basket, 181
slovenliness in practice forbidden, 171
summary, 182–183
obligation of coach to squad, 182–183
Three-on-Three All Over the Court, 182
Two-Line Loose Ball, 174

Aggressiveness of squad determinant of team quality, 182

Agility drills, 37

All Over the Court Keep-Away drill to improve aggressiveness, 181

All Over the Floor Loose-Ball drill to improve aggressiveness, 181

American philosophy of demanding excellence, 6–10

Appeal to fans of fast break, 47

Arm and shoulder exercises as conditioning drill, 35

Automatic switching of defense, 117

Awards for superlative effort to encourage aggressive play, 13

B

Baseline, driving, 90

Baseline man, guarding, 90–91

Basketball Research in Fatigue, 25n, 31

Bicycle against resistance as conditioning drill, 34

Blisters, treatment of, 29

Block-Out All Together drill to improve aggressiveness, 177

Blocking out, offensive and defensive, important for small men to control boards, 160–161

Blocking out in rebounding, 72–73

Boards, controlling, to control game, 71

Body Extension drill, 73, 74–75

Body position important in rebounding, 71–73

"Boxer's" drill to improve body position, 92

"Broken knee" position in defensive play, 88

Browning, Robert, 171

Bunn, John W., 30n

Bunn technique, 27, 30–31

C

Carlson, H. C., 25n, 31

Carlson Spot Run Technique, 31

Characteristics, twelve, of aggressive player, 4
of coach, 4–6

197

Also by Perri Klass

RECOMBINATIONS

I AM HAVING AN ADVENTURE

A NOT ENTIRELY BENIGN PROCEDURE

OTHER WOMEN'S CHILDREN

PERRI KLASS

OTHER WOMEN'S CHILDREN

 RANDOM HOUSE NEW YORK

Grateful acknowledgment is made to the following for permission
to reprint previously published material:

American Academy of Pediatrics: Excerpt from "Nonorganic
Failure to Thrive" by Donald M. Berwick, from *Pediatrics in
Review,* March 1980, Volume I, Number 9. Copyright © 1980.
Reprinted by permission of Pediatrics.

Random House, Inc.: Excerpt from *Happy Birthday to You!* by Dr.
Seuss. Copyright © 1959 by Theodor S. Geisel and Audrey S.
Geisel. Copyright renewed 1987 by Theodor S. Geisel and Audrey
S. Geisel. Reprinted by permission of Random House, Inc.

Manufactured in the United States of America

Quality Printing and Binding by:
Berryville Graphics
P.O. Box 272
Berryville, VA 22611 U.S.A.

I am inundated with imploring letters recommending poor little Nell to mercy.—Six yesterday, and four today (it's not 12 o'Clock yet) already!

—*The Letters of Charles Dickens*, 24 November 1840

I am slowly murdering that poor child, and grow wretched over it. It wrings my heart. Yet it must be.

—*The Letters of Charles Dickens*, 6 January 1841

CONTENTS

CONTENTS

OTHER
WOMEN'S
CHILDREN

CHAPTER 1
INDEPENDENT SCHOOLS

Before she falls asleep, Amelia allows herself a fantasy. The same fantasy every night, rationed out to those last few minutes in the dark. A little boy named Darren sits cross-legged on a travel-poster beach, his toes dug deep into wet sand, his face turned up to the blue, blue sky. He is laughing. Amelia takes the details from a memory of her own son, Alexander; last summer he chased the outgoing waves at Crane's Beach in Ipswich, Massachusetts, then ran shrieking back up the beach, to collapse, sticky from Popsicles, covered with sand, on Amelia's lap, to sit still for one brief hug, then up again to dig in the wet sand on an endless search for pirate treasure.

Darren, in her fantasy, has traveled farther than Ipswich; she imagines him on some tropical paradise island, Bermuda or Bali, Tahiti or Tobago, endless smooth sand, palm trees waving against a cloudless horizon.

Amelia's son, Alexander, is white; Darren is black. Alexander is healthy. Amelia imagines that Darren is shouting with pleasure as the cool water tickles his toes.

Wednesday, Amelia skips work in the morning, doesn't go to the hospital. Instead, she and Matt drop Alexander off at the day care center, then drive to the Conservatory School. The slush is thick on the ground, the sky is gray. The school is in two big nine-teenth-century Cambridge houses now joined by a modern glass-roofed addition. Amelia and Matt are escorted around the school by the director of admissions, Colette Friedberg, chic and even mildly glamorous, but professionally bouncy and friendly. She wears glossy boots with high thin heels, a tight black skirt with little slits front and back, and a hot-pink silk shirt. She has curly blond hair, and she makes Amelia feel distinctly dowdy, though she has dressed up for this visit. Colette moves fast down the hallways, boots kicking in and out of the slits in her skirt, heels tapping along the polished floors. She is on display, she is displaying the school, and luxury is the order of the day. The computer center, the wood-working shop, the ceramics studio. Colette ushers Matt and Amelia into the back of classroom after classroom, where none of the students even look up at their arrival. The classrooms are full of color and noise on this cold gray day. The student artwork decorating the halls is intimidating: enormous scrolls of Egyptian gods from the fourth grade, portrait painting by the sixth. Amelia checks out the Conservatory: according to rumor, there should be exactly one child in each class the precise color of café au lait. First grade, check; second grade, check; third grade, she can't find the kid, either absent or too much au lait to be recognized from the back of the room; fourth grade, check.

The fourth graders are having a dictionary lesson; a bald man in a tweed jacket points to the word "fiduciary," printed neatly on his blackboard. How can you use the guidewords to help you find "fiduciary"? Suppose you open your dictionary and see that the guideword on the upper right-hand side of the page is "farm"—do you need to go forward or backward?

"Mr. Mullinmark has been here for more than fifteen years," Colette Friedberg confides as they slip out of the room. "We're very proud of our record in holding on to our teachers."

Amelia sits in the admissions director's office, sipping excellent coffee from a Styrofoam cup. She is resolutely not thinking about her patients, about Darren, waiting in the hospital. Matt is asking polite but searching questions, designed to indicate a serious inter-est in the school, but also to let Colette Friedberg know that he and

Amelia are not just petitioners. No, they are serious consumers, comparison shoppers, out to find the best possible education for their child. Tee hee, please let us in, please give our little darling access to your superb woodworking facilities, your computer system, which is better than that of many small colleges, those teachers you hold on to so well. Amelia toys with the beeper that is hooked on to her blazer pocket: see, I'm a doctor, you like doctors, don't you?

Colette is asking them about their son now, what kind of a child he is. Last night when Amelia and Matt talked about this interview, made up those all-purpose searching questions to ask, they also made up an answer for this one: oh, he's a pretty average kid, nothing special in the way of brains, can't even get it together to be interested in dinosaurs like the other kids in the day care center. Likes junk food, noneducational TV, and playing with guns. They laughed together over this, knowing perfectly well the true and unusable answer: we have the most beautiful sharpest smartest wisest most graceful child this world has ever seen.

"I think the thing that strikes most people about Alexander," Matt is saying slowly, as if thinking this out for the first time, "is how focused he is, how he sets himself these little projects and just carries through on them. I mean, for example, he and I have been doing some work on the house, we've been restoring a section of gingerbread trim on the porch, and I thought he was just going to get bored and walk away after a while, but he just keeps at it."

"That's often the sort of child who stands to benefit most from our type of independent school," Colette Friedberg says. "A child who doesn't have to be pushed to achieve, but benefits from constant stimulation and opportunity."

"I suppose every parent says this," Amelia says, doing her part, "but I *am* a pediatrician so I *do* get to see a wide range of children, and I really think Alexander has an exceptional ability to absorb new things and make them part of his life. He doesn't just listen to a story, he takes it over, starts to add to it, uses the characters in his own games." Suddenly she smiles helplessly and finds herself saying simply, "He's just an unbelievably delightful kid."

"He certainly sounds wonderful," says the director of admissions. "We'll look forward to meeting him later on in the process. Now, have you looked at any other independent schools for Alexander?"

"This is the one that interests us the most," Matt and Amelia lie in unison; they are resolved to give this answer at every school they visit.

Amelia takes Matt's arm walking back to the car. He looks at her, purses up his lips, and gives a Bronx cheer. "Snaky sadistic double-talking sleazes," he comments.

"Rot in hell and die, their toes should fall off one by one," Amelia agrees.

"And what's with this 'independent school' shit? We don't use the term 'private school' anymore?"

"Well, no, we seem to prefer 'independent school'—perhaps because, well, the school is independent. Independent of the *state,* you see."

"Or do you mean to imply intellectually and spiritually independent?"

"Well, yes, that too. But what I really mean when I say '*independent*' is that the parents of the students pay *money* to the school so their children can attend and that therefore people who are *poor* can't send their children. Do you see what I mean? Perhaps you will, later on in the process."

Amelia sits in her clinic office, filling out WIC forms. The welfare office wants to know if the children are anemic, if they have any serious medical problems. The yellow forms are ticktacktoed with creases; they travel to the doctor folded many times in mothers' purses, another incomprehensible form to be filled out, a signature to be obtained. Amelia goes through a small pile of test results, lead levels, required by the state. All negative, no children with lead poisoning in this batch. If not for the lead laws, would one of these children be poisoned, retarded, neurologically damaged? And here is Carmel Gutierrez's hematocrit, up over thirty-three for the first time—her mother has been dripping iron drops into her faithfully. At one time, Carmel's blood count was so low that Amelia worried about malignancy. But no, just the mystery of body chemistry; avoid lead, eat iron, and grow up healthy. The door to the hallway is open, and a plump and naked baby totters in, stomach round and punctuated with a proud and pointed outie belly button. A little girl maybe fourteen months old, with two tiny blond braids wispily escaping from red velvet bows. She looks around Amelia's office with interest, then pulls hard on the loose end of the big paper roll, the liner that is hanging over the edge of the examining table. The paper makes a satisfying crackling noise, and the child waves it as violently as she can. Then pauses to urinate on the office floor.

Amelia drops a handful of paper towels on the puddle, takes hold of one pink hand, and leads the child back out to the waiting room. No one seems to be looking around anxiously. She goes to the microphone the nurses use to call in patients and announces that she has found a little girl with two blond braids, et cetera, et cetera. A mother, carrying a naked newborn, comes hurrying out of one of the examining rooms to claim the child, drag her off to be weighed and measured.

Amelia is tired when she gets home. She thinks about collapsing on the armchair after supper, drowsing over the newspaper. Instead, Alexander directs his parents to the little couch, a Victorian loveseat upholstered in tattered cabbage roses, which Matt wants to reupholster as soon as he has time to learn how. Alexander himself ducks down behind the big couch opposite the loveseat, and his hand appears, clutching a little wooden ice-cream spoon decorated with a Magic Marker face. "I'm all alone," announces this figure. "I guess I'll dance. Da da da da da da da da." He dances wildly back and forth along the back of the couch. Another hand appears, presenting another ice-cream spoon; the two dance together as the music continues, "Da da da da da da," then draw closer, and kissing noises issue from behind the couch. Kiss, kiss, kiss, and then, "Yikes, a monster!" and the newcomer disappears. Puppet number one takes this phlegmatically. "I'm all alone. I guess I'll dance. Da da da da da da da," and soon a new partner appears. "Da da da da da da da da, kiss, kiss, kiss. Yikes! A monster!" Exit. "I'm all alone. I guess I'll dance." And so on.

Every now and then a small blond head inches up from behind the couch, beaming with pleasure, checking out the audience. And he is always satisfied; on the loveseat, Amelia and Matt are enchanted by the puppet show. Matt's arm is tight around Amelia's shoulders, and the two of them are leaning forward, laughing and laughing. Alexander continues. "Da da da da da da da, kiss, kiss, kiss. Yikes!"

This is not the story I was intending to write. This is not what I was intending to write about. How can anyone write about children who get sick, children who die? What is most heart-piercing in life can turn to bathos, melodrama, sentimental nonsense in fiction. Unless perhaps you are a genius, and even then—remember what Oscar Wilde said about Little Nell? "One must have a heart of stone to read the death of Little Nell without laughing." And Dickens was a genius, and I am not.

I do not want to write about children who are sick. If I could, I would show the cruelty of life through the little pains and the helplessness of the well-intentioned, but I would not invoke the agony of the parent who stands by a hospital bed and watches a child fight for breath. See how the sentimental tear-jerking comes as quickly as that; the child is clutching his teddy bear (his teddy bear! for Christ's sake!) and his little chest sucks in and out. Is there nothing ahead for him but darkness and pain, or will his parents see that anxious face smile up at them again, that fevered body relax back into comfort? And who will save him, who will make the difference? Could it be me? Talk about melodrama!

They dominate my days, they appear in my dreams, these children I am supposed to save. They wear their pajamas with the little feet, they drag their teddy bears by the arms, they suck their thumbs. I stand at their bedsides and watch them scream as tape is pulled from their arms so IVs can be changed, as needles slide in yet again to take blood, yet again for more tests. My life does not feel like soap opera to me, but sick children on camera are automatically suspect. In soap operas, children grow up easily, automatically; no one puts in two thousand hours changing diapers and walking floors for colic and spooning in the baby cereal, weaving those connections, only to feel them ripped out by the roots as the child lies ill or dies, dies despite all the clean diapers. This is not the story I was intending to write.

Two of her patients are hospitalized, and she goes to see Melinda Finley first, putting off her visit to Darren. Melinda is a nine-year-old girl with severe asthma. Her attacks are triggered by cats, and by very cold weather, and by severe emotional upheaval. She came into the hospital wheezing badly after a fight with her mother about what she was going to be for Halloween, a fairy princess or a singer just like Madonna. After two days on IV antiasthma drugs, her breathing is now almost clear, and her mother has given way. The intern has changed Melinda over to her usual oral medications. Amelia listens to the little girl's chest and gives her blessing: home tomorrow. Privately, she wonders how Melinda and her mother are ever going to make it through Melinda's adolescence. Still, for today, Melinda is sitting up in bed, watching game shows, guessing ahead of the contestants and winning a fortune. No trouble breathing. Home tomorrow. Have a good Halloween.

Amelia braces herself, tightens up inside, and goes to see Darren. In the hospital she walks differently, she sometimes thinks, especially now. Outside the hospital, she also walks well when she is with Alexander, clearly and plainly his mother. With Matt, she is less and less sure who she is; with him she is aware that she is fatter and plainer and stranger and that her head is full of sick and dying children, while he is strong and handsome, and she cannot help wondering what people think, looking at the two of them together. But now she is in the hospital and she adopts the quick step of the doctors, never enough time, always an appointment running overtime, a page to answer, two meetings back-to-back with no time scheduled to get from one to the other. You wave at people in passing, you drum your fingers while you wait for the notoriously slow elevators, you stab the button repeatedly as the elevator stops at every floor. And going down, you always take the stairs, even from the eighth floor.

Amelia knows the intern who is responsible for Darren. In fact, she and this intern have a somewhat illicit deal. The intern is Christine, a gangly girl from Louisiana with a heavy accent. She wears only hospital-issue white pants and oxford button-down shirts and she has apparently no vanity. There is something resolutely undecorated about her, about her unpierced ears and her scrubbed face, her ponytail of lank brown hair held back with a rubber band. She is considered an excellent intern, Amelia knows, and besides that, Amelia likes her. She likes her, most immediately, for taking time and trouble over Darren, who is a difficult and frustrating patient, who will never get well. She suspects that Christine does not entirely approve of Amelia's high level of investment in Darren's case. Christine might well feel that Amelia is interfering, might call her "inappropriate," a favorite hospital term for doctors who somehow cross unwritten lines. But ultimately, Christine is sympathetic and willing to bend, as witness the illicit deal.

The illicit deal is this: in the morning, the blood-drawing technicians come around and draw blood from all the patients. If they can't get the blood, the interns are supposed to try. Christine and Amelia have agreed that the blood-drawers will never try to get blood from Darren, and that Christine will not either. When Darren needs blood tests, Amelia will draw his blood; no one else is allowed to try. This is highly irregular, but Darren has spent so much time in the hospital, has had so much blood drawn from him, that his veins are all scarred and he is what is referred to as a hard stick. His grandmother, crying, asked Amelia a long time ago to promise that no one but she would try to draw his blood, no more new interns, no more techs who don't know him well. In fact, Amelia can always draw his blood on the first try, though it makes no particular sense that knowing someone would help you get your needle into his vein. Still. She cannot cure the woman's grandson, but she can offer this much.

"I'm sorry," Christine says to her today, knowing that Amelia tries to minimize Darren's blood tests. "I'm sorry, but we really do need to send a candida antigen, and while we're at it, we could get a CBC. I didn't know if you were coming in today, but I held off."

"I'll get you the blood," Amelia says, thinking automatically of how Darren will cry and beg, how he will begin to cry as soon as he sees the syringes.

This is how you draw blood from a three-year-old boy with AIDS. Before entering his room, you have to put on a mask, a yellow cotton precaution gown, and gloves. The gown and gloves are required for anyone handling his blood and body fluids, the mask is not because of the AIDS itself, but because he is suspected of having that far more communicable scourge tuberculosis. You would leave off the mask and the gown, take the infinitesimal risk, but you know that it is bad policy for a doctor to ignore the rules that nurses and family members are forced to follow. Makes for bad feeling. So what if he probably doesn't have tuberculosis anyway, but has a related infection, *Mycobacterium avium-intracellulare,* which is unlikely to infect an immunologically normal person. So what. So you go into his room in your mask and your gloves and your gown. A little boy is lying in the bed, eyes wide open, staring at you. In pediatrics, when you come upon someone who is really sick, someone with volumes of charts, piles of lab slips stamped with his name, with PRECAUTION signs on his door, someone who carries the weight of diagnostic conferences and detailed plans of care, you find a little boy in a bed. He is not even half as long as the bed. He lies perfectly still on his back, connected by clear plastic tubing to his IV bottle. The window is behind him. The TV is off. The room is full of toys, but they have a dead look to them. And you walk in and sit down on the edge of his bed.

Do you see what I mean? It is difficult for me to write about this. Listen: Darren has a tattered stuffed animal next to him, called Mouse, brown and pilling, one of its floppy ears almost off. When he sees that I carry a syringe, big clear tears flow up out of his eyes and down his cheeks, though he doesn't make a sound. I know from experience that he is working himself up to loud hysterics. I also know, register automatically, that the HIV virus, which causes AIDS, has been isolated from tears. I'm not afraid of Darren's tears, but they contain this virus which is killing this child, and I look at them almost with awe.

So imagine then how I feel about his blood, which also holds his death. My tourniquet is stretchy yellow tubing with little knots tied in it to hold it tight as I loop it round his arm. His nurse stands across the bed, also wearing the gown and the gloves and the mask;

her eyes look tired because of what's ahead, and she grabs his arm maybe a little harder than necessary.

I see Darren for a few minutes a day, though I've known him for a long time, and I hate to hurt him. Each of his nurses spends eight hours a day cleaning and feeding him and trying to make him smile, changing his diaper and putting medicine into his IV. How can they bear it when he has to be hurt? The rules say the nurse will hold him down for every procedure. Actually, we have done away with the word "down," we just say, Can you hold while I do this or that. Can you hold for an IV, can you hold for a spinal tap. And they do, and he shrieks at them. How nurses do it I don't know. So much taken-for-granted female tenderness. When you care for a child eight hours a day, you fall a little bit in love. Eight hours a day is what I spend with my son, Alexander, on the good days, the days when I'm not too busy.

I swab Darren with Betadine and alcohol. I feel his antecubital with my gloved finger. Antecubital, the inside of his elbow, where the big veins draining his arm and hand should be close to the skin. His arm is pitiful and thin, straining up against the nurse. I feel mostly scar tissue, from the hundreds of needles. But I can feel the shadow of a thin and tortuous vein, up a little ways, and with a hurried ritual count of one-two-three, I stab my needle down and watch the red travel up into the tubing. The nurse's eyes crease at their corners; she is smiling at me for getting it, first try. I pull all the blood I need up into the syringe, and as the level of red rises, I become aware again that there is a screaming child on the bed, a baby in pain. You can't exactly see them when you're sticking them.

One thing about being in the hospital all the time—Darren knows that when a stick is over, it's over. He stops fighting, he sobs hard for another ten seconds or so, and even before I've finished injecting his blood into the various tubes, he is recovered, back to lying still and staring.

What a life they have, these sick kids. Begin with, they don't feel good, all the time they feel lousy. Then go on to the way they live, lying in their beds, not understanding it all. Even adult patients can't usually understand the reason for the pain we inflict on them, and here are little children, lying there wondering if each new person walking in the door will bring a needle, or a tube to go down the nose. I imagine their parents' lives, the lives of the women who live in the hospital, changing clothes in the patients' bathrooms, sleeping on the fold-out chairs, just so they can be there in the night if the children want them. I could do that (cross my fingers, touch wood). Then I try to imagine the children, watching us come into the room, eyeing our stethoscopes and the bulges in our pockets, the plastic-wrapped sterile objects we casually put down on the bedside table.

I tell you, it's all a lot easier when they're going to get better. Like Melinda got better. Darren is never going to get better. Darren is one of the ones who have been cheated, now and forever.

"Special interests?" Amelia squints at the application.

"Murder and mayhem," Matt suggests, "guns and bombs."

"Music," says Amelia, looking over at Alexander, who is banging on the dinner table with a plastic dinosaur, banging somewhat rhythmically, it is true.

"Art, humanitarianism, and The Dance."

"Magic Markers and Gummi Bears."

They have a little pile of these applications in front of them, all written by people from other planets. And what are your four-year-old's particular intellectual strengths? And which five adjectives best describe your four-year-old? And why would your four-year-old benefit from an independent school?

"'Well, above all, we don't want him to go to school with black people, and we hear that at your school they aren't allowed.'"

"Is that what makes it independent?"

It is Matt, finally, somewhat shamefacedly, who actually begins to fill in the applications, printing their names, Alexander's name. Amelia pages through the booklet for the Canfield-Rowbotham School, staring at the page that shows the schedule for the Beginners. Alexander sitting in a circle, doing Math Readiness? Alexander and Nature Study? Alexander practicing French?

"So who are we going to get to write his recommendations?" Matt has sorted out a pile of recommendation forms.

"Maybe one of his grandmothers would do it. They think he has a lot of promise."

"I'm sure it helps to have celebrities."

"'I would like to recommend this four-year-old child whom I have never met as a highly superior candidate for your school. His intellectual virtuosity, his superb oratorical skills, and above all his newly acquired ability to poop in the potty all make him a must for Canfield-Rowbotham.'" But Matt is serious now, looking at the papers on the rug between them. Matt is imagining his son in some awful mean classroom, picked on by children and mocked by the teacher beause he is bright and sweet and funny. Matt, tortured all through his own education, is going to buy his boy, if nothing else, a place where he will feel safe and happy. "Fuck the education, I want the privilege," Matt says.

This is a moment when things are badly out of balance for me. How can I go back and forth, how can I hold these two realities in my mind at the same time? Alexander needs to go to a school where he will be kept safe from bullies, a school that will keep him laughing, keep his eyes bright when it is time to go in the morning. It is the most important thing in the world, that Alexander should be happy. I know this with no irony at all. Why do I earn money, save money, if not to keep Alexander safe, happy, interested. Alive.

Darren, on the other hand, needs to die. Among the interns, I imagine, that must be said openly. He is in pain, he is feverish, he has no future. His prognosis is zero, as we say.

A brilliantly warm autumn day, the sun so bright outside the hospital windows that Amelia is aware of it wherever she goes, aware that she is in a little fluorescent box inside the blaze of sunlight. Melinda Finley has gone home, breathing easily in the pleasant air—winter will make her wheeze, when it comes. Still, she's been hospitalized less often this year than she was the year before; maybe she's outgrowing the worst of it. One other patient of Amelia's was admitted with a badly fractured arm and Amelia stops by to say hello, to reassure the boy's mother that, yes, he'll be fine in the end. Children heal so fast, she says, it's amazing how quickly their bones knit back together.

And now Darren. Darren's grandmother, Roberta, is waiting for her in the hall outside Darren's room. She is short and plump and dressed, as she always is, in a suit. A dark red skirt and matching jacket. She makes these suits, in various fabrics, flowered prints for summer, tweeds for winter. Before she retired Roberta taught third grade, and Amelia pictures her, wearing those suits, in front of a classroom. Definitely in charge. No one went to the bathroom without a pass, no one chewed or talked or passed notes. In Amelia's mind, Roberta teaches the kind of classroom she has never herself set foot in, where the good children clap the erasers and the bad children copy sentences over a hundred times.

"Good morning, Doctor," Roberta says.

"Good morning, Mrs. Wilson. How's Darren today?"

"Darren's not good, Doctor. He won't even try to stand up now. He just shakes his head and tells me it hurts him. And you know as well as I do that before he came in this time, he was running around. And talking—you know as well as I do that he was talking to beat the band. So why won't he talk now? Is it the sickness that's making him stop walking and talking?

Always "the sickness"—she does not use the word "AIDS."

"I think it's more the hospital than the sickness. I think he's mostly weak from lying in bed and not eating."

"Not eating, now that's another thing, Doctor. Now, Darren likes sweet things. I won't say he's usually a good eater, because he won't eat the vegetables or the meat very much, but sweet things he will eat. And now I bring him Jell-O or Tootsie Rolls, things I wouldn't let him eat usually until he finished all his food, I bring them to him and he just shakes his head."

Amelia has had this conversation before. But Roberta Wilson comes every day braced to feed her grandson, to get him up and walking, and the least Amelia can do is cheer her on.

"It's just beautiful out," Amelia says. "And it's very warm. Why don't we get Darren up into a wheelchair and send him to the patients' garden?"

Roberta stares at her. Darren has been in this little room now for almost a month, and Roberta has almost forgotten what it is like to take him outside, about their daily outings all summer to the park and the playground, about how Darren finally learned to go down the slide alone, about how he sat in the sandbox and dug happily, not so far perhaps from Amelia's picture of him on that tropical beach. Roberta now only imagines him in this hospital room, still and silent on his sheets.

"Mary Pat," Amelia calls to the head nurse, "how can we get Darren out to the garden to enjoy the sunshine?"

"We can't," Mary Pat says, shaking her head, regretful. She is a slim young woman with smooth short blond hair and a tiny waist. Her white skirt is crisp, her blue turtleneck looks ironed, and she wears large Mickey Mouse earrings to amuse her patients. "Because of the TB," she says. "He's a risk to the other patients."

"What if his grandmother keeps him away from all the other kids? They'll sit way over on the side of the garden. What about if he wears a mask?"

Mary Pat shakes her head again.

"Look," Amelia says, "you don't believe he has TB and neither do I. He almost certainly has MA-I, which isn't transmitted by coughing, and doesn't infect anyone who isn't immunocompromised anyway. And look, even if he did have TB, he's been treated for almost a week now, so it shouldn't really be infectious."

"Listen, I don't make the rules." Mary Pat grabs a looseleaf binder from a shelf over the nurses' station, pages through it looking for the precaution instructions. "The *doctors* make the rules, for your information. So if the rules don't make sense, go make different rules. But I say that if you have Darren on TB precautions, he has to follow the rules which the *doctors* set up for TB precautions, and I'm not letting him leave his room unless Infection Control says he can." Then she turns, smiles at Roberta, and says much more mildly, "I'm sorry, Mrs. Wilson, I'd really like to see Darren get out of that room. But I just plain can't let him."

It takes Amelia almost an hour to arrange Darren's trip down to the garden. She has to page two different doctors and a nurse from Infection Control, explain Darren's medical situation to each one, then wait to be called back. Finally, after they have talked to her at length and then to Mary Pat, it is agreed that if Darren wears a mask and is not allowed near any other patients, he can go down to the garden for an hour with his grandmother.

Amelia can feel that her voice has gotten louder, that she has become more emphatic, the triumphant crusader. She bustles around with a wheelchair, padding the back with an extra pillow. It is still too big for little Darren, so Mary Pat gets her a go-cart, a wooden chair on wheels, long and low and better for little children.

Roberta Wilson has pulled Darren's sweatpants onto his chicken-bone legs, wrapped a blanket around his shoulders, ready to lift him into the go-cart. But when she tries to put the blue paper surgical mask over his nose and mouth, Darren refuses. No, he won't wear it. He starts to cry. He turns away from his grandmother's hand as she attempts to stretch the elastic over his head. Amelia and Mary Pat and Roberta all stand over him, all eager now, imagining him out in the sun.

"Darren, we'll go sit outside and see the trees," his grandmother tells him. "We'll see the birds and we'll see the sky, the clouds."

"No mask!" Darren screams, and Amelia thinks, Well, at least he got his voice back.

"Darren, I'll read you your books outside. We'll take Mouse." Roberta reaches for the stuffed toy.

"Oh, Darren, wait till you feel that sun on your skin," Mary Pat says suddenly. "Oh, it feels just like summer out, we won't see sun like this again all winter. You may have to wait till next summer for another day like this."

Amelia thinks immediately that Darren may not have any more summers. She is sure both the other women are thinking of that too. Darren has burrowed into his pillow, hiding his face from all of them.

"Darren, please, honey," Roberta says. "It'll be like you've come home from the hospital, being out of this room. It'll be almost like you're not sick. It'll just be the two of us under the sky."

People in the hospital, Amelia has noticed before, often say the things you expect them to think but not say. Amelia cannot bear this, she cannot bear it.

"Darren," she says firmly, as doctorly as she can. "Let your grandma put that mask on and go out with her. If you stay in here, I will have to do a blood test on you."

As Roberta pushes the go-cart down the hall toward the elevator, Darren's tears still leaking out from under the mask, Amelia whispers to her, "When you get him off in a corner of the garden, take the mask off, for God's sake," and Roberta nods, but without looking at her.

Still, later that morning Amelia passes the glass doors leading out into the garden and sees a bright landscape, children on a green lawn, a fountain sparkling in the sun, some late flowers still in bloom, asters and a few pale roses, and if you ignore the IV poles and the wheelchairs and the hospital pajamas, it's really just children in the sun. And way off on the side, lying on his blanket with his grandmother, is Darren, his mask off, and Amelia finds she can in fact ignore his IV pole standing over him like a leafless tree, as if winter were already here, and see him as a child not sick, with his grandmother, who loves him, just the two of them under the sky.

Matt had seen them off in Boston, kissed Amelia, hugged Alexander, lifting him off his feet and kissing him noisily all over the head while Alexander squealed and wiggled. Take care of each other, Matt had said, and have a good trip. The thought came almost automatically into Amelia's mind as the plane took off: What will Matt do when we're not around, whom will he see? She closed it out, erased it, staring past Alexander's head. Outside the window, Boston turned slowly beneath the airplane.

The sun in Los Angeles is warmer, and there is no suggestion of oncoming winter in California. Alexander is trying hard to keep his eyes open as Amelia carries him out of the airport building. Amelia's old friend Dodie carries Amelia's suitcase, leading the way to her car, where Amelia straps Alexander into the backseat and herself in beside Dodie and finds herself also drifting off to sleep as Dodie drives them onto the freeway.

All across the continent, Amelia slept on and off, read *People* magazine, worried ritualistically that the plane was about to crash, and at intervals pretended that she and Alexander were striking out on their own. In fact, she is in Los Angeles to attend a conference and give a talk; she has brought Alexander along to show him off to Dodie, her oldest friend, and to take him to Disneyland. And in four days they will be home, met at the airport by Matt, husband and father, who will drive them back to their comfortable house, their accumulated medical books and Lego bricks. But on the airplane, for six hours, they might be a mother and son who have nowhere they belong, have only the possessions in their one gray zipped suitcase and each other. Flying from no one to no one, the two of them, Alexander sleeping against her.

Instead of flying to no one, of course, they are met by Dodie, carried off in her car. Amelia and Dodie went to high school together; their friendship has lasted more than twenty years now, since eighth grade. More than half their lives. Amelia has a copy of *To the Lighthouse* Dodie gave her at graduation, inscribed, "Time passes; someday we will have been friends for fifty years." And in fact, remarkably, they have stayed close; it is still Dodie whose phone number Amelia tends to dial, almost aimlessly, late at night. Dodie does not expect her to have a reason when she calls. Because their friendship goes back before adult destinies, before jobs and marriage, it somehow stays clear of such complexities. They see each other only rarely, and their lives do not match at all, and perhaps they are best friends only by default, since adults do not form such best friendships.

Alexander is sound asleep in the backseat. In the front, Amelia is dozing, waking up as they pull into a parking place. There are palm trees on Dodie's street but the little modern bungalows are squat and ugly. Dodie has lived at this address now for almost three years, after her romance fell apart, the romance for which she moved out to California in the first place. Amelia has never visited her before.

"Currently," Dodie says, "I need to be a get-ahead career woman with a child, who is discovering that she can't have it all. I can pick your brains, since you *are* a get-ahead career woman, and you *do* have a child."

"Give me a break." They are sitting on Dodie's king-sized mattress, which takes up most of the floor of her small living room.

The mattress is covered with an Indian bedspread, the fabric of which almost exactly matches Dodie's wraparound skirt.

"No, really, haven't you heard? Don't you read any magazines besides medical journals? Family and career don't mix this year; I'm doing three different articles right now about giving up my career because my baby is so rewarding."

"What careers are you giving up?"

"In one I was a lawyer, very high-powered, but it's all worth it because never again will my little girl call the housekeeper Mommy."

Amelia makes a fart noise with her mouth.

"In the second, I was an executive secretary, and in the third I was a reporter, but then I had twins. The little devils."

"Pass the wine, Dodie. You're making me sick."

"The nice thing about a word processor is that I'll be able to use all the same details in a couple of years when they want articles on how boring it is to stay home with your kid, and how great it is to shove the kid in day care and get back to work."

"Back to being a lawyer, an executive secretary, and a reporter."

Amelia is slightly drunk already. Alexander is sound asleep on the bed, arms and legs splayed out, unwakable. With Matt and Alexander in a car speeding through a rainy night, Amelia has sometimes felt this tremor, this sense of all I love is right here, just keep this little can of people safe. She feels it now, on Dodie's mattress, picturing the mattress rising above Los Angeles like a flying carpet. Don't let us fall off, please. But where is Matt?

"So how's Matt?" Dodie has met him once or twice only. Her friendship with Amelia goes back before Matt was invented.

"Matt is fine. And he's making lots of money."

"Fixing up people's houses?"

"Artistic renovation, painstaking reconstruction of period detail. They pay whatever you ask."

After you are married and have a child, even your best friends no longer ask how you two are getting along, how you guys are doing. Amelia considers saying, Matt is now much more attractive than I am; what do you think that means? He is sexy, and women look at him at parties, and I don't think anyone ever looks at me these days. And besides, my head is full of such strange, sad things, and I can't always put them aside. Do you think Matt bargained for all this? Do you think he can tell how often I am with him but thinking about mess and pain and death? Do you think he screws his clients, all these house-proud women whose cabinets he builds? Do you think he is alone tonight, three thousand miles from me? Talk about soap opera.

"I am having the affair with the proverbial shit married man," Dodie tells her, speaking of soap opera. "So far it has generated four articles and one diamond bracelet."

"A real diamond bracelet?"

"The minute he leaves, I type up everything he said and did, into the word processor it goes. This is the first time in my life I've ever written off contraceptive gel as a business-related expense."

When Amelia and Dodie were friends in high school, Amelia thought Dodie was the most beautiful girl in the school. She looks almost exactly the same now, with lank absolutely straight blond hair parted down the middle, hanging in split ends almost to her waist. Still thin, still wearing a T-shirt and an Indian wrap skirt. Amelia feels conscious of her own outline, fuller since motherhood.

Dodie has never lost that slightly surprised air of irony that went with being an ostentatiously sophisticated adolescent. Whenever she drops it for a minute, Amelia is startled.

"He's beautiful, your son."

"They're always especially beautiful when they're asleep; you just want to protect them and hold them." It seems an embarrassingly intimate thing to say, even to Dodie. Why doesn't she just say, matter-of-factly, he's the most beautiful child in the world? She wouldn't say that, actually, any more than she would have said it in the private school interview. There is only one person in the world she would tell this particular truth, and he, as it happens, already knows. So does it really matter where Matt is right now?

Her hand smooths back Alexander's slightly sweaty hair, stroking from the damp silk to the wrinkled coarse cotton weave of the bedspread.

"I put that in the one about the lawyer; I watch my little girl sleeping and realize I have to be there when she wakes up, not the housekeeper."

When Alexander finally does wake up, Dodie takes him into her back room, which was meant to be the bedroom. Part of the room is set up with her word processor on its black Formica table, her white metal filing cabinet, her shelves of magazines and self-help books, pop sociology and diet advice. In another corner of the room is a maze of cages, tubes of chicken wire and Plexiglas tunnels connecting them, a city of rabbits. Dodie gives Alexander some lettuce, and he hesitantly pokes a piece into a cage. A rabbit snatches it, and Alexander crows with triumph.

Watching her son, Amelia is thinking that he really ought to have a pet. She remembers a series of white mice from her own childhood, the odor of the uncleaned cage and the terror of finding them dead. Matt has said, maybe a dog. But neither of them is really eager for the responsibility of a dog; maybe when we have another baby, Amelia has said, meaning, that will tie us down anyway.

"Mom, I gave them all the lettuce." Alexander, wildly excited, is pulling at her shirt. "Mom, I need more lettuce, they're still hungry. And I didn't even feed the other ones yet, Mom."

Dodie gets him a Tupperware container full of lettuce, and he crouches beside an enormous cage, where three black rabbits sleep in a heap. She unlatches the little door, reaches in, and hauls out a rabbit. As she cradles it, Alexander feeds it pieces of lettuce.

"How did you get so many animals?"

"Alexander, this is what happens if you start out with two horny rabbits."

Amelia can already see the request looming up ahead, Mom, can we have? "Alexander, it's time to go pee and wash your hands and face, and we're going to go out and get something for us to eat. The rabbits will still be here when you get back."

"Tomorrow, when your mother's at her conference, we'll take some of them out in the backyard and exercise them."

Awed, Alexander goes off to pee.

Amelia says to Dodie, "Do they do calisthenics?"

"No, aerobics. This is California, remember? You should see them in their little spandex outfits."

At the conference the pin on her name tag is defective, and the tag keeps turning upside down. But her paper goes well; for the rest of the day people seek her out the way a success is sought out. At the afternoon reception she is monopolized by a big bearded man from UCLA, a pediatric oncologist who wants to talk about the cancers that children with AIDS get. Why don't they get Kaposi's sarcoma, he demands of Amelia. He brings her a vodka and tonic, brings himself a beer, why don't they get KS? Amelia doesn't know why not, no one knows why not. But she is somewhat interested in the question. The big bear's name is Al Markowski, and he is not bad-looking, if you like them big. Nothing at all like Matt. Amelia is not exactly attracted, but she knows she is being given the business, so she is watching him closely. He swings his bottle of beer. Listen to this study design I'm working out. Something tells her that he wants to come to Boston, to her own hospital. And then there is a certain category of men who like to court the successful, the good speakers. She can imagine the aggressive good fellowship Al Markowski would offer if she were a man herself, the two of them chugging their beers and shredding other people's research.

"Excuse me, won't you," she tells him. "I'm afraid I desperately need to pee."

In the bathroom mirror she can see that the tag is upside down again. She is amused at herself; mother of a four-year-old, she is always on the brink of asking her companion, Do you have to go pee? Of warning an adult, Go now, there may not be a bathroom later. What a make-out artist I am, Amelia thinks. Soon she will get out of this reception and go back to Alexander and Dodie. Once upon a time this would have seemed like an opportunity for flirtation; Dodie even now would not be the least bit shocked if she called, said, I'm going out with someone for dinner, see you later. Amelia realizes that the vodka drink was too strong for her; ever since she came to California she has felt slightly tipsy. Jet lag, probably. When she leaves the bathroom, three medical students find her, serious and full of questions. Amelia is kind and encouraging with them, feeling a little giddy and a little foolish. Al Markowski finds her again: There are a couple of issues you raised in your talk I really wanted to go into further. Maybe this isn't the place . . .

At the podium I thought of how my voice would sound. My voice is nasal, always has been; I do not like tape recordings of myself. I looked out on my audience, some snoozing in the after-lunch haze of any conference. The white-coated doctors on loan from their hospital duties would snooze too, until beeped out. There was a man in the front row with a foolscap pad, already making confident felt-tipped-pen notes, even though I hadn't started to speak. My voice is my voice, after all; it's all I have. I cleared my throat and launched myself. I do not like the way I sound particularly, though I keep on talking.

Next slide please. This chart shows the opportunistic infections that we diagnosed in the patients in our study, which you see follow a very similar distribution to the CDC data we've been hearing about. But there are a couple of differences I want to point out. First, look at the prevalence of pneumocystis carinii pneumonia in our study population.

A somewhat more interesting story comes to light when we plot the immediate cause of death of those children diagnosed between 1984 and 1986.

Our patients underwent a battery of special studies.

From a primary care point of view, this information raises some special concerns for pediatricians taking care of children at risk for HIV infection.

Thank you very much; I'd be glad to take questions now.

With Dodie and Alexander, the day after her speech, Amelia goes to Venice, to the beach. They walk along the boardwalk. Alexander is not interested in the ocean, but the crowd along the boardwalk is as good as a circus. People on roller skates go zooming by, and he clings tight to Dodie and Amelia, but screams out in pleasure, "Here comes another one!" They pass an enclosure where masseurs and masseuses stand waiting for customers, their little signs advertising rolf, shiatsu. A muscular man of maybe sixty-five is being worked over, with copious oil, by a pipe-cleaner-thin young woman dressed as a cartoon witch; her fingers sink deep into his muscles. Frozen yogurt for everyone; Alexander is blueberry-blue and happily sticky. A skateboard competition, young men in heavy-metal T-shirts weaving in and out among orange traffic stanchions.

"The edge of the continent," Dodie says, as they watch a skateboarder hurtle toward the sea so fast that surely he could keep on going, catch a wave. Sparks fly from his flint wheels on the concrete.

"This is a wonderful place," Amelia tells her friend. "Can you imagine if we'd had somewhere like this to go when we were in high school?"

"I'll always be a shopping-mall girl at heart. This is too fucking sunny and bright for me." But Dodie is enjoying herself; her hair gleams in the sunshine and filaments leap up in the wind to scatter round her head. Dodie likes to be at the show, and Amelia is happy to be there with her, to stretch Alexander between them, a sticky hand to each. Amelia's real life is far away and the air smells of suntan oil and pizza and everyone is wearing turquoise, hot pink, or electric yellow.

On the beach itself, they release Alexander and he runs, looking down to find shells. Frisbees fly overhead, and kites with rainbow tails, and seagulls. Amelia thinks suddenly, overwhelmingly, of Darren. Darren on a beach, a quiet faraway island beach, not this California circus place. She watches Alexander running away from her, kicking sand with every bounce of his strong little legs, and she thinks about Darren's skin, loose over his bones.

I thought, I have to get Alexander away from here, keep him safe. This landscape, this beach, was something I had imagined into being for Darren. Eastern city child that I am, the beach is no big part of my mental terrain, and it was an alien place for my child. I shouted his name, but he didn't hear me, or else didn't turn around, and Dodie comfortingly told me that he was nowhere near the water, that he was too smart to go in the water. I could not possibly have explained that what worried me was that when I caught up to Alexander, he would look up at me not with his own happy evil eyes, the eyes of a child who heard his name and didn't turn round, but with the wary eyes of a child who expects pain, a child whose legs will not carry him down the beach.

"How is 'being a doctor'?" Dodie inserts the quotation marks ironically, matter-of-factly; no occupation is exactly real to her. "I'm used to it." Once Dodie was the one person on earth to whom Amelia could say anything; back then, everything was susceptible to irony: teachers, boys, parents. Amelia has various lines she gives out on the subject of her work, the take-me-seriously line, the let's-not-start-talking-about-sick-children deflection. "How's the writing?"

"It's a living. Give me another little nugget—besides watching the kid sleeping. What else makes me decide to give up the rat race and stay home with Junior?"

"Dodie, articles like those give me a pain."

"But doesn't it make you feel good to think that someone like me is writing them? I've never held a regular job or had a kid."

"Did you use having the kid get sick and not being able to stay home with it?"

"Give me a good disease for an infant, nothing fatal, no brain damage."

"Diarrhea and dehydration."

Amelia had enjoyed helping out much more when Dodie had been doing articles on the joys of casual sex (What You Can Learn from Your One-Night Stand; Different Kinds of Romance; Choosing Your Next Fling; Nice Girls Just Want to Have Fun). Up ahead of them, Alexander has wormed his way into a Frisbee game going on among a group of blonds in running shorts, who look irresistibly like frat boys. In fact, Dodie, looking at them, is already singing softly into Amelia's ear, "Where the boys are. . . ." The boys are being nice to Alexander, snagging the Frisbee out of the air, bending down to offer it to him. With a corkscrew whirl, he sends it madly out into the air, a different direction each time, and the boys cheer him. When he sees Dodie and Amelia standing by, watching, he leaves off throwing to come running up to them, screaming, Mom, look at me, I'm playing Frisbee, I don't have to go yet, do I, watch me throw, watch how far I can make it go. Amelia grabs her son up into her arms to hug him hard; he wriggles like a frenzied fish. Mom, put me down, Mom, I have to go play Frisbee. She releases him, and he goes dashing back, but the boys' game has gotten fierce and is now going on way above his head, with howls and leaps and occasional collisions, and the boys do not really notice Alexander charging into their midst, waiting for a hand-off. So Amelia collars him and Dodie gets hold of his hand, and they pull him away, Dodie telling him about the carousel up ahead, at the Santa Monica Pier.

One day Amelia was sitting in the cafeteria with Christine, the intern who has taken care of Darren for the past month. A man sat down at their table: Mark Curry, a pear-shaped anesthesiologist, who listened for a while to their discussion of Darren's pneumonia. Amelia and Christine were both eating wilted Greek salads; Mark began forking down the breaded pork chops. And listening in; he and Amelia were on a hospital committee together so he assumed they were friends. Finally, Mark asked, "Does the kid have AIDS?"

"Yes, of course," Amelia had said, wishing Mark, unctuous, prurient, and not really all that smart, would get lost so they could continue their conversation.

Mark shook his head heavily, tsk-tsk-tsk. "The sins of the fathers," he pronounced.

Christine rolled her eyes.

"In this case I don't think the sins of the fathers have anything to do with it," Amelia said irritably. "This child is infected because her mother got a blood transfusion almost ten years ago when some drunk asshole plowed right into her car."

Christine, who knew Darren's medical history as well as Amelia did (father IV drug abuser, mother dead of AIDS-related pneumonia), sat pushing pieces of mushy tomato around her bowl. Mark was tsk-tsking even more energetically; he was a self-styled sensitive, caring doc, which gave him an excuse to be a busybody, always prying for details to shake his head over (So how did the parents take the news their kid was brain dead, gee, what a shame, what'd they say?). "What a terrible thing, that poor woman. And now the kid, too."

Actually, I remain confused about the politics and ethics of this. I would like Darren to be considered just as a sick child, obviously, I would like it to make no difference at all how or why he got sick. By making up a story and pretending he got sick in some less unsavory way, I am admitting the importance of the moral judgment, hiding details of his history as if they were shameful. On the other hand, I would like the jerks of this world to keep their tongues off him, or at the very least, I would like even Mark Curry to weep his crocodile tears for Darren without any feeling of smug superiority. This could happen to you, too, you big lug. I think of the lines I draw to protect my own child: Alexander will never get sick if I don't do this, or that, or any other bad thing. The thing that scares me most in this world, I think, is that a serious illness for Alexander would be some kind of justice, some kind of irony. So, little lady, you think you know what to say to parents, you have your set speeches. There's still hope, let's try to be optimistic. Let's try to make the most of the time he has left. Let's try to manage things so that she doesn't have any unnecessary pain. And above all, your special song and dance: You are so lucky to have known this child, if only for a month, a year. Your child was a gift; in your sorrow, sir, ma'am, think for a moment about the joy you had. I never say myself, of course, The Lord giveth and the Lord taketh away, blessed be the name of the Lord, but it seems to me one of the more comforting thoughts in the liturgy.

Yes indeed, I pride myself that even in those impossible moments I can find things to say that touch those parents. That I reach deep into my own love for Alexander and my own soul is touched, for even a few minutes, with a sense of their sadness and the vacuum of their loss. What the Lord should say to me is, So, little lady, let's see how those brave words sound in your own ears. Or maybe not the Lord, maybe a chorus of those weeping mothers and fathers I have tried to comfort, thinking of my own thriving boy.

Disneyland is a tremendous success; Dodie takes Alexander on the Thunder Mountain roller coaster, while Amelia holds Alexander's half-eaten cotton candy and half-drunk Coke. When he comes off the roller coaster, he goes immediately for the cotton candy again; Amelia is impressed. And patiently, she and Dodie wait through the line at Pirates of the Caribbean a second time, inching along through the realistic tunnels lined with cannons and barrels of rum and the occasional imprisoned skeleton. The second time, in front of them there is a family of four, all wearing lime-green shorts, a ten-year-old girl trying to scare her five-year-old sister. "There are real cannons that shoot at you, only usually they don't hit anybody, but this time they might hit our boat! Too bad if you can't swim."

Alexander, who was quite unnerved by the cannons his first time through, pushes into the conversation. "They aren't real pirates," he assures the small girl, who is maybe three inches taller than he is. "They're just robots, and the cannons are just a record of cannon noises."

The small girl considers. "I don't want to go on this," she announces. Her mother, without saying a word, smacks the older sister hard across the shoulder.

When they finally creep their way to the front of the line, a smiling mouseketeer named Brad manhandles them into the front seat of a boat and they sail off to the music of the singing pirates, "A Pirate's Life for Me." The first time through, Amelia had to keep whispering to Alexander, They aren't real, it's not a real knife, the cannons are just a record, but this time he shushes her when she tries to whisper to him. "I can't hear the pirates when you talk to me," he tells her, leaning forward eagerly in the front seat, scouting for buccaneers.

The exit leads them out of the ride into a pirate-theme souvenir shop, where Alexander selects a pirate hat, a pirate vest, a cutlass, and a small rubber knife in a sheath decorated with a skull and crossbones. Dodie insists on buying it all.

That evening, their last in Los Angeles, Amelia reads idly through an article Dodie has just finished writing, the joys of commitment in this age of sexual peril, how AIDS is bringing back romance. Dodie has two single-girl identities: one sleeps around, or used to, and one has a steady boyfriend with whom she has problems. Between them, they enable her to cover the territory pretty well—loneliness, commitment, sexual etiquette, gift ideas for your man.

Dodie is making hollandaise sause for the salmon. Alexander of course has no intention of eating salmon, with or without hollandaise, and has already eaten his dinner, plain macaroni, a toasted hot dog roll, a small bowl of frozen corn kernels. Frozen corn is one of Alexander's staples lately; at Amelia's suggestion, Dodie tries a kernel and agrees that it is surprisingly good. Eaten straight from the package, the cold little nuggets yield up sweetness as they warm in your mouth.

Dodie's hollandaise sauce is a fancy version with fresh ginger and orange zest in it. It is supposed to thicken in the food processor but it doesn't, and they end up with a bowl of melted butter with egg yolk in it. When Dodie, in desperation, heats it on the stove, the egg cooks and separates out, little filmy bits visible in the butter like egg drop soup. So Dodie good-naturedly peels five cloves of garlic and crushes them into the butter, and they eat their salmon with garlic butter.

Alexander is on the bed, wearing priate hat and pirate vest, his cutlass and his knife stuck into Dodie's old hand-tooled leather belt around his waist, muttering to himself in absorbed singsong, yo ho, yo ho. Suddenly he stops, looks up at his mother and Dodie, as they eat their cheesecake.

"Actually," he says, his face slowly opening into a grin, "actually, you don't know what I really am."

Obligingly Amelia guesses, a knight, a soldier, last month's enthusiasms. An astronaut?

Alexander is giggling, almost writhing with his triumph, shaking his head emphatically, no, no, wrong again. He points to the skull and crossbones on his hat. "One more guess?"

"I give up," Amelia tells him.

"I'm a pirate!" he screams, struggling to pull the cutlass loose from the belt.

"Help, help, a pirate! Dodie, help, it's a pirate!"

"Jesus fucking Christ, pirates! Call the coast guard!"

Alexander has to come to Dodie for help with the cutlass. After she has freed it for him, he brandishes it but says to her reassuringly, "Actually, I am a good pirate, not one of the bad ones."

Dodie, you seem somehow stranded, out here at the edge of the country in this little box bungalow, writing these slick little confessions of conventionally insightful women who don't really exist.

I sit here and eat the salmon, and there across the table is the face that was six inches away from me in the dark of her room the night we first smoked marijuana, at the ripe age of fourteen, having obtained the single sacred joint for an inflated price from her older sister. The phone number of her parents' house I still, twenty years later, know by heart; I dialed it a minimum of once a day for years and I doubt I will ever not know those seven digits. All information, all events, everything, had to be analyzed, giggling, every night, with mothers standing by to remind us that we saw each other in school all day anyway. I have never since had so much to talk about with anyone, and I cannot recreate a single instance of dialogue. What on earth did we say to each other? What was so funny, anyway?

"He has to go for an interview tomorrow," Matt says. "It was the only date they had."

"What are we supposed to tell him to do?"

Matt reads from the letter, in the squeaky and didactic voice of an unhinged computer. *It is not necessary to prepare your child in any way. This is our opportunity to get to know your child, to help you figure out whether Canfield-Rowbotham is the best place for him or her to be. Your child is not being 'judged' against any set of standards, but rather offered the opportunity to show us what kind of educational environment would really meet his or her needs as a person."*

They tell Alexander that he is going to meet a nice lady, and if he does everything she tells him to, and is very polite into the bargain, they'll buy him a whole bag of Gummi Bears. Prudently, Matt adds that if he tells the lady about the Gummi Bears, he'll have to share them with her. While Alexander is having his interview with the early childhood education specialist, Amelia and Matt, all dressed up, sit stiffly in a waiting room, under the impression that they are being watched through a two-way mirror.

"You pick your nose once, and it's all over for Alexander at Canfield-Rowbotham," Amelia whispers.

"Sit up straight, Amelia! Don't slump—bad posture counts against you."

"Did I ever tell you about the little kid I met at the hospital, Alexander's age, wearing a tie and a little blue blazer? His parents had brought him into the emergency room one day when I was moonlighting. I asked what he was all dressed up for, and he told me very seriously that he'd just been for an interview at the Woodbury School. You know, it was three years ago, before I knew about any of this stuff, so I just thought it was joke, a four-year-old in a jacket and tie. I asked him, 'So how did the interview go?' and he said to me, very mournfully, 'Not so good. I threw up.'"

"You told me."

On the wall are a number of pictures of Canfield-Rowbotham athletic teams; neither Amelia nor Matt refers to it, even in a whisper, but she is sure they are both thinking of the Canfield-Rowbotham scandal; two months ago, the boys' lacrosse coach in the high school division of the school was arrested for having sex with some of his students. The story got good play in all the local papers, especially since Canfield-Rowbotham is the snootiest school around (and lacrosse itself is considered a rather snooty sport), and, most important of all, word is there may be fewer applications than usual this year, especially from the parents of little boys.

"Did you like the lady, Alexander?"

"What did you and the lady do, Alexander?"

"Did you play games?"

"Did she want you to do puzzles?"

"Did you do what the lady told you to, Alexander?"

"I didn't tell her about the Gummi Bears, so I get to eat them all. I told her I was getting a treat if I did everything she told me to, but I didn't tell her what it was. So I get to eat them all, don't I, all by myself? And you and Mom can't even have one, because you said."

"I love him so much," Amelia says to Matt, as they lie in bed, still laughing at the idea of Alexander and his Gummi Bears.

"I wish we'd let him bring his cutlass to the interview, that's all I have to say."

Amelia turns over, her face in her pillow, the familiar warmth of Matt's body behind her. She cannot summon up her fantasy anymore, of Darren on the beach. It is gone, ever since she watched Alexander run along a real beach in California. When she tries to imagine Darren, happy and healthy in the sun, she sees only danger and menace, a beach threatened by tidal wave, typhoon, or perhaps by pirates who are not Disney creations, pirates who hurt the weak and defenseless and glory in the pain they cause. And she cannot be sure what child that is who plays so foolishly at the water's edge.

CHAPTER II
THE MOMENT BEFORE THE CRASH

What Amelia does on airplanes, when Alexander is with her, is make up her poem. When Alexander is not there, she reads a magazine, or leans her head back against the seat and sips her white wine spritzer, a childless grown-up who can accept a drink in a plastic glass full of ice without worrying even for a minute that a splayed little arm will send it splashing over her business-suited neighbor. Once last year she flew out of the Pittsburgh airport on a little commuter plane, Allegheny Airlines, to Akron, to give a talk at yet another conference. The plane had seats for thirty passengers, a strange rectangular aircraft like a disposable Styrofoam box made to hold a fast-food burger. Amelia and her companions walked out to it across the field, climbed the staircase, their clothes whipped by a hot airfield wind. The plane seemed too small to rate its own stewardess, its own pilot, but a stewardess settled them into rows two through eight, and a pilot flew them off.

It was the bumpiest flight ever. It felt like an amusement park ride; you could feel the plane dog-paddling along through the air, imagine every little bump of cloud, every blast of breeze. Reading was impossible as they bobbed along. The stewardess made it down the aisle dispensing drinks, which jerked up out of their cups in her wake, splashed down on the knees of childless adults clutching their armrests.

Across the aisle from Amelia was a very improbable woman to find on the commuter flight to Akron; cascades of golden curls in a hairdo like a showgirl's wig, and dressed all in snow-white frills, an eyelet blouse, a ruffle-edged skirt, lace stockings, and ankle-high spike-heeled white leather boots. Amelia looked out her window; the moving cars and the clearly visible houses and farms and even cows would have delighted Alexander. But Alexander was not there, and if this bumpy little box of a plane fell down onto one of those farms, only Amelia would fall—and the lady in white, of course, and the stewardess. Actually, before she had a child, Amelia never worried at all about flying. She wasn't named for Amelia Earheart, she was named for her father's great-aunt Amy. Still, she liked the idea of her famous namesake, and she liked flying. Off into the unknown, brave and true, here goes Amelia. If Alexander had been there, Amelia would have gripped him tight, smiling, and worked on her poem; instead, Alexander was home safe, on the ground, with Matt, and Amelia took cautious sips of Pepsi and looked out the window and enjoyed the bucking of the plane, all the way to Akron.

The poem is called "The Moment Before the Crash." At times it is in iambic pentameter, at times in rhymed couplets, often in blank verse. Almost automatically, she looks around the plane for details, she listens for scraps of conversation.

The moment before the crash, the lady in green sweatpants let her table down,
The retired hospital administrator gave up on Robert Ludlum,
And Jonathan DiAmato, five years old, missed the bowl and got pee on the floor when the plane jiggled—not the crash yet.

Nowadays Amelia rarely flies alone. She is accustomed to having Alexander there beside her, often Matt, too. The moment before the crash. She waits for the look of doubt on the flight attendant's face, the beginning of an announcement over the loudspeaker which will never be completed, the drop, the spin, the sudden understanding that this is what it will feel like, nothing else. Scary but also intoxicating; this is not her disaster, not her responsibility, there is nothing she can do, nothing she is supposed to do, to prevent a crash.

On the last airplane flight I took, just the shuttle back to Boston from New York City, with Alexander sleeping against me, worn out by his grandmother, Matt over by the window reading Agatha Christie, I was working on my poem, and across the aisle was an overly thin very possibly gay young man, and I kept putting him into the poem as dying.

And the man across the aisle feels a little short of breath.
He relaxes, says his mantra, breathing slower,
Doesn't know it's pneumocystis and the whispering of death,
And he reaches up and fiddles with the blower.

Darren has frequent fevers, which is not surprising; kids with AIDS often have fevers. He is already on three different IV antibiotics, on Bactrim to treat the pneumocystis carinii pneumonia for which he was originally admitted, also on mezlocillin and gentamicin, which they are using because even on the Bactrim he continued to have fevers; he may have some other bacterial infection and they are treating it, whatever it is. This particular cocktail of bug juices was worked out for the chemotherapied children on the oncology floor, their immune systems stripped bare as their heads. They get fevers, they get mezlo and gent; covers pretty much everything. Of course, the little leukemics will get their immune systems back (it is to be hoped), while the disease will die out of their bone marrows and the healthy white cells will gradually redivide and conquer. Darren's immune system is gone for good.

Darren is also on two antituberculosis medicines. But he is still spiking fevers, almost daily. For every fever he gets a blood culture, little bottles of bacterial medium injected with Darren's blood, sent to the laboratory to be tended in warm incubators, to see if any bacteria grow. If something would grow, they would have an explanation for the fevers, maybe a disease they could treat. No bacteria ever grow; Amelia calls up Darren's lab results on the computer in her clinic office and sees a long list of blood cultures, and after each, NO GROWTH TO DATE (NGTD, the interns write).

Every couple of days Darren gets a chest x-ray, and the radiologist always says it looks like PCP. How aggressively they should be looking for the source of Darren's fevers nobody really knows. He hates getting his blood drawn for those blood cultures. He hates x-rays, even though they don't hurt. Face it, he hates all of them, he hates everything. His life is one long unending series of examinations, stethoscopes tracking across his chest and back, and some eager intern always pushing a plastic funnel into his ears because they joked on rounds, or half-joked, Wouldn't it be funny if the fever is from a regular old ear infection? It would have to be some monstrous ear infection, to survive over the antibiotics he's on; an ear infection of bubonic plague, maybe.

Every week Darren's blood is sent to be tested for candida antigen. Candida is an omnipresent yeast, lives everywhere, on everyone. Causes diaper rash in babies, yeast infection in grown women, then, in people with immune deficiencies, causes doom and death, just like so many other microbes. When candida has invaded deep in the body, in the blood, in the tissues, it shows up in this blood test, the candida antigen. So every Monday a candida antigen is sent on Darren, a sentinel watch for a yeast attack. Eventually one comes back positive.

Sitting at the supper table, Alexander eats his noodles and his frozen corn, eyes glazed, letting Amelia and Matt talk back and forth about the shelving Matt is building into Leora Kagan's alcove, Leora being one of the women Amelia suspects Matt might service. So the conversation, at least on Amelia's side, is a little tight, but overtly friendly and casual. Leora wants the shelves made of oak, she wants them specially designed to hold her collection of occupation Japanese porcelain, she knows exactly what she wants, but she changes exactly what she wants every two days. Matt complaining, these crazy ladies, but actually liking her for caring. Matt maybe laying her on her pale pink upholstery (she and her husband have no children), saying to her, with a smile, Just part of the service, ma'am.

Alexander has lately mastered the technique of excuse me, excuse me, excuse me, over and over until he has the attention he wants, whether the parent he is besieging is on the couch, on the phone, on the toilet. "Excuse me, excuse me, excuse me, excuse me, Mom, excuse me, Daddy."

Amelia and Matt break off their conversation and turn to their child, who announces, "I can talk while I am eating food, know how? I push the food all over to one side of my mouth, and then I talk with the other side!" And he laughs, in sheer delight at this new accomplishment, while fragments of noodle fall out onto the table, and Matt and Amelia look at each other and finally end up laughing too.

The candida antigen is positive, but only borderline positive. Not strongly. What to do? A repeat blood sample is sent, but it will take a week to get results. The question is whether to treat Darren for candida infection, assume that is what has been causing the fevers, and start him on the antiyeast, antifungus medication, amphotericin, which the nurses call ampho-terrible.

Amelia confers with Christine, with the infectious disease specialists. Amelia would like not to start Darren on this new drug, but there's no way out; he has fevers without any known source and now he has a mildly positive candida antigen and candidiasis is a treatable disease. In her heart, Amelia doesn't believe that Darren's fevers are being caused by that yeast, doesn't believe that his borderline positive test result means serious disease. But what can she do; she can't let the yeast eat away his body.

Ampho-terrible the nurses call it. Look it up in the infectious diseases textbook: "Toxicity of intravenous amphotericin B is formidable, but nearly all patients can complete a conventional course of therapy." "Toxicity" means lots of people react to the IV infusion with fever, shaking chills, drop in blood pressure, shortness of breath. There are serious long-term dangers, mostly kidney damage, but the nurses hate it because of the daily horrors of infusing it. Medical protocol dictates that the first dose should be a small test dose, and after all the discussions are done, Christine finally writes the order (Please give 1 milligram amphotericin B IV over twenty minutes, check temperature, blood pressure, heart rate, and respiratory rate every fifteen minutes during infusion and for next half hour, then every half hour for four hours). It is late afternoon when the drug arrives from Pharmacy. Amelia, finished with her clinic for the day, drifts back up to Darren's ward to see how Darren does with amphotericin. All afternoon she has been doing a little special pleading, Please, could Darren be one of the lucky ones who have no bad reaction to amphotericin? It doesn't seem like so much to ask, that a child who has already had such enormous life-shattering bad luck should have the good luck to be able to take one particular drug without added suffering. It is of course exactly the kind of luck you so often don't get in medicine, when you pump toxic substances into people already stuck with the short end of the stick.

Darren is not one of the lucky ones. The small test dose of amphotericin drips in slowly through the plastic tubing leading into his left arm. Within five minutes of the start of the infusion, Darren's body shakes with tremors, his fever is shooting up, and he is beginning to break out in a rash. Even as she watches over Christine's capable coping ("Let's stop the amphotericin, let's give some rectal Tylenol and a hit of IV Benadryl, please"), Amelia is feeling furious. Darren looks like death right now, shaking in his bed like a child having a seizure—Christine and Amelia have both checked that out, as a matter of fact, but his eyes are not deviating to left or right, and he can respond to voices, so it isn't really a seizure, only a shaking chill. He's burning hot to the touch, his skin puffy and his breathing fast and shallow. Looking at his grandmother, wanting to know, why is this happening to me, why something else, and his grandmother knows why; they explained the side effects of amphotericin to her this morning.

Amelia leads Roberta Wilson out of Darren's room, murmuring that Christine and the nurses need room to work. In the parents' room, the TV is on eternally, leaning down from the ceiling. The color is bad; an aging orange-skinned mouseketeer is talking basketball. Amelia wants to turn it off, but like others before her, she cannot find a button that will do that; she turns down the volume all the way, sits Darren's grandmother down on the green vinyl couch, and starts making promises: from now on we will pretreat Darren every time he gets the amphotericin, we will give him Tylenol and Benadryl first, we will give the amphotericin even slower.

"I don't want him ever to get it again," says Darren's grandmother. "It's not going to save him."

Amelia nods, doesn't argue. Tomorrow, after Darren has had a peaceful night, Roberta will listen to reason and allow another dose of amphotericin, with premedication.

A new baby at the clinic, for his two-week visit. His mother, sixteen years old and proud as can be, has dressed him up in a stiff sailor suit with a blue bow at the neck, spotted already with dribble. She herself is trying to squeeze back into her old clothes; she wears a very short denim skirt, pulled drum-tight around her hips and buttocks, a black cotton sweater stretched over her breasts. She has a gold chain around her left ankle, over her nylons, another around her wrist, a third around her neck, with a cross on it. She is Somerville Irish Catholic, a sophomore in high school.

"Do you have a pediatrician yourself, Marcelle?"

"I go to the clinic doctor, the one who delivered Michael."

She is not breast-feeding, of course. Few of the mothers in Amelia's clinic breast-feed, despite her wall full of pamphlets from the La Leche League, despite her own eagerness to teach and advise and encourage. A couple of the mothers nurse—one of the Cambodian immigrants, one girl who dropped out of Boston College to have her baby. But none of the lower-class whites, blacks, Hispanics, who make up most of her population. Bottles, bottles, bottles. Amelia remembers very clearly the sensation of Alexander nursing; it is one of the few things she can recall so distinctly from when he was a little baby—most of his infancy is blurred over by the slow changes, small baby to big baby, toddler to little boy. But the nursing remains clear and specific in her memory: she loved the absorbed look on his face, the way he fastened on and sucked for dear life, pulling the milk out from her toes, it felt like, the narrow-eyed glares he would snake out at Matt if he came too close. Amelia and Matt called that expression I'm-on-the-booby-and-you're-not.

Amelia wishes that Marcelle was breast-feeding. She feels sure that a field team for the World Health Organization would have had better luck convincing Marcelle's third-world equivalent. Actually, Marcelle is in her way a sort of third-world character, though of course she does have access to clean water to mix her formula, for which we should all be thankful, Amelia thinks, examining Michael.

He is an uncommonly beautiful baby, with pale cornsilk hair and beautiful long arms and legs. He still has the newborn aura, at least when his mother takes off the sailor suit. Still looks more like a blind being from outer space than he does like a baby. Still moves his hands aimlessly in underwater ballet, still smells of the dark waters of the womb, however well anointed with baby powder, baby oil, baby lotion. Amelia undoes his Pamper but keeps it in position to avoid being spritzed; she owns no garment that has not been peed on by her patients. They save it for the genital exam, when she has to uncover them, though she's good at noticing the infinitesimal stiffening of the penis which precedes the blast, and often she gets it covered up just in time.

Maybe, like a musician's scales, certain things get so familiar to your fingers that you would have to watch yourself before you could describe the routine. Amelia has already seen how Michael watches her, turns toward his mother's voice, holds up his head. Something in Amelia is poised for disaster, for a newborn who does not seem able to do those few things a newborn should do. Floppy, limp, listless, poor muscle tone. Amelia has been the one, several times in her life, to break the news to new parents: something is wrong. She is braced for the next time. But not Michael. The sailor suit off, the Pamper loosened, Marcelle burps her baby against her shoulder while Amelia gets at his back and then his front with her stethoscope. The lubdublubdub of his heart is without any whisper of a murmur fogging up the beats, the air moves clearly down to the bottoms of his lungs. He is wriggling with impatience at this cold metal disc on his body, but by the time he cries, she has heard enough. She gets into his ears, sneaks a look down his throat when he opens up for a good big scream, presses down on his belly, manipulates his hips. There is nothing more alive than a healthy newborn, nothing more reassuring than this exam; under his pink and powdered skin, muscles and vessels and nerves are all in proper place. He is a little growing machine, no business in life but to absorb food and get bigger; if you filmed him at night, you would see by time-lapse photography how his body is enlarging. Normal, normal, normal. No masses in his stomach (germ cell tumors), no clicks when she wishbones him at the hips (congenital dislocation). He sucks like a demon on Amelia's finger, well equipped for the most basic infant survival duties, and Amelia feels another brief regret that Michael will not get to suckle at Marcelle's ample bosom.

"He's just perfect," Amelia tells Marcelle, who knew it all along.

It's normal if he has five or six bowel movements a day, normal if he has only one, normal if he spits up a little after eating.
If his stool is yellow, brown, greenish.
Don't worry about spoiling him, pick him up when he cries.
He gets his first shot when he's two months old.
Get sleep and good nutrition yourself, Marcelle, stay healthy.
Enjoy him.

And the baby in the second row awakened from his nap,
Just when his mother got the *Cosmo* open on her lap
  And the tall guy with the calculator eases off his boot,
  While the cop up on the movie screen decides to turn and shoot,
  And the crossword puzzle lady, who is just across the aisle
  From the frat boys on their second beers, is writing all the while.

Properly premedicated, Darren does a little better with the amphotericin. By the third day, he has caught on to the routine, swallows his Tylenol and lets them shoot the Benadryl into his IV without protest, but then when the nurse comes in to start the amphotericin going, even if his grandmother is trying to distract him with a story, Darren begins to wail. He knows that the stuff the nurse is putting into his medication burette is the stuff that makes him burn and shake, and he cries; already by the third day he understands that this is some new torment added to his routine.

Also on the third day, Christine pages Amelia, troubled; the lab
that does the candida antigen tests called her to say something is
wrong with their assay this week, and they are worried that some
of the positive tests may be false. They're fixing up their process,
running some tests—by next week they should be able to do it right
again.

"Do we really need to treat him?" Christine asks.

"Yes, I think we do." As Christine expected her to answer, to
play the heavy. But what can she do? It might be a false positive,
but it might also be a real positive, and if it is real, then et cetera,
et cetera. "Christine, I feel morally certain that Darren doesn't
really have candida, but then, I don't *want* him to have candida.
So he gets maybe four or five more days of ampho, and then it'll
turn out he's not positive, and never was—but I don't see what
choice we have."

"Well, it bothers me a lot—and even if he did have it . . ." Her
gentle drawl trails away.

"If he does have it, it's a treatable condition, and we treat it. And
if a lab error buys him a few days of amphotericin, that's better
than giving up on him just because his ultimate prognosis is lousy."
Amelia is not sure she believes this. But then, if you give up on
people as soon as you make a fatal diagnosis, then much of the
medical profession is out of business. "Christine, we are trying to
get this child home to have some time with his grandmother. We
are not going to let treatable diseases eat him up alive."

"Okay, ma'am." Christine sounds hurt and distant. "Good-bye.
I'll let you know when the results come in next week." Christine
is gone.

Slippery ground. How much is it worth torturing a small child
with a fatal disease? If he could vote, how many needle sticks would
he endure for how faint a hope of how much time at home? The
battle won will mean what?—television in his grandmother's living
room, walks in the park, if he is strong enough to walk, a sick
child's approximation of childhood with temptations brought in
from McDonald's to slip calories into him, with medications eight
or nine times a day, with anxious examinations every day to see if

he is getting worse, with all those trips to the clinic for weighing and measuring and listening to the chest. How many needle sticks, how many doses of amphotericin, for how many days, Darren?

A sense of duty sends her up to the ward to talk to Roberta Wilson: I am the one who insists on the daily amphotericin, but it may turn out to be unnecessary—and if it does, we have to be happy about that. Right?

"Doctor, I clipped this article I wanted to show you, and you know as well as I do that normally I don't hold with this kind of thing, but Darren just is not making any improvement. And it says here that people with damaged immune systems should not be eating any meat, because human beings were never designed to eat meat, so you need your immune system to handle the alien substance. Now, I have been ordering meat for Darren, lunch and dinner, trying to get him some protein—is this to say I have just been using up the little that is left of his immune system?"

"If he eats the meat at all, I think you should keep ordering it, Mrs. Wilson. There's so few things he's willing to eat at all, and he does need the calories so badly."

All she does this day is stand up for principles that don't matter. Why not let Darren's grandmother try a vegetarian diet, make her feel she's doing something to help? A few more days of amphotericin when she doesn't really believe he has candidiasis, a few more bites of hospital hamburger when he is wasting away one way or the other. It's what medical training teaches you. It's the kind of plan you make: Number one, treat with amphotericin until candida definitely ruled out; number two, maximize calories. Christine takes care of him every day when the ampho-terrible goes in, his grandmother sits by the bed and tries to spoon the food in, no wonder they persist in bringing reality to my attention. But for all that, Amelia must recite the doctor's lines: He needs the amphotericin. He needs the meat.

Between Amelia and Matt there are various scars, of course, various fights settled or unsettled, various acts of contrition and gifts of forgiveness. The little fossil invertebrate that Amelia calls to mind, buried in its accumulated rock, is the affair Matt had with her best friend while she, Amelia, was an intern. Almost ten years ago.

It was a bad year, when Amelia was an intern. Matt was working for a bad-natured, though talented, carpenter in Brighton, coming home every evening aggrieved and injured in his pride—or his arrogance. Amelia was not at home ever, practically. She stayed late at the hospital, she slept at the hospital, she ate standing up at the hospital. She came home to sleep, every now and then, in clothes she had been wearing for two days straight. A fairly standard internship: she was conscientious, stressed out, and she loved what she was doing. Matt hated what she was doing; he felt betrayed and abandoned.

Amelia learned that around him she must never show any affection for her job. He insisted that she regard it as he did, as an unbearable imposition on their lives. He was angry at the hospital, angry at medicine, angry at her. He constantly forgot her schedule; he would buy concert tickets for the two of them on a night when she had to stay over at the hospital, then look affronted and outraged when she reminded him. He would try to keep her up late when she had to be at work early, and if she protested he would say, Call in sick. Interns are not allowed to be sick, Amelia learned quickly not to say.

In other words, he behaved badly, for quite a sustained period of time, the only such time in their life together. And then rather suddenly he reformed, he began to keep close track of her on-call schedule, he greeted her with a hug when she came home late, he was solicitous of her sleep, her fatigue, her completely wrung-out state.

It took Amelia quite a while to catch on. His solicitude was nothing more than what she had felt dimly entitled to all along; other doctors had spouses (well, wives) who didn't pout and whine all the time about being internship widows. So Matt had finally pulled up his socks and decided to behave.

Well, actually not. He had started sleeping with her friend Vicky.

At the time they were living in an unpleasant little apartment near Massachusetts Avenue, and Vicky in the next building over.

Vicky has since gone to law school, moved to New York City, and now earns over a hundred thousand dollars a year; she works at least as hard as Amelia. But at the time she was a free spirit, selling second-hand clothes in a chic and grubby little shop in Central Square and maintaining the living room of her apartment as her studio, where she made mammoth mountain-and-valley landscapes out of papier-mâché and then covered them with collages of faces and words clipped from magazines. She was a friend of Amelia's from college, and quite a good friend, but prone to romantic crises, seductions and betrayals, and Matt began sleeping with her, presumably to divert himself and hurt Amelia all at the same time.

Unfair, maybe. Maybe they were swept away by passion, forbidden but irresistible. Vicky was always around; Amelia and Matt were her stable couple friends, her surrogate parents, and when she had romantic crises, she came over to rummage in their refrigerator and lament her wild unsettled state. Matt hung back from these displays; she was Amelia's friend, after all, really.

Amelia caught on, though it took her a while. Just like in the magazines, you had to notice a tender intercepted glance. A night Matt wasn't home and should have been, so with a little free time on her hands in the neonatal intensive care unit, Amelia called Vicky, who sounded flustered to hear from her. Amelia eventually guessed, and felt hurt and betrayed from both sides, but also felt a wonderful sweeping relief: after all, I am in the right and they are not, Matt has done something wrong, the moral advantage is mine, after all. She let it go until her precious two-week vacation in February, when she and Matt went to Mexico and dutifully drank fruity alcoholic mixtures in the warm evening air and made love every night.

"Matt, you'll tell me if I'm out of my mind, but I think you're sleeping with Vicky." She said it almost casually, surprising herself, the two of them wandering through the marketplace at Oaxaca, through stalls crammed with sewing notions, bolts of cloth. Matt looked at her sideways, sheepish and maybe a little bit relieved, and quoted back to her her call schedule. "Every third night," he said, and squeezed her hand, and they took a horse-and-buggy ride around the city and smooched a little in the buggy.

And went back to Cambridge slightly giddy with their own tolerance and adaptability: so if I am gone every third night, working, why shouldn't he indulge in harmless fun and games with someone we both like? That sank it all forever, of course; Matt and Vicky didn't last and Amelia and Vicky were washed up for good.

That was the last official infidelity. The last time Matt and I allowed it. We have not discussed it, really, but up till a year or so ago, I would have said it was understood, our wild oats were sowed, we were going to be faithful together till death did us part. And we had a baby, of course, and that changes things. Nights at home are now family nights, and there is a child who wakes, and for years there were bottles to prepare and a wet diaper in the morning. You pass out of one stage and into another, and I know that when I did my internship we were still in a stage where infidelities were possible and would not wreck us, though there was pain and tension, and there are still scars. But now there is AIDS, and now we are a family, not a struggling young couple, and now I do not want to know if Matt is doing it with this lady or that one, because I don't know what will happen. Or actually, I suspect that the same thing will happen, since we can't just take our family apart, but I won't like it. It won't be like my internship, when I left *him* behind every day and every third night, and there was no child to hold him in place.

I will never ask him. How brave and sure of myself I was ten years ago in a market in Mexico, my arms full of clay bowls wrapped in newspapers. You will always love me best, go ahead and have your fun—was I really so little hurt? I remember occasional nights in the hospital, feeling sorry for myself, imagining the two of them squirming around in my bed, wishing on them impotence, mutual disgust, and a white-hot electrical fire that would leave them both charred skeletons. But I felt such power, it seems to me now, such a sense of certainty, as if I knew I would win in the end. But win what?

My husband and I are very happy together is what I would say if you asked me. Maybe, if I were being somewhat more honest, I would say, We went through some rocky times when I was doing my internship, when he had a job he didn't like, but now we have a child we both adore, we have a family life that matters so much to both of us—my husband and I are very happy together. Only sometimes I think maybe he resents the way I insist on dirtying my hands, the deaths I have to see. Why can't I make the world beautiful as he does, restoring houses, building fine wood cabinets. If I have to see sick and dying children, children he doesn't want to think about because the thought might hex his own, must I then come home dragging it all with me stuck to my shoes? And compel him to be concerned, morally whip him into solicitude?

And also, only sometimes, I think that he is good-looking, more so than he used to be, and I am not, and I wonder what that imbalance does to us. I am embarrassed that this thought returns to me so often, such an obvious trivial self-consciousness. I don't know if I would ever have another lover if we were separated. What exactly does that mean? If-we-were-separated is not even a real thought to me anymore, because of our boy, and what exactly does that mean? Sometimes I think that if I spend much more time around shattered children, I will need my own family too badly, too pathologically, like a world inside a snowflake globe, asking to be smashed. Is that why I keep a copy of *Little Women* next to my bed?

Alexander on the floor with his friend Jeremy, talking seriously; Amelia, reading the Sunday paper on the couch, can hear them. The game has faded, the army of miniature plastic zoo animals is abandoned.

"Whales don't bite you, they swallow you whole," Alexander tells Jeremy.

"No, whales can bite you. Whales have hundreds of teeth." Jeremy is a little bigger, a little older, a little braver.

"Sharks are the ones that bite you." Alexander sticks to his guns.

"No," says Jeremy, "whales can bite you with their big teeth, but a shark can swallow a boat."

This, Amelia thinks, is no doubt the result of some day care unit on Our Friends the Marine Mammals.

"You kill a whale with a harpoon," Alexander says. "That's a kind of long spear attached to a rope that they carry out in boats."

"I would kill a shark with a gun," Jeremy proclaims, "so it couldn't swallow me up."

"What if it swallowed you up before you could shoot it?"

"Then I would shoot it from inside its belly!"

Both little boys hoot with laughter, and Amelia shoos them up to Alexander's room, where they will no doubt make guns out of Tinkertoys and massacre the stuffed animals.

The copy of *Little Women* Amelia has been keeping at her bedside is the copy she read when she was little. It would be only a very slight exaggeration to say that she knows the book by heart—certainly she could pass a trivia test on any chapter. (What was Amy punished for in school? How did Jo first meet Laurie? What was Beth's pseudonym in the Pickwick Club? What did Meg look like when her wealthy friends dressed her up?) She took that copy with her to college, and to medical school, and now she keeps it by her bed, to read a little bit before she goes to sleep, to drift, as she has done all through her life, into a house where long graceful skirts rustle across the floor and Marmee knows the answers. The March household welcomes her easily in the evening; she has slipped into it so many times that her imagination takes her easily through the rooms and hallways of their house.

The fungi have generally been considered to be members of the plant kingdom, but many taxonomists have argued that they are entitled to a kingdom of their own—the Kingdom Fungi. (It all depends on whether you are a lumper or a splitter, since Kingdom is the largest and most inclusive of the taxonomic categories—is everything either Plantae or Animalia, or are there other kinds of organisms just as basic?) Unlike proper plants, fungi have no chlorophyll and therefore cannot photosynthesize. Instead they are either saprophytic, helping to decompose dead animals and plants, or parasitic, feeding on the living. Fungi have a number of original methods of reproducing themselves, including budding and spore formation, and there are those who find their genetic details absorbing. The fungi (or The Fungi) may be divided into the yeasts and the molds, and *Candida albicans* is a yeast.

Candida organisms are our constant companions as we make our way through this world; along with many other interesting bugs, they find safe passage and a bountiful supply of nutrients on our skin, or in the moist welcoming caverns of our orifices. And the complex community ecology of the human body keeps all these visitors in balance; our own cells protect us from invasion, and the competing pressure of the rest of the flora and fauna prevents any one colonist from multiplying out of all proportion and taking over, like the rabbits in Australia.

Darren's defenses are weak. Parts of his immune system continue to limp along, trying to wall off his body from invaders. But he is thin and wasted, and that compromises him further. The virus has wiped out many of the cells he needs to repel unwanted visitors. Amelia, in her more histrionic moments, can imagine the microbes massed round him, jostling for the openings. The infectious diseases textbook has this to say about disseminated candidiasis: "Multiple organs are usually involved, with the kidney, brain, myocardium, and eye the most common. . . . The hallmarks of the pathologic changes are diffuse microabscesses with a combined acute suppurative and granulomatous reaction and small macroabscesses." So bring in the fungicides and wipe it out, if you can, and wait to see what comes along next.

Win I did, I suppose, if you mean by that the survival of the marriage, Matt and I still a happy couple, now with beloved child. But here I am now, trapped—I would countenance anything, I think, rather than take apart our family, so have I somehow won only to lose self-respect, and power? I will never pay him back now, I think. And those bowls I would never eat out of, because I was afraid of lead in the paint—how could I not have thought of that, walking through the market in Oaxaca.

Amelia rarely goes on overnight trips alone; she turns down many conference invitations. But the invitation from Tampa is from an old professor, now gone south to the sun, and she flies down alone one evening, relaxed in the airplane, no child, no poem. Is met at the airport by Mira, the professor, now sixty or so, large and dignified and highly formal, incongruously driving a BMW convertible. Some cross between Grandmother retired to Miami and Frau Doktor Professor among the savages. The climate, she informs Amelia, is very congenial, though there are multiple cultural disadvantages. This is how she talks. And drives five miles below the speed limit in her flashy car in the center lane, people whizzing past them on both sides, occasionally honking, which she ignores. One does not exceed the speed limit, which is set optimally for road safety, is that not so? When she taught the interns, Amelia remembers, they used to do imitations of her speech patterns, claim they were translated directly from the Swiss, or the Romanian, or the Serbo-Croatian; in fact, Mira speaks perfect unaccented English. She was of an old school, fierce, formal, and supremely knowledgeable, raised four children, all of them now doctors, buried her doctor husband, and moved to Florida.

The apartment to which she takes Amelia is new and high-rise, quite lavish, overlooking blue water. Sleek and modern inside with glass tables and a white leather couch. And, dominating her living room, an enormous TV screen, the biggest Amelia has ever seen in someone's home. The white leather couch and the screen make her think of the *Playboy* mansion. She is embarrassed even to think such a thing in connection with Mira.

There is a guest room, double bed turned down, thick lavish magazines on the chrome nightstand, thick white towels in the guest bathroom. Thank God I didn't bring Alexander; imagine what he could do to a white leather couch. Amelia thinks about him, far away up the Atlantic seaboard, and misses him acutely. She and Mira sit on the couch and sip ritualistic sherry, gossiping rather uninterestingly about people changing labs and getting promoted. Mira complains at some length about the interns she now supervises when she does teaching rounds at the local medical center: they are just not as good, not as thorough as the interns in Boston. Amelia can remember very clearly how Mira used to berate the interns in Boston; she remembers being an intern and being terrified of Mira's tongue. She knew so much, she expected information to be given correctly and completely and without excuses, and she mourned the young doctors of her own day, who had studied harder, remembered better, and respected their elders. Amelia and the other interns had feared her but grudgingly acknowledged that, unlike many of the distinguished older doctors who supervised them, she had kept up avidly with the medical literature, and her clinical instincts were golden.

At Mira's suggestion, after a second glass of sherry, they watch a National Geographic video about the Bengal tiger, its intriguing habits and vanishing habitat. The lush jungle music is interrupted by the ringing phone, Matt, calling to tell Amelia that they are trying to reach her from the hospital, Christine has to talk to her.

Christine is at the end of her rope. "This is unreasonable, this doesn't make any sense to me, Amelia. He was real sick tonight, his blood pressure went down, I thought he was gonna code on me, and we've never even discussed whether he gets the full court press. I don't feel comfortable with this at all, Amelia."

Christine, usually so calm and so reassuring, is on the edge of tears. All evening she has been worrying that she will have to call a code on Darren, send him to the intensive care unit.

"Didn't you talk to Bob Berkowitz? I signed out all my pages to him."

"He's not gonna come in here and do a DNR status on some kid he doesn't even know."

"Christine, I'm not sure we're at the point where we're ready to talk about DNR."

"You want Darren intubated? You want him on a respirator?"

"Christine, for tonight there isn't anything I can do. Even if I were in town, I can't suddenly grab his grandmother in the middle of the night and ask her if it's okay to make him Do Not Resuscitate. You take as good care of him tonight as you can, and we'll plan on a sit-down meeting as soon as I get back . . ."

"Just so you know, Amelia, the nurses are up in arms. They don't want him DNR, and they're all pissed off at me because I said I didn't wanna code him."

"Are you okay, Christine? You don't sound so good."

"This fucking deathwatch is getting to me, okay?" Christine's voice cracks and she is obviously crying. Amelia says nothing for a few seconds.

"Christine, call up your senior resident, get someone over there to help you out. You just go ahead and do your job; you're a very good doctor, and you shouldn't have to take any flak over this."

"Amelia," Christine says, still with tears in her voice, "if I have to put this kid on a ventilator, we are committing child abuse. Just so you know I think that. Page me tomorrow whenever you're ready for that meeting. Now I gotta go, someone else is crashing too."

"Good-bye, Christine, hang in there," Amelia says, and is left holding the phone and feeling like a fool.

She is glad to let Mira take a break from the Bengal tiger and discuss the case with her, though she can't help thinking that back when Mira was in charge, no intern would have dared call her up at night and harangue her, let alone use profanity. Mira wore a white starched coat and she compelled formality; even now, Amelia is a little bit astonished to be lolling on a white leather couch with her. She finds herself presenting Darren's case rather formally, as if at a conference, half expecting to be grilled on her data.

"In this state," Mira says, "certain private hospitals are not willing to take care of AIDS patients. There is a great deal of what the residents call dumping, sending them to the county hospital. And one orthopedist in Miami has made a name for himself, making speeches about how surgeons should test each patient's serology before agreeing to operate and thus keep themselves safe from contaminated blood."

The next day, in some anonymous conference room, carpeted and air-conditioned, speaking into some anonymous microphone at the obligatory symposium on AIDS, which has to be included in every scientific meeting, Amelia imagines herself saying to the assembled doctors, all busily accumulating their required continuing-medical-education credits, Listen, how about if there is a child, and I think he has a chance to get well enough to go home, but the intern thinks I'm torturing him. Listen, isn't the time at home worth everything to a kid who'll never have anything else? Or is it actually a quick death that is worth everything?

Listen, there's a lady, Roberta, who used to teach school, and she had a daughter, whom we take for granted she loved very much, and then, to hear her tell it, her beautiful romantic-minded daughter got mixed up with a lying cheating slimy drug abuser who gave her AIDS and an illegitimate baby, and the former killed her, and the latter is dying now. And the lying cheating slime still walks the earth, though last week Roberta told me she had heard he was developing symptoms. Now, tell me, what does this lady's quite considerable human decency come to in the end? What point can there be to this story? Lose a daughter, but gain another child to love and raise and lose? And gain as well, maybe for the first time in her life, a truly murderous ambition: she wants to see this man die in horrible agony, and she feels rather guilty that her wish is likely to come true. Can we have this symposium address the moral of that story, please.

Amelia gives her talk badly, anyway. The whole symposium is somewhat lackluster, perhaps because one of the participants, who reads aloud a very long paper in a metronome monotone, belabors over and over his point: a hospital must treat patients with AIDS if such patients fall into the category of patients treated by that hospital. A hospital that was exclusively for obstetrics need not treat male AIDS patients. A pediatric hospital need not treat adults with AIDS. And so on and so forth, and the pages turn one by one and the voice ticks on into the endless distance.

I am going to sound like a horrible prig if I try to describe Vicky, my friend, my ex-friend. I will say nasty things about her, and you will think, with friends like Amelia, who needs enemies. Vicky has been my friend since college, and has always been very anxious about herself, about her life, but—how can I put this?—anxious about the wrong things, anxious about things that reveal she is, really, not a good, moral person. How obnoxious I sound, how snide, to disapprove of a friend because she has *bad values*—don't you mean, because she screwed your guy, honey? Vicky is often in a tizzy, but she would be sitting there in a tizzy about her thighs while all the time I would be saying, but this guy is a vicious liar;

who cares if he likes your thighs? Or something like that. Vicky used me, used all her friends, in her endless crises: this one doesn't love me, that one is having me followed by detectives, I'm getting old and all I really want is a baby, I don't have enough money to go to Guadeloupe for the weekend. Vicky's friends, I suppose, sometimes used her in return—she made us feel romantically successful, stable, and balanced. I am making this all sound so ugly because she screwed my guy, honey.

I was supposedly her friend, but I took her with an ugly edge of irony, I made fun of her with Matt. Then he went to bed with her and that meant by definition he had to take her seriously, be part of her endless intrigues, and that was one of the signals I couldn't possibly misread. That I was shocked that both of them were capable of this betrayal brands me as at least 50 percent pure mushhead.

I don't like it in books when one fatal sex act, one seduction or betrayal or infidelity, echoes across the years, poisons lives. But sometimes I do think about the time that Matt betrayed me with my friend while I worked in the hospital, and I wonder whether anything was poisoned.

I am becoming generally a little bit unbalanced on the subject of sex, I think. My fantasy life is taking me over. It is more real to me than my sex life, such as it is, or mostly isn't. And one of the fantasies I can't escape is a younger Matt and Vicky. I see every lurid detail; he is acting with her as he never does with me, selfish, lying back, expecting to be made love to, as if he knows that she is the one with something to prove. She is all over him, giving a performance, for him, for me, for the centuries, moaning and writhing, she is lying between his legs and sucking ferociously on his cock.

It does not surprise me that she is successful as a lawyer.

Hospitals that normally provide a certain range of medical services are obligated to provide those same services for patients with AIDS, whereas hospitals that do not normally provide given services shall not be required to extend the list of those services in order to meet the needs of patients with AIDS.

Amelia imagines Christine, tired after her night on call, dragging through the day. Darren in his bed, waiting for his amphotericin. What is child abuse in this context—giving it or not giving it? I did not go into this business to treat children who will never get better, and neither did Christine. You go into pediatrics because it's full of happy endings. Most sick children get well.

"It is already cold in Boston?" Mira asks her, somewhat wistfully, on the way to the airport in the convertible.

"We've had a string of nice days, but the nights are chilly."

"It's a tropical disease, really, when you think about where it comes from originally. AIDS, I am talking about again. So it is strange to think of it so well established in a cold climate."

"Well, it's a tropical disease in that it came out of Africa. But the transmission is direct person-to-person, so it doesn't depend on climate or mosquitoes."

"Still, it would somehow seem more appropriate here in Florida. Do you know how many children I have seen with hookworm since I came here, Amelia? I cannot think that any statistics are being kept with even remote exactness, because I believe there are towns where hookworm is endemic and every growing child has a worm burden."

Frau Doktor Professor among the savages. Imagine her in her starched white coat in a jungle hospital, and the natives bring their children by canoe through the perils of the jungle, past the lurking tigers, to offer them to this formal lady, her hair always pinned severely back, her fingers probing down into the little belly, her light shining down into the throat. She does not ever recoil, not from the most fetid sore or the most wasted child. And not from the far-off roar of the tiger.

The moment before the crash, the lady who had ordered the special diet
    dinner spooned up the last bite of canned peach and cottage cheese,
And promised herself a stop on the taxi ride home to pick up an order
    of Kentucky Fried,
Leaned back in her seat, imagining her own kitchen, her shoes off, no
    one to watch her wolfing down one piece after another,

And her lips formed the order, practicing, as she chewed the mush in her mouth.

But flying back to Boston alone she doesn't have to write her poem, of course. It may be the moment before the crash or it may not; it isn't her problem. She thinks instead about this meeting she will have to arrange. The nurses will want everything done for Darren, no holding back. They will be suspicious, they will intuit a cabal among the doctors, a wish to give up on this child because he has no chance to live long, a wish that will translate into telling the nurses to let him die. They will probably be right.

"We missed you," Matt tells her. Alexander is polite about the shell box bought in the Tampa airport; he would prefer a submachine gun, of course. She wishes she had brought Matt something, even from just a one-day trip.

Suddenly I realized, picking up *Little Women* after a night away, what chapter it is that I have not been reading. I read over "Amy's Valley of Humiliation," or "Meg Goes to Vanity Fair," skip from Jo refusing Laurie to Jo and Professor Bhaer under the umbrella, or I read Jo's journal from her stay in the boardinghouse. She needed money, and she wanted to be a writer, and she found that the newspapers would buy sensational stories. But how could an innocent girl from a small New England town write stories of sin and degradation? She had to educate herself about the evil underbelly of the world. She had to look into the gutter, and carefully categorize what she saw there. It reminds me of medical training: "Mr. Dashwood rejected any but thrilling tales, and as thrills could not be produced except by harrowing up the souls of the readers, history and romance, land and sea, science and art, police records and lunatic asylums, had to be ransacked for the purpose. Jo soon found that her innocent experience had given her but few glimpses of the tragic world which underlies society, so regarding it in a business light, she set about supplying her deficiencies with characteristic energy. Eager to find material for stories, and bent on making them original in plot, if not masterly in execution, she searched newspapers for accidents, incidents, and crimes; she excited the suspicions of public librarians by asking for works on poisons; she studied faces in the streets, and characters, good, bad, and indifferent, all about her; she delved in the dust of ancient times for facts or fictions so old that they were as good as new, and introduced herself to folly, sin, and misery, as well as her limited opportunities allowed." There it is, medical education. Take the sheltered middle-class good child, whose idea of tragedy to date is a high school classmate killed in a drunken car crash. Here is the emergency room, here are the homeless and the drunks, the elderly poor and the abused children, the suicide attempts and the stab wounds. And they bleed all over you and you ram tubes down their noses to suck the vomit out. Medical education, it was once thought, would coarsen any nice girl. A reasonable point.

When Matt shrinks from me, from my life, this is surely what he is thinking, though less explicitly. Why would I choose to be exposed to the ugliness of the city? Why not make things beautiful, or make beautiful things, and enjoy my own beautiful child? Do I think I am piling up credit, that the world will be kinder to Alexander, if he should get sick, because I have been caretaker for other women's sick and dying children? Actually, Matt would never ever put that question; he does not countenance the idea of Alexander's sickness, he does not allow for the possibility. The two of us, faced with a magazine article about some child's heartbreaking illness, some family's heartwarming struggle—I would read it, he would skip it.

He would, of course, be right to skip it, since it would in all likelihood be cornmeal mush. Dying children, soppy, soppy. Dying children are the sweet, creamy centers of literature; bite in and reach the dying child, and suddenly there is nothing for your teeth to chew on, there is only sickly oversweetness, goo, and tooth decay.

"She thought she was prospering finely, but unconsciously she was beginning to desecrate some of the womanliest attributes of a woman's character. She was living in bad society, and imaginary though it was, its influence affected her, for she was feeding heart and fancy on dangerous and unsubstantial food, and was fast brushing the innocent bloom from her nature by a premature acquaintance with the darker side of life, which comes soon enough to all of us."

As I say, I finally realized what chapter I have been avoiding.

The battle lines in the meeting are familiar. Amelia and Christine represent the doctors; for reinforcement, they have called in Peter Hillyard from the infectious disease team, a doctor mildly famous in the hospital for being a full six foot four. Thin and nerdy and more than a little awkward, but fundamentally a nice guy, he sits now at the table, teetering back in his chair, making conversation with the nurses. Mary Pat and Kathleen, the two nurses who most often take care of Darren, Mary Pat sure of herself and controlled, Kathleen newer at her job, visibly unwilling to speak up, taking refuge behind Mary Pat's pronouncements.

Although Christine is by anyone's standards the most junior person present, she is the intern in charge of the patient, and therefore by convention it is her job to run the meeting. Amelia defers to her elaborately, and Christine, looking tired but determined, opens up. "I spent a long time talking to Darren's grandmother today. She has a very good understanding of how sick he is, I think—remember, her daughter died of this same disease. And I told her that I felt that we might not be doing Darren any favors if we put him on a ventilator, or if we sent him to the ICU."

"How did she take that?" Mary Pat asks. She is plainly displeased; she feels that Christine has exceeded her authority in raising this issue with the grandmother before the meeting.

"She said she understood, and she's thought about this a lot. She told me she wants us to help Darren, but if he looks like he won't be able to come home, like he won't get any better, she wants us to let him go."

Mary Pat is not afraid of doctors. Also, she wears a gold cross around her neck, and she takes her religion seriously. In her opinion, Amelia knows, the doctors are all too ready to say good-bye to a living soul just because there is no hope of a cure. "Darren does not seem to me to be immediately terminal," Mary Pat says. "If he gets sicker, if he crashes, I don't think you have any alternative. You have to code him, intubate him, send him to the ICU. He has a good chance of getting better from any particular illness."

Amelia says her piece. "If he develops respiratory distress, the likelihood at this point is pneumocystis. And if he has pneumocystis, and we put him on a ventilator, we'll never get him off. So there'll be all kinds of trauma to him, and emotional trauma to his grandmother seeing him on the vent—you know, sedated, in the ICU. Come on, Mary Pat, you know what dying in the ICU is like."

Mary Pat looks completely unconvinced. "I think that just because he has a fatal disease you guys are ready to give up on him. And that is not something you are entitled to do, M.D. or no M.D. You can't make that child DNR until you prove to me that he is going to die anyway *right away,* and that interventions will only mean extra pain."

Now, in her heart Amelia agrees with Mary Pat about Darren. That is, she thinks that the DNR issue is being raised here largely because Darren's ultimate prognosis is fatal, not because he is by any means ready to die. But she wants to end his pain, or at least not increase it, and if he gets much sicker and the question of a ventilator comes up, then in all probability he will never get well enough to go home. And further, she feels locked into the position of the doctors, almost always more inclined to pull back, to make the patient DNR. The nurses are Catholic, by and large; the doctors, by and large, are not. The nurses become more attached to the patients, standing by their beds day and night—maybe they see better the value of a life even out on the rim. Or maybe they are blinded by sentiment and don't really see the hideousness of a life of hospitalized pain.

"Mary Pat, he's not going to die right away. What we have to think about is what if he gets sicker, specifically what if he needs to be intubated, go on a vent. And what I'm saying is that if he develops lung disease so bad that he needs a tube, then it's all over for him. AIDS kid with pneumocystis don't come off the vent."

Mary Pat looks to Peter Hillyard. "Is that true?"

"Yes," says Peter. Amelia knows he is lying, just a little. So is she. Darren *could* deteriorate and need a breathing tube for other reasons. Children with pneumocystis *do* sometimes come off the vent. But Mary Pat wants absolutes.

"You're sure about this, that his chances for coming off the vent would be nil?" Now she is grilling Amelia.

"Given his underlying disease, given what we know about pneumocystis, Mary Pat, I don't think he would ever come off." She is lying, just a little. She doesn't know for sure whether he would come off or not. She knows she sounds definitive, invoking this doctorly knowledge, which, in the final analysis, the nurses will not challenge. Christine and Peter Hillyard are nodding.

And Mary Pat and Kathleen, who will be the ones to find Darren, if he stops breathing, the ones to hold back and not give the alarm, the ones who will not clasp an oxygen mask to his face and try to push air into his lungs, Mary Pat and Kathleen look at each other and accept these assurances.

It is agreed, then, that Amelia will go to Darren's grandmother and make a formal suggestion that Darren be made DNR. No tube down his throat if he stops breathing, no thumping on his chest if his heart stops. She knows that Darren's grandmother will agree; she sees only a child in pain, a child with a fatal disease, and Amelia knows that she thinks every day about taking him home, disconnecting the IV, getting him out. At home she could hold him on her lap in a room full of his favorite toys, she could feed him all the things he used to like, and she is sure that without doctors and needles he would eat them again. And at home, if it was time for him to die, she could lie down with him on her own bed, and they could listen to the classical music station on her radio, until one of them was dead. Would that be such a bad way for a three-year-old to die? Amelia has no ready answer, only a continuing hope that she may be able to buy them something a little better than that, some time for Darren to grow a little, learn a little, make some more memories for his grandmother—another dubious kindness.

Sure enough, Roberta Wilson agrees to the DNR status. But Darren does not stop breathing, his heart does not stop beating. And three days later, word comes that the positive candida antigen result was indeed false, and the amphotericin therapy has been unnecessary.

Little Women, Chapter 40, "The Valley of the Shadow." "The pleasantest room in the house was set apart for Beth, and in it was gathered everything that she most loved—flowers, pictures, her piano, the little worktable, and the beloved pussies. Father's best books found their way there, Mother's easy chair, Jo's desk, Amy's finest sketches, and every day Meg brought her babies on a loving pilgrimage, to make sunshine for Aunty Beth."

They know, you see, that Beth is dying, that there is nothing they can do, and they accept it. Don't get me wrong, I'm not going to tell you how much better they handled death way back when. Dying at home, no medical heroics. Sometimes better that way, perhaps, but give me modern medicine and antibiotics any day. No, the reason I find I cannot read this chapter without anger is that for me it serves as the archetype of all dying-children literature. It occurs to me that before I say that, I ought to go and read the real Little Nell—I will buy a copy of *The Old Curiosity Shop* tomorrow. But here is Beth, as good and golden and not-long-for-this-world as she can be, the dying child as plot device, to wring our hearts and make us better people, to open our eyes to the suffering of this world. The dying child as Christ, but also as spear-carrier, as guaranteed measure of guaranteed pathos, as, eternally, too good to live.

"Here, cherished like a household saint in its shrine, sat Beth, tranquil and busy as ever, for nothing could change the sweet, unselfish nature, and even while preparing to leave life, she tried to make it happier for those who should remain behind."

And for those of us who watch children get sick and die, over and over, there will always be questions of the nitty-gritty: yes, but who empties the bedpan, and what do you do when she misses the basin and vomits on the sheets? But this I suppose is quibbling; all births and deaths have always been attended by bloody linen and the smell of excrement, and that does not necessarily make them any less holy and wondrous, any less close to the mysteries of the eternal. And as for pain, which is the real filth, the real horror that hovers around a child's deathbed, well, Louisa May did not ignore it. "It was well for all that this peaceful time was given them as preparation for the sad hours to come; for, by-and-by, Beth said the needle was 'so heavy,' and put it down forever; talking wearied her, faces troubled her, pain claimed her for its own, and her tranquil spirit was sorrowfully perturbed by the ills that vexed her feeble flesh. Ah me! Such heavy days, such long, long nights, such aching hearts and imploring prayers, when those who loved her best were forced to see the thin hands stretched out to them beseechingly, to hear the bitter cry, 'Help me, help me!' and to feel that there was no help."

Why do I mind this? I have cried over it and cried over it in my time; I must have read the book through ten or fifteen times. Nothing so unusual in that. Everyone reads it, everyone identifies with Jo. And Beth's death can still stir me to tears (so does Jo's cutting off her hair), but I mind it. Because even if Louisa May really did lose a beloved sister, still, this chapter is pathos by the spoonful, this is the holy death of one too good to stay with us, whom the Almighty called to His bosom too soon. It is the whole damned nineteenth century, if you ask me.

"With tears and prayers and tender hands, Mother and sisters made her ready for the long sleep that pain would never mar again, seeing with grateful eyes the beautiful serenity that soon replaced the pathetic patience that had wrung their hearts so long, and feeling with reverent joy that to their darling death was a benignant angel, not a phantom full of dread."

So I guess by those standards I did right to fudge things with the nurses, to help Darren earn his DNR order. If it truly comes as a benignant angel to a suffering child. Horseshit and double horseshit.

How am I supposed to encompass this material? If part of my life is making the decision about Darren, then how do I downshift and find the right way to navigate the other parts, my own darling child, for example?

No wonder I find it mildly soothing to contemplate an airplane crash, a disaster that is beyond my decisions, my interventions, my expertise.

"This is aimed at us," Matt tells her, passing over a photocopied note from the day care center about the monthly meeting. Their room's meeting will focus on the question "Do we need a policy on sweets and junk foods in the lunches?"

"Why at us?"

"Amelia, I have a confession to make. I have been putting Twinkies in Alexander's lunchbox."

"*Twinkies? Are you serious?*"

"We saw them in the store, and he wanted to try them, and he thought they were just absolutely the best things he ever ate, so I've been sending one every day. And I knew the gestapo would be after me eventually, but hell, I ate Twinkies every day when I was growing up and it never did me any harm."

"Maybe we ought to skip this meeting," Amelia says, but knows Matt wouldn't miss it for anything. She loves him for putting the Twinkies in his son's lunchbox, for rebelling against his position as Mr. Groovy Cool Dad of the Month. All those children with their wholewheat-oatmeal cookies, their granola bars, their fresh figs, the sucrose and the glucose just clinging to their teeth, bathed in sanctity: no white sugar.

"Do we have any extra Twinkies in the house?"

"Why? Are you having a Twinkie attack?"

"I think that before we go to this meeting we should each eat one. As a pledge."

In the event of cardiopulmonary collapse, please DO NOT RESUSCITATE, by request of family. May give oxygen by facemask for respiratory distress, but no intubation, no mechanical ventilation, no cardiac medications, no chest compressions. Order will be renewed by attending every week.

"Max told me that the other day he tried to trade his whole lunch for one of Alexander's Twinkies."

Mrs. Max is something of an argument for you-are-what-you-eat, Amelia feels; her brain must be as smooth and white as tofu. She tends rather to whine, and she is whining now, sitting straight up on the orange shag carpet in the day care room. She omits no detail, however small or insignificant, refusing the cheap white wine to drink ostentatiously from her own container of apricot nectar, wearing an overtly handwoven shirt, and jewelry that was surely made by political prisoners somewhere. She is a plump and very dumb lady, and Amelia, who has never liked her, finds herself roused to anger: who is this cow to attack my lovely child?

"Max has a real problem with junk food," whines Mrs. Max. "If I let him, he would eat sweets all day long. Now, I'm trying to help him deal with that, and I don't put any sweets in his lunch, and I just feel we should reach a consensus here. If some children are going to bring just the kind of food I'm trying to help Max learn to avoid—I mean, he tried to trade his *whole lunch* for a Twinkie."

"I assume Alexander wouldn't trade," Amelia says. Matt catches her eye; they are both thinking of Max's lunches, lentil loaf on whole wheat with miso sauce, carrot sticks, rice cakes with margarine. Amelia wants to laugh, and so, she imagines, does Matt: good for you, Alexander, stick to your Twinkies.

Now speaks the day care parent Amelia truly hates. Mrs. Max and Mrs. Brandon are the only two she even dislikes, but they are the two who always hold forth at meetings. Which is no coincidence; they are both enamored of their superior techniques for raising perfect children.

Mrs. Brandon is less furiously New Age; her hair is frosted and shaped into a ladylike little flip, and her dress code is strictly preppy. But she is such an Involved Mother, she makes Amelia's skin crawl. Here she is now, with her Isadora Duncan hand gestures, to tell them how she manages with Brandon, who is easily the least appealing, worst behaved child in the room. Little Mr. Booger; Amelia has never seen him without one, and often two, fingers deep in his nose.

"What I have always done with Brandon"—a sweeping swoosh of the arms—"and I really think it has worked out well, I have always kept sweets in a jar where they are *available* to him"—a downbeat of both arms on *available*—"and he knows that it is his *choice* to take or not to take. And that way, it just defuses the whole issue, and he regulates himself very well."

"If I did that with Max, he would empty the jar in two minutes."

"But in any case," Mrs. Brandon swooshes on, holding up her hands to the heavens now, "I make it a point to use healthy sweets,

I would never fill my jar with junk, because that is not the *message* I want to send to my child."

The message *I* would like to send to *your* child is Take your fucking fingers out of your nose.

Mr. Emily, who is a lawyer, assures Mrs. Brandon that in point of fact it is not a question of what message we send, but rather, if he may say so, a question of medium.

But Mr. Rachel, who is a take-charge kind of guy, wants to know if we can all just agree on some basic rule and move on to the next item on the agenda, extra socks for cold days.

"Well, to begin with," says Mrs. Max, "I think we should agree on no white-sugar desserts in the children's lunches."

Amelia puts on her doctor voice, the same one she used last year when Mr. Emily didn't want the kids to pee out in the corner of the yard because he was afraid it would spread disease, and Amelia, who was sure that what he was really worried about was sexual immorality, informed him that urine is a sterile fluid. "There is essentially no difference nutritionally between white sugar, brown sugar, honey, or even molasses. That apricot nectar you're drinking has enough sugar in it to rot anyone's teeth."

"I like Twinkies," Matt says, loudly and clearly. "I ate Twinkies every day when I was a kid, and I've never had a cavity or committed a murder. And for that matter, I like Devil Dogs, and Ring Dings, and I like pink snowball cupcakes." He smiles right into Mrs. Max's eyes. "I'll be happy to talk with Alexander about not trading at lunch, so the other children will be safe."

Mrs. Jason moves that the rule of no trading at lunch be instituted, and the motion is carried over Mrs. Max's dissenting vote. And Amelia and Matt giggle themselves to sleep imagining Max, a very normal, stolid, cheerful child with a hopelessly frustrated sweet tooth, trying day after day to trade his tabbouli for the demon white sugar.

Three days later, a notice comes home from day care: by general agreement of the parents, teachers, and administration, no desserts containing white sugar in the lunches, please, since white sugar can cause hyperactivity in small children.

Roberta Wilson has lived a long time. When she was a girl, did death come to children the way it came to Beth March? Surely never, nowhere. Could such a death come to Darren? The pleasantest room in the house is set apart for him. Amelia imagines a sunny neat room, next door to Roberta's sewing room, where bolts of material lie neatly folded, put aside while she has been keeping vigil with her grandson. Plants in the window, but no unruly profusion, a row of flowering geraniums and well-disciplined ferns. Mementos of her vacations, shells from a trip to Florida, back when Darren's mother was a strong and healthy child in a flowered bathing suit with a flounced skirt. Family photographs, that same little girl growing tall and slim and lovely, and then perhaps no more photographs after a certain age. Do you stop putting pictures in frames when the child starts destroying herself?

Never mind. No mother of a lovely four-year-old can contemplate too closely the possibilities of adolescence, drugs, doom. Back to the pleasantest room of the house, in it gathered everything that Darren loves. Amelia has to guess at this; Darren is closed off from her, frightened, withdrawn, regressed, retreating from her, from her hospital, from his illness, in every way he can. She can only guess at the child he might be, the child she wants to send home. And like it or not, she can only use her own son to guess by. So the things Darren loves best, a large fire engine with a realistic siren, a stuffed octopus, Dr. Seuss's *Happy Birthday to You* with its promise of endless presents, endless celebration. A picture of the pirate ship from Walt Disney's *Peter Pan,* with Hook and Smee leering over the bow. And there, cherished like a household saint in its shrine— no. There, busy with fingerpaints. There, squishing up Play-Doh.

She still feels shy in public, but the baby has to eat,
So she tucks the baby underneath her clothes,
And the college boy beside her is trying not to see,
That every now and then her nipple shows.

She closes both her eyes, and she concentrates on milk,
Like the booklet from the doctor said to do,
And she cradles close her baby, and pretends she is a heifer,
And the milk is spurting freely, moo moo moo.

"Darren's father called me last night," Roberta tells Amelia. "He wants to come see Darren."

"How is he?"

"I didn't ask." Roberta does not say, I hope he's sick, I hope he's dying. "I told him I don't want him coming while I'm here, so I told him what times would be okay. Then I was thinking about it. Doctor, you know as well as I do that man is not to be trusted. I couldn't bear to be there myself, but I want to ask you if you would sit in if he comes to visit, they could page you; I'm sure it wouldn't be but once. I don't want him alone with the child."

Amelia agrees. She wants to be able to do something, something for Darren, something for his grandmother, something to make up for the amphotericin. She imagines herself facing an angry man, a deranged man, a dying desperate man. Not long ago a father had pulled a knife on one of the interns, demanding his son, who had cancer, who was living bald-headed and supported by a multitude of drugs, in the glass cage of the bone marrow transplant unit. The father wanted to take the boy home, let him live normally. Security came and took the father away, and the boy got his bone marrow transplant, and some weeks later he went home, no one prouder of the medical miracle than his father. But there is no miracle to promise Darren's father, not for his son, not for himself.

So for a week, Amelia walks around worrying every time her beeper goes off, dreading not only the call from Darren's floor, he's worse, he's dying, but also the call to say his father's here to visit him. It never comes. He never comes.

Amelia reads the book to her own son, who knows it by heart.

"'I wish we could do what they do in Katroo
They sure know how to say "Happy Birthday to You!"'"

When she urges, he will sometimes say a line with her, but he prefers to let her read, while he stares at the pictures of the lucky little boy and the Great Birthday Bird.

"'Today you are you! That is truer than true!
There is no one alive who is you-er than you!
Shout loud, "I am lucky to be what I am!

Thank goodness I'm not just a clam or a ham
Or a dusty old jar of sour gooseberry jam!"'"

Alexander thinks that's pretty funny. "A dusty old jar of sour
gooseberry jam!" he hoots at his mother. "*You* are a dusty old jar
of sour gooseberry jam!"

CHAPTER III
HAS THERE EVER BEEN A CHILD LIKE EVA?

The second week in November a blizzard hits the whole Northeast. The morning that Amelia wakes to find the windows whited out is already a morning with an unfamiliar feeling. Matt has gotten up early and gone out to work, but Amelia has planned to stay home and finish her grant proposal, and has allowed herself to sleep late. The weekday morning routines of her household are unfamiliar to her; since she is usually in the hospital before eight, she leaves Matt and Alexander sleeping, drives away alone. Waking her son, dressing him and packing his lunch and taking him to day care, these are things she rarely gets to do. Now, Alexander still asleep, Amelia scoops him out of his bed and holds him, so warm in his fuzzy lavender pajamas with the feet, and he keeps his eyes closed and buries his nose in her neck. It is not possible to resist, so she carries him back into her own room and gets back into bed, she in her flannel nightgown and he in the fuzzy pajamas, pulls the comforter over them both, tells him, Let's cuddle together.

Into her mind, with clarity, comes a sentence: This is perfectly happy. This is perfectly happy, having him here in my arms, where I can hold him and see him safe, and we can both be warm, and outside the window snow is falling, and we are warm together inside. And I will keep him safe. She tightens her arms around the

little boy and he settles into the embrace; she can smell his nighttime scent, which is last night's toothpaste and the musty acrylic
of his flameproof pajamas, and beyond all that some pure candylike
smell which is perhaps the smell of perfect happiness. I love you,
she tells him, and you are the best boy in the whole world. She
wants to tell him, always remember this, always remember how we
cuddled together under the blankets on a snowy day and were safe
and completely happy. He will not always remember, of course, but
she believes that the knowledge of that state of safety and happiness
will be with him always, he will know that it is possible to be loved
absolutely—surely that has to count for something. You are my
favorite kid, she tells him, and he is by then sufficiently awake to
purse his lips at her and ask, Why do you always keep *saying* that?

Finally she gets out of bed, sorry to leave behind the softness and
warmth, but her son is already hurrying down the stairs, pulling
on the zipper of his pajamas, eager to dress himself. Then she gets
very busy, telling him they are late for day care, thinking of the
grant proposal to be written. The snow is still coming down, thick
and wet, and she digs out last year's snowsuit while he eats his toast
and jam. The snowsuit still fits, thank God, and she zips him in,
and out they go. Alexander begins to whimper as soon as the cold
sharp wind hits him; this is not how he has been imagining snow.
So she bundles him into the car, where he sits, eating his toast, as
she shovels the snow off the windshield. As she scrapes away an arc
of snow, she sees his face through the cleared glass; his eyes look
dreamy and he leans back against the seat, slowly bringing the
bread up to his mouth, taking neat little bites. He is not really looking out the window, he does not really see her, out in the snow,
though his eyes are staring straight ahead. The job of clearing off
the car seems pleasant, thinking of her son, warm and protected,
and eventually she too is able to get in, buckle their seatbelts, and
drive off down the snowy street, driving very carefully, creeping
along behind her windshield wipers.

The day care center is bright and full of colors, its electric lights
are welcoming on this stormy day; the watercolors and the finger
paintings and the yarn and tinfoil collages hanging in the hall are
vivid and cheerful, and so are the children's coats and snowsuits,

dripping from their hooks, and the lunchboxes waiting in their cubbies—everything seems so *decorated* and so inviting. In Alexander's room there are only five children; most have stayed home because of the storm. The five sit around a table, eating graham crackers and orange segments, and her son immediately sits down on the floor, pulls off his snowsuit, then runs to take his place at the table. Amelia would like to linger, in the color and warmth, in this friendly room where there are art projects to do and a trunk overflowing with dress-up clothes, where the children are all so strong and healthy, but instead she goes back out to her car, and has to clean off the windshield again because the snow is coming down so hard, and drives herself home.

Trying to park, on her unplowed street, Amelia gets stuck in the snow, whirring her wheels first backwards, then forwards, to no effect, getting out and clearing the impacted snow out from the front of her wheels, then getting back in again to spin uselessly against the slush, the car sticking out into the street. A woman knocks on the car window, offers to push. She wears a red knitted hat, a matching scarf, and a thick parka, and she refuses to take the wheel and let Amelia push. Her accent is strong, maybe French, her cheeks are flushed, and her lashes frosted with snow. She braces herself behind the car, and Amelia hears her yelling through the opened window, her foreign voice carried in with the cold air: "Okay now! One, two, three! Again!"

It takes quite a bit of pushing, but finally Amelia feels her wheels slide up over the ruts and out. By the time she turns off her ignition and gets herself out of the car, her helper is already back at work, down at the far end of the street, building a snowman on the playground. Amelia trudges down to thank her and sees, coming up close, that it is in fact a snowwoman, as tall as an adult, with two enormous cone-shaped breasts, and branches snipped off a pine tree for hair. Amelia thinks of her own warm house waiting nearby and says, by way of thank you, Would you like to come in and have a cup of coffee?

"Oh, no, I cannot!" says the stranger, turning to look at her, and Amelia realizes that this woman is much older than herself, in her fifties at least, her face lined and leathery between the bright hat and scarf. "I must go very soon, I just wanted to finish this," says the stranger in her accented vivacious English. "I am afraid I am to give a seminar at MIT in only one hour, and I must finish my statue and imagine my conclusion." And she bends over again to fortify the snowwoman's base.

Inside her own warm house, Amelia finds herself at first unable to work. She lies on the couch and watches the snow come down, the branches accumulating their topping; she makes herself toasted cheese for lunch and thinks about Heidi and children snug in children's books. It feels like an enchanted day, the gift of those moments in the morning with Alexander, the beauty of the natural disaster outside her windows, the snowlady on the corner, standing guard.

Darren's discharge planning is under way; he is going to go home. His fevers are milder and less frequent, his chest x-ray is improved, he looks stronger though he has not yet gained back any weight. Still, he has stopped losing; evidence that his intestines can absorb nutrition and his body can use it is very welcome, since otherwise he would need to go to the operating room and get a central line, a semipermanent surgically implanted IV to use for intravenous nourishment. Amelia has been resisting the idea, mostly because central lines are very vulnerable to infection; candida, for example, just loves a nice central line, and so do lots of other bugs. Still, if Darren had continued to lose weight . . .

Discharge planning is complicated, for a child as sick as Darren. There is a visiting nurse who will come in every day. There are appointments to arrange with Amelia herself and with a couple of other doctors, and with the physical therapist. There is financing for his medications, which cost more than two thousand dollars a month, and for the home nurse, and for a wheelchair. All this is done by the nurses and the continuing-care specialists, and Roberta Wilson is rehearsed over and over in Darren's routines, his medication schedule, techniques for lifting him without straning her back, all the extra help he needs because he came into the hospital walking and he is leaving it bedridden. But she is bright and hopeful; when she gets him home, she will get him walking again, they will do the physical therapy exercises morning and afternoon, she will tempt him out of bed with toys and games, and there will be no more needles, no more tests, no more pain. Amelia assumes that Mrs. Wilson plans, if Darren gets sick again, to keep him home and let him die. She will be slow in bringing him to medical attention, she will ignore danger signs. Amelia wants to tell her, please don't call me, make your decision and keep to it. What, after all, is Amelia supposed to do if she gets a call to say Darren isn't breathing right, Doctor, what should I do?

Finally, two days before Darren is scheduled to leave, she sits down with his grandmother.

"I'm so happy," Amelia says, not sounding it. Now, when it is close, all she can imagine is disaster. Darren will be too hard to care for at home. He will be sick again in a matter of days. There will be no rest for his grandmother, no peace, no pleasure, just a close-up of the agony, the helplessness, and the failure.

"I just want to get out of this place," says Roberta Wilson.

"I know. Do you have any questions for me, are there any things I could be helping you with?"

"Why, no, Doctor. I just have to get Darren home to his own room. And I have to get myself away from this place. Every time I walk into this building, I think about my little girl dying. Something about the smell."

"It's going to be up to you when to call for help now," Amelia says. Then, even more directly, "Darren's going to get sick again, you know. If you want to keep him home, not bring him back in to the hospital, he could go on and get even sicker at home."

Darren's grandmother looks her in the eye. "I'm going to keep him home from now on. No more hospitals. Are you with me, Doctor?"

Talk about direct. "If you want to keep him at home, we'll try to keep him there."

"Seems like he's been getting stronger every day. You think maybe the sickness is weaker in him than it used to be?"

"I think he is better. I think if he's lucky, he might go on getting stronger and stronger. I wish I could help him more."

"Don't worry, Doctor. I'm going to help him. I'm going to get him home where he belongs, and start him being a child again."

"No more needles," Amelia says, smiling, even though she doesn't really believe that Darren will go on getting stronger and stronger.

"By Christmas I'm going to have that boy up and walking again. I'll give you a picture, Doctor, I'll take pictures of Darren under the Christmas tree, and I'll give you one."

"Thank you. I'd like that."

Amelia feels resolved and uplifted. How Darren feels is anybody's guess. In the clinic, a patient who was scheduled for one appointment slot has brought four children: One with severe asthma, ran out of medicine two weeks ago, and now wheezing because of the weather change. One with a weird skin rash spreading out from her belly. One with no medical problems, but also no vaccinations since the age of six months, now almost two years old. And one who is doing very badly in the second grade; his teacher thinks he's hyperactive.

Thanksgiving is a holiday Amelia likes. Best of all she likes it small, herself and Matt and Alexander and a moderate-sized turkey. No religious overtones, no gifts to buy for an already lavishly indulged child. Just cook and eat with your family, and make a little speech to your son about being thankful, and find that you mean it.

Matt's parents usually have their own Thanksgiving, in Philadelphia, a Thanksgiving for his younger brother, who still lives at home, and his sister, who lives nearby with her own husband and children. Every year Matt and Amelia and Alexander are invited, and every year they decline, pleading Amelia's work schedule (a useful habit they got into back when she was an intern) and the difficulty of travel with a small child. And every year Matt says, with false regret, If only you could come to us instead; we'd love to have you. And this year the bill comes due. Matt's sister is going to her husband's family's Thanksgiving in Ohio; his brother is going to Florida with a friend. And we're coming, Matt's parents announce exultantly. God help us, every one, says Matt.

Amelia is not eager for this larger Thanksgiving but finds herself planning a menu, fantasizing about a groaning board. She invites her own parents, separately, but her father and his second wife, who live outside San Francisco, are having dinner with her sister in Berkeley, and her mother says she has to stay in New York to serve a Thanksgiving dinner to the homeless. Amelia finds this suspect; her mother may just be trying to avoid Matt's parents. Maybe Amelia herself would rather eat with a bunch of street people. At this thought she abruptly stops feeling cheerful about the coming holiday.

Alexander, on the other hand, is thrilled. His grandparents coming, a turkey that Matt promises him will be almost as big as he is. And Amelia tries to feel kindly toward her in-laws, tries to manufacture affection by reminding herself how much they love Alexander, how they are members of that small, select club that counts him the most miraculous child on earth. There will be no lack of compliments and gifts and admiration; Alexander will have a happy Thanksgiving.

Amelia is rather subject to New England fantasies. Here she is, a transplanted New York Jew, in Massachusetts, where she has absolutely no roots. No relatives came on the *Mayflower*, heaven knows; no forebears were executed at Salem; no one prowled Beacon Hill. But if you know *Little Women* by heart, then of necessity you have a Massachusetts fantasy. In Amelia's secret Massachusetts fantasy, she is a New England spinster, an old maid, living neat and useful among the frugal artifacts of her life. After all, Louisa manufactured a man for Jo, but she herself never married, just got rich and famous and toured Europe and supported her relatives. And in *Little Women* wrote this: "At twenty-five, girls begin to talk about being old maids, but secretly resolve that they never will be; at thirty they say nothing about it, but quietly accept the fact, and, if sensible, console themselves by remembering that they have twenty more useful, happy years, in which they may be learning to grow old gracefully. Don't laugh at the spinsters, dear girls, for often very tender, tragical romances are hidden away in the hearts that beat so quietly under the sober gowns, and many silent sacrifices of youth, health, ambition, love itself, make the faded faces beautiful in God's sight."

So Amelia would have "quietly accepted the fact" a couple of years ago already. Baking for the neighborhood children, but sweeping the floor neat as a pin each night, settling down with secret novels by her own fireside at night. A reasonable secret life for a busy overweight Jewish woman living with husband and son in a house bursting with toys and books and odds and ends, never neat, never calm, never everything in its place. A reasonable fantasy for someone who grew up not only on *Little Women* and *An Old-Fashioned Girl* but also *Rebecca of Sunnybrook Farm.*

She tries to think about Thanksgiving in that spirit; the old maid aunt roasts a turkey for the assembled family, for the eccentrics and the difficult, welcomes them into her polished dustless home, knows they will be gone again tomorrow.

Amelia loves the used-book stores, all used-book stores. She stops at Cambridge yard sales to sort the piles of old economics textbooks and diet manuals. If a book is meant for you, to interrupt your life and change your mind around a little, that book will not be all new and glossy on the shelf with all its clones. It will be dusty and unique, battered and abandoned in a basement where faded diagrams on shirt cardboards direct you to Fiction—Popular, Science and Nature, Women's Studies, Fiction—Literary.

In the basement of the Book Case, in Harvard Square, the air is thick with book dust, as if all the books crumbled and gone persist in this miasma. It is a comforting place; Amelia can imagine that any book is welcome, none ever to be turned away as too old, too obscure, too certain never to find a home—like a private humane society run by a batty old lady who would never send any cat to its death.

Amelia browses in Hardcover Fiction—Literary. Here and there a bright dustcover, a recent novel, but most are without their protective paper, old MLA editions and older singletons from dispersed sets of Dickens, Thackeray, Robert Louis Stevenson.

Here is *The Old Curiosity Shop,* but someone has vandalized it, underlining with blue ballpoint pen. She takes another book off the shelf and stands remembering a hot New York summer when she was ten years old. A week she spent huddled over *Uncle Tom's*

Cabin, skimming, racing ahead, crying secretly in the bathroom. She had read her parents' old copy, but this one she holds now is older, a dull green book, the spine frayed at top and bottom.

God, how she had cried and shivered. The children torn from their mothers' arms, the beautiful young girls sold to a fate worse than death—she had been vague about all that at the time, but still. The whippings and the deaths. It was too much for a ten-year-old; it almost sank her. Even as she tore through the book, she was always on the verge of giving up, admitting defeat. She cannot remember the main thrust of the plot, she cannot remember in what states it takes place—Louisiana? Mississippi? She remembers a woman killing herself by jumping from a riverboat. And she remembers Eliza on the ice, and little Eva, and little Eva's death, and fragments of other things, the "thee"s and "thou"s of the abolitionist Quakers, the scene where the beautiful slave is sent by her cruel mistress to a whipping house. And she remembers, too, the feeling of being lectured by the author, that boldly hectoring nineteenth-century approach in which the author makes no bones: I am the writer, you are the reader, listen to what I have to tell you.

And the other thing I remember is confronting my mother: How could this have happened, how could it be allowed. Mama, this is the greatest book ever written. And God help her, she tried to explain to me why it wasn't, why the noble Uncle Tom was an uncle tom, why Harriet Beecher Stowe, for all her lofty aims, was imprisoned in the prejudices of her time. It was a very good book for when it was written, she told me, and it did a lot of good. It made people angry about slavery. But when we read it now, she plunged on bravely . . . Jesus, the responsibility of mothers! Imagine finding it on your shoulders to explain to your child about slavery (and whipping houses, and concubinage, and God knows what else), and then to explain the politically correct modern opinion of the saintly Uncle T. The weight of it: what if you tell it wrong, or change it around, and then your child never quite gets it right, always hears the echo of that first inadequate explanation.

In retrospect, you know, those may have been my mother's best years, right around when I was ten. I remember her as beautiful and full of what seemed to me at the time a special kind of good energy, an energy that other people's mothers never had. She was going to school, she was getting a degree to be a social worker, and she read me stories, occasionally, from her textbooks, to show me that the city was full of unhappiness, full of people waiting for her to help. She would find homes for whole families crowded into one dirty room. She would find parents for orphans. She would find jobs for poor but honest folk, who wanted to work, not beg. It made perfect sense to me, listening, that what people in trouble needed was my mother.

And she was beautiful. She was tall and she wore her hair in a thick braid almost to her waist in the back, like some big, triumphantly healthy schoolgirl. She is still beautiful, I suppose, though her figure has thickened and her hair is now cut short with an efficient little bang in the front, and she has taken to dressing in weird clothes, military surplus items dyed in bright incongruous colors. She gets them at a store run by a group of ex-addicts, and she knows the ex-addicts from their halfway house, where she volunteered for a while.

When I was ten, she dressed in jeans and sweaters, like the student she had become, and she took me for milk and cake to the college cafeteria, and I wondered whether people looking at me might imagine that I was also a student—perhaps I could pass for thirteen, and surely there were thirteen-year-old prodigies who went to college.

Unfortunately, my mother never finished her degree, never got a proper job. She is still perennially on the brink of one credential or another, a work-study degree that will give her credit for all the years of volunteering in a soup kitchen, a master's, which is hers if she takes another four credits and writes up that door-to-door survey she and a friend did, examining community attitudes toward the mentally ill. She has yet to finish a degree program, but she does keep busy, my mother. She and my father separated eventually; he waited her out stolidly through one love affair after another till I was grown up and gone, and then somehow he was in California, and then he was remarried. Marriage is probably his right and proper state, and probably not hers; her boyfriends still seem to arrive regularly, one after another. And which of my parents do I resemble, still with the man I met in freshman chemistry? And who was I reacting to when I decided, back in high school, to march on through and get myself the most emphatic of credentials, the ultimate two letters to top off my signature? But she did a good job, my mother did, explaining *Uncle Tom's Cabin*. And, for that matter, she was right about people in need, too; they do need homes, parents, jobs, soup.

Amelia opens the elderly book and finds herself staring at a colored frontispiece opposite the title page (*Uncle Tom's Cabin; or, Life Among the Lowly*). In the picture, two little girls stand face to face; the caption is "Eva stood looking at Topsy." Eva is on the left, with golden ringlets and a pink dress with a full skirt, short enough to show snow-white pantalets, and little black slippers. She holds a doll, equally well dressed, though in blue. Topsy is slightly taller, her hair in tiny braids and curliques. She wears a plain short orange dress, which reaches down to her knees, and a polka-dotted apron tied round her waist, the apron strings trailing on the carpet behind her. She is barelegged and barefooted. And black; the advantage of color illustration is that Eva can be truly pink and white, Topsy soot. Almost against her will, Amelia turns to page 264 to read the scene that goes with the picture. She does not allow herself to dwell on the picture, to look any more closely at the faces of those two children; she does not let herself think about other children, rich and poor, black and white, sick and healthy.

"Eva stood looking at Topsy.

"There stood the two children, representative of the two extremes of society. The fair, high-bred child, with her golden head, her deep eyes, her spiritual, noble brow, and prince-like movements; and her black, keen, subtle, cringing, yet acute neighbor. They stood the representatives of their races. The Saxon, born of ages of cultivation, command, education, physical and moral eminence; the Afric, born of ages of oppression, submission, ignorance, toil, and vice!"

Amelia thinks of herself, ten years old, lying sweaty on her bed through all those summer days, galloping through this sort of stuff and never cringing. She cringes now, for her childish self, and thus aligns herself with Topsy, cringing but subtle. That could be a family motto. Oh, lord, always the same thing, two children, one pampered, one abused, and the heroine is the Shirley Temple child, because if you love them and treat them well they are sweet and good, but if they are bad because they have not been properly loved, well, then.

This is getting a little feverish; Amelia stops herself. Why does she get so worked up so easily these days? Where is her sense of proportion? The world is full of healthy, happy children, bringing joy to their families. This is a picture in a book, for heaven's sake. And Harriet Beecher Stowe meant well, after all, though all she would probably have seen in that picture was Eva's saintly mission to raise up Topsy by her beauteous example.

But wait a minute. Little Eva is the one who dies. Don't go feeling too sorry for Topsy. Eva may have the doting father and all the pretty dresses in the world, and lace-edged pantalets and a beautifully pious disposition too—but she dies. She is brought onstage, really, only to die—and suddenly Amelia is feeling a murderous anger. She knows she is out of control, somehow. She knows her sense of proportion has deserted her completely. She can't help it; she is standing in the bookstore, almost shaking with rage.

Children are jerked around in every direction. Need some pathos? Need to make people cry? Bring on the child. Conjure up its endearing graces, the intensity of parental love which cannot protect it, the frail little limbs, the eyes, the smile—then kill the child off.

Amelia's clinic office is crowded with the four children, their mother flopped exhausted into one of the available chairs, her bag of bottles and diapers and coats plopped onto the other. Amelia knows there will be another patient here in half an hour, she feels irritated at having to sort out these four and provide for them—but then again, this mother deserves a medal for single-handedly bringing in four children under the age of seven, maneuvering them through the streets. Only an ogre would say to her, Take three of them away and bring them back when you have appointments.

"Youngest first, Mrs. Awallah, we'll have to go as quickly as we can."

The youngest is the one with the skin rash; six months old, she has a red and peeling patch around her groin, flaking skin and tiny red bumps on her belly, advancing up toward her shoulders. Most likely candida again, though this baby is safe from invasive disease, and Amelia prescribes an antifungal cream. The almost-two-year-old gets an oral polio vaccine, and a DPT shot, and a measles-mumps-rubella shot; he is still screaming when Amelia is trying to listen to his older sister's lungs, renew her asthma prescriptions. And the oldest gets a quick, rough eye-and-ear check, and then gets referred to the school dysfunction clinic for more thorough testing. And after all that, Amelia goes back and listens to Fatma's lungs one more time, now that the two-year-old has calmed down, and decides that the wheezing is worse than she originally thought. So she gives Fatma a breathing treatment, aerosolized medicine blown in her face by a nebulizer machine, and Fatma gets somewhat better right then and there; Mrs. Awallah gets a lecture on how important it is to get Fatma's prescriptions filled immediately and keep giving her the medicines, every single day. By the time they leave, Amelia is forty-five minutes late for her next appointment, and dissatisfied with almost everything she did. (Was that really candida, and should she have scraped the rash and looked for fungus under the microscope to be sure, and why is the two-year-old so behind for shots—she should have discussed that with the mother—should Fatma be observed in the clinic for a little longer to see if the wheezing gets worse, and will she really get the medicine she needs, and why didn't Amelia try a little more energetically to sort out the older boy's school problems?)

What I really wanted to do was call up Dodie in California and cry to her, Dodie, I had a fight with Matt, I stomped out of the house, I'm sitting in my office, I'm so mad I want to kill him.

I've noticed that once you're married, you stop doing that. None of my married friends call me; sometimes I get the word: We've been having problems, we're seeing a counselor, even, we're separating. But no overwrought calls in the middle of the night from the married ones: We're fighting, I hate him, I don't know what to do. Probably because the other person is always there, is in the other room, maybe listening, is sulking in front of the TV.

Dodie, we had a fight, in front of Alexander, about Alexander. A stupid fight, starting out with whether Matt should make curried pumpkin on Thanksgiving, when his father hates unfamiliar food, and I told him he only wanted to do it because it would irritate his father, and he ought to be too old for that, and he exploded, and told me not to bless him with my nickel-and-dime insights, he could read *Psychology Today* too, if he wanted. And I knew, of course, that he was just tense about the approach of his parents, and the inevitable nagging and criticizing, and the way he will be reminded for one celebratory day that he is unsatisfactory in every way. But I told him he could just do Thanksgiving himself if he wanted to, shop and cook for it all alone if he was going to use it as an excuse to play games, and he accused me of being flat-out lazy, and began on a litany of all the shopping, home repairs, cooking, laundry, he has done in the last month, and challenged me to match his list, which of course I couldn't do, and I tried to make a virtue of that, telling him *I* don't keep lists that way, and he said, no wonder!

Dodie, the worst thing I did was I said in front of Alexander, well, if you think I contribute so little, maybe you would rather I bowed out altogether, and he said, smugly, just as you like. So I said, well, I'm leaving, and ran out the door, and dawdled down the street, hoping he'd clop out behind me and so we could make up in the middle of the street, apologizing and laughing and kissing in the dark. But even while I was imagining that, I was unlocking the car door and turning on the lights and driving away.

"Hi, Dodie? It's Amelia."

"Hi, Amelia, My rabbit just had quints."

"Congratulations."

"How's your cute little only?"

"My cute little only is fine. I'll tell him about the baby rabbits."

"Tell him if his parents don't treat him right, he can come on out here and take care of my rabbits."

"Anything else new? How's the shit married man?"

"How's your own shit married man?" asked Dodie, who is no fool.

"We had a squabble, and I walked out. Right now, I wish he was dead."

"You can't live with 'em, you can't live without 'em. I think that could be an article."

"You can't have my squabble for your trashy analyses. I don't want any nickel-and-dime insights into *my* domestic life."

"We're a little touchy tonight, aren't we? Are you having just ordinary squabbles, such as all healthy couples have, or is it Can this marriage be saved?"

"We're fine, Dodie. It's just, his parents are coming for Thanksgiving, and he gets all wound up about that."

"In-laws," said Dodie pontifically, "are one thing you don't have to deal with when you have an affair with a shit married man."

"Two things."

"Will they pick at Matt for not being a doctor?"

"And at me for being one, and at Alexander for being ours, and at the pumpkin curry for not being candied sweet potatoes, and at the oil heat for being so dry, and at the wine we serve for being wrong with turkey."

"This sounds like the kind of shared trial which ought to bring you and Matt closer together, not drive a wedge between you."

"Dodie, sometimes I just can't stand being part of a family. I said unnecessary mean things to Matt, I frightened Alexander, and now I don't have the energy to go home and soothe them both and gear up for the descent of the in-laws."

"Now she is working up to a declaration of how she envies me my independence, my idiosyncratic dwelling arranged just to suit myself, and even my lover, of dubious motives and dubious morals, who confided in me yesterday that he has always wanted to make love to a woman who was wearing only thigh-high boots. He thought this was rather original of him."

"Dodie, you never told me you had thigh-high boots!"

"I don't. But Christmas comes right after Thanksgiving."

"How's your other line of business?"

"I have a book contract, to my own endless surprise. I wrote a proposal for a book about men, and since I am such a renowned expert, I got enough money to live on for two years. The only problem is, all the good titles are already taken. *Sex and the Single Girl; Smart Women, Foolish Choices; Total Woman.* I'm thinking of calling it *Just Because You Have a Penis, Don't Let It Go to Your Head.* It will be a little bible of womanly wisdom, helping today's single girl through this vale of queers."

"Dodie, that's wonderful, that you're writing a book!"

"No, it isn't," Dodie said flatly. "Don't pretend I really believe in what I'm doing. Crap is crap, but it's a living."

"Why don't you write something different?"

"Amelia, I gotta go. Rest assured, when I write my two-hundred-page experimental prose poem, you'll get a copy."

Before she leaves her office, Amelia gathers up a folder of articles. A new patient is coming tomorrow, not an impoverished clinic type but a difficult patient, referred by a frustrated private pediatrician. Printed on the folder, in her own neat writing, is FTT.

Failure to thrive, FTT, is a frustrating and potentially fatal illness, a syndrome of chronic malnutrition in childhood. Failure to thrive is when they don't grow. Every time a young child visits the pediatrician, weight and length are marked off on a growth chart, and when a child falls below the third percentile for age, failure to thrive is suspected. Now, the syndrome of failure to thrive is divided into two main categories, organic and nonorganic. Organic failure to thrive is growth failure that can be traced to some definable physical problem, and any ailment can make a child stop growing, from recurrent ear infections to leukemia. Every pediatric textbook contains a lengthy list, the differential diagnosis of failure to thrive, everything from cardiac disease to milk allergy. But of all the children with failure to thrive, only 20 percent or so turn out to have any such organic etiology; the rest are failing to grow for what are called nonorganic reasons, usually assumed to be social, behavioral, environmental conditions—in short, usually perceived as reflecting parental failure.

Amelia does not let herself back into her own house. She rings the doorbell and stands there on the cold porch, thinking, what if they've left, what if Matt's taken him and gone off somewhere, what if right now they're eating a pizza and the house is empty? But the door opens, and Matt is there, and Alexander is calling out to her reproachfully, But, Mom, you shouldn't get so grouchy!

You're right, I shouldn't, she tells him, as Matt finally does wrap his arms around her, welcoming her in.

The disturbing thing about nonorganic failure to thrive is the outcome. Though these children have no identifiable physical ailment, though nutritional and behavioral interventions are applied, still they do not turn out normal. Some catch up in growth, while others remain small, but many have severe personality problems and learning disorders. So, are those children somehow different right from the beginning, or is the interplay of factors in their lives which led to the FTT just impossible to mitigate? It's not a good disease to have, nonorganic failure to thrive—and it's deeply frustrating to diagnose, because you have to rule out all the organic possibilities. Amelia sits up late that night, reads over a few basic articles. Well, there it is: "On the one hand, the differential diagnosis of the infant with poor growth or weight loss is practically coextensive with the lexicon of serious disease in childhood; on the other hand, the indiscriminant 'ruling out' of one occult possibility after another assures only high cost, iatrogenic complications, persistent anxiety, and, in most cases, diagnostic failure."

Amelia's medical practice is part of that institutional paradox, a teaching hospital. On the one hand, clinic patients are the poor, the disenfranchised, the ones who can't shop for or pay for a private pediatrician and end up being cared for by whoever staffs the clinic. Amelia supervises the residents one afternoon a week as they take care of these patients. She takes care of a large population of her own in the mornings, including now seven children with AIDS. She also puts in an afternoon in the second-opinion clinic, where she will see this FTT kid tomorrow, and an afternoon in the AIDS clinic, checking out the general health of the children who come in for special treatments and experimental drugs, for neurologic examinations and batteries of blood tests.

On the other hand, to a teaching hospital, along with the

unwanted, the poor and tired and huddled, come the people looking for expert care, the entitled, demanding consumers, the educated parents whose children have problems; we want the best, we want the professors. As a doctor who has hung on in a teaching hospital, but without becoming a specialist of any kind, Amelia sometimes feels like a superannuated resident, still practicing pediatrics in this unreal academic world. She has never made the transition to the rhythms of an office practice, never left behind the wards, the emergency room, the public address system announcing emergencies.

I tell myself that I like the poor better, and certainly that old joke about how God must, because he made so many of them, applies to poor children. I like the respect I get from clinic patients, like to see myself as Lady Bountiful, I suppose. Like to imagine myself doing something to help these children start out on their way—here I am, after all, doing what may be the one thing everyone in the whole world could agree is good, vaccinating the innocent, helping them through their infections and their asthma attacks. Sure, they'll grow up and get pregnant and no one will give them prenatal care; sure, they'll grow up and take drugs and no one will notice because they will be the drugged-out dregs. But for now, when they're cute, we all care. I care.

I tell myself I like the poor ones better. Tomorrow this family will come, the lawyers from Newton with the kid who doesn't grow, and I will be with people who talk my language, who understand what I explain to them, who appreciate my education and my skills. And I will wonder, Is it time to turn into that kind of pediatrician, don't these kids need their vaccinations too, and why not work somewhere where such parents are the order of the day? And then I tell myself firmly that I like the poor kids better.

The truth is, the poor kids are making me crazy. I think about all the effort, their parents and their teachers and even me, and then about how little is out there waiting for these kids, what all this effort is probably going to come to.

What I mean is, Amelia, face facts. You like the kids who have a place in the world. You like to imagine yourself allied with good, well-meaning parents, mothers struggling against the odds of poverty and urban life to bring up happy children; one reason you invest so much in Darren is his grandmother.

Amelia knows she evaluates the medical profession through her mother's eyes. She was sent out into the world with an old-fashioned do-gooder sensibility, and something in her still sneers at those who tend the bodies, the uteruses or the stomachs, the backs or the nervous systems, of the well-to-do. Matt's parents may somehow sense this; can they tell that even though she is that best of all possible things, a doctor, she is not really in their corner? Amelia knows what her mother would be too polite to say to Matt's mother, who is a psychiatrist—that she thinks psychiatry is nonsense, that she has sympathy for the mentally ill only when they are so sick they have to be institutionalized—or deinstitutionalized, to join the homeless. Perhaps, though, Amelia thinks, as her mother grows older, and her friends grow older, she will give a little more credit, at least, to the doctors who tend their ailments. So far, Amelia's mother is as healthy as a horse and has only scorn for her ex-husband, Amelia's father, who is obsessively and endlessly interested in the well-being of his own body.

I am making her sound much less human than she really is. My mother tends not to think things through properly; she has no particular intestest in being consistent. I mean, she is devoted to Alexander, and any little twinge that pained him would seem to her a matter of great moment, and any doctor who relieved the twinge would be a hero ten times over. And I suspect that secretly, against all her principles, she wants to see me send him to the fanciest private school in Cambridge, though she will mask this as concern that he will be stimulated with all the proper free and innovative education techniques. Secretly, I know, she wants the same thing for him that Matt and I do. She wants luxury and comfort and attention and protection. She wants him to stay, always, beautiful and confident and interested, engaged and engaging.

When I met Matt, we were both premed students, pounding away at inorganic chemistry. We were friends through that, and through the first half of organic, then boyfriend and girlfriend through the rest, and through basic biology. From the start, I would have to say in all honesty, I was much better at the premed stuff than Matt was, or at least I was much more willing to be doing it. He complained, somewhat idly, that he had never been allowed to think of *not* becoming a doctor; the child of two physicians, he had been programmed. Lots of premeds talked that way, but many of them went on happily to become doctors. Not Matt. He finally said, at the beginning of physics, Look, you be the doctor; he dropped physics, and then a month later dropped out of college, moved into my dorm room when he had to vacate his own, and had the satisfaction of not giving the phone number to his parents, who thought he must be having a breakdown, by which they meant that they were having one together.

I was the better student, I was the one who really wanted to become a doctor, I was the one who went to medical school. I don't think Matt would make a particularly good doctor. I don't think he has any interest in science, I don't think he likes to have his life intruded on, indiscriminately, by moans and excrement and sputum. But still, he had been groomed for medicine. His family had a slot ready for one more doctor. They would have bought him white coats when he graduated, and had his name embroidered over the pockets, a little ritual my parents knew nothing about. Sometimes I do get this feeling that it is all a mistake; the wrong one of us became the doctor.

Matt's parents have never forgiven me for going on and succeeding, for being the doctor. I don't know if they would explicitly accuse me of having sacrificed his career to my own, but I suppose that, at the very least, they mind having me around to rub it in. And they resent my parents, neither one a doctor, broken marriage, why should *they* have produced a doctor child?

Matt's success, of course, is nothing to them, dust and ashes. Never mind that he is very good at what he does, that he makes more money than I do, that he is more in demand, that he comes very close to the line between artisan and artist. His parents buy their furniture from good department stores; they are house-proud, in the manner of the urban bourgeoisie of their generation. They have no idea of the insane perfectionist decorating of the young professional class, the ceaseless shopping around for experts, which makes Matt more sought-after than any doctor he might have become. They would rather have him a modestly successful internist, or perhaps a cardiologist—once none of those terms would have meant much to me, but now, from within the profession, I see clearly where they would have wanted their boy. A smart Jewish boy, thin and tense, with his hair a little messy and his good-quality loafers a little scuffed. With an expensive pen in his white coat pocket, and an unreadable handwriting. I wonder if they even notice his personality change. Matt has remade himself slowly, over the years. He is laconic and easygoing and reassuringly sweet-tempered, like some boy who grew up poor in a small town somewhere, but with loving, strong-valued parents, a father who taught him everything about carpentry, a mother who always believed in him. Not with a mother, Dr. Markovsky, who is a psychiatrist, and a father, Dr. Markovsky, who is a gastroenterologist. The two Jewish specialties, Matt calls his parents' fields, for those who know they're neurotic, and for those who don't and take their neuroses out in ulcers and colitis and irritable bowel syndrome. Matt is resolutely not neurotic and has a stomach of steel.

Sara Blake's mother is beautiful, one of the most beautiful women Amelia has ever seen in real life. She has yellow-gold hair cut abruptly at her shoulders and features that belong on an Italian primitive fresco, touched with gold flake. A serene, slightly sad, ethereal face, a slim figure, a royal carriage, expensive muted clothing, gray wool skirt, thick cream sweater, Geraldine Blake. Amelia notes, automatically, that she has taken her husband's last name, disapproves, automatically. Frank Blake is as tall as his wife, balding on top, but not unattractive. Both of them seem to Amelia tight, angry; they are upset and embarrassed to find themselves in her office.

Dear Dr. Sullivan, I saw your patient Sara Blake in the second-opinion clinic this morning. As you know, she is a thirteen-month-old female who presents with failure to thrive. She was originally the six-pound-two-ounce product of an uncomplicated full-term gestation, born by cesarean section for failure to progress. She did well as an infant, was breast-fed for three months, then fed Similac. Although consistently small for her age, she grew steadily along the curve for the fifth percentile in weight, length, and head circumference. She had no serious illnesses during her first year of life. Around the age of nine months, her parents noted that her appetite seemed to be diminished, and she began to fall off her growth curve. This was initially attributed to a series of ear infections and colds, but her appetite did not improve when these resolved. Her parents, as per your advice, have attempted various dietary modifications, with some limited success, but despite apparently adequate caloric intake, Sara has failed to gain weight. Her weight is now significantly below the fifth percentile for her chronological age, though her length and head circumference have thus far been spared. Medical workup to date has been minimal, since inadequate caloric intake was presumed to be the cause of her failure to thrive. She is now referred for more extended medical workup, and possibly for hospitalization and trial of controlled caloric intake. Thank you very much for allowing me to be involved in this interesting case. I will, of course, keep you apprised of all developments. Sincerely yours, Amelia Stern, M.D.

Actually, though Amelia sends off the letter punctually, the Blakes have made it clear they want nothing more to do with Dr. Sullivan, who is one of the poshest Newton private pediatricians. They don't like him. They don't trust him. They are convinced that there is something seriously wrong with their daughter, something *medically* wrong, and this bum has let months go by, worrying about calories.

Frank Blake opens his briefcase, takes out a folder, a photocopied article. Frank has been to the library, and he comes prepared with one of those lists, the possible etiologies of failure to thrive. The many things Dr. Sullivan has not looked for, has not bothered to rule out. With a sinking heart, Amelia accepts his invitation to review the list: C is for celiac disease, and congestive heart failure, and cystic fibrosis. H is for hepatic insufficency, and hyperaldosteronism. How could Dr. Sullivan have missed Fanconi syndrome, renal tubular acidosis, and all the rest? All these reasons for poor little Sara to be losing weight, and what does her doctor do? Tells us to keep a food diary, for Christ's sake. Tells us to clap our hands whenever she takes a bite!

Sara herself is completely engaging, a tiny curly-headed blond child, clinging to her mother at first, but consenting to Amelia's exam, a bright-eyed child who is so small for her level of physical control that she gives an impression of adorable precocity. She makes a grab for Amelia's African bead earrings, and giggles obligingly when her concave tummy is tickled. There is of course nothing about her physical exam that is the least bit abnormal; Amelia could have predicted that. If there had been anything funny, her pediatrician would have jumped all over it; Amelia is sure these parents made his life hell. Everyone's nightmare, an FTT kid and two lawyer parents.

Privately, Amelia would put her money on the same diagnosis: inadequate caloric intake. A thirteen-month-old who has gotten out of the habit of eating enough, a family in which mealtime has become a battleground, some kind of mismatch between child and parents. In her office, they seem a tense and unhappy family, but of course this long process of failure to thrive could have done that to them. In any case, it is time to take steps.

"I'd like to do some tests today, have the lab take a little blood, get a urine sample." The Blakes look at one another in triumph; finally, a doctor with sense! "I also think it's time we arranged for a hospitalization for Sara, no emergency, we'll do it electively, schedule it when I can get all the tests I want lined up. There are two reasons I want her in the hospital: one is to have a number of tests done, but even more important, I want to try having other people feed her, keep track of calories she gets, and see if she grows. And also, I want to give you two a break."

"We could use a break," says Geraldine Blake, speaking for almost the first time; her voice is low and forceful, probably a good voice to use in court. "The doctor says establish a routine, feed her dinner every day exactly at six, but real families don't work that way, and if something comes up, then dinner isn't on the table at six. Sara is not the only person in the house, you know, Doctor. Or he says, Sullivan that is, cheer and clap whenever she takes a bite, and we've spent our meals cheering and clapping. You know what that does to meals? Or to her older brother? He wants to know why we don't clap for him, too."

Amelia buys Darren a good-bye present, a little pink plastic kangaroo with elongated feet. Wind it up, and it does sudden somersaults, the feet flipping it up and over. When she goes up to present it, the PRECAUTION signs are down off Darren's door. Darren has no IV in. He is wearing denim pants with an elastic waist and a Red Sox sweatshirt. But he lies back against his pillow and stares straight ahead. Do not be fooled. I am not getting better. I will never get better. He will not meet Amelia's eyes.

She winds up the kangaroo and sets it on his table, and it begins to flip. Darren directs his steady stare toward the kangaroo. In pediatrics, you always try to make the dying kids laugh. Sometimes, with the older ones especially, you get the feeling that they laugh to make you feel better, to make their parents feel better. See the funny clown, look at the mask, was that Big Bird I just saw walking down the corridor? Darren doesn't crack a smile.

Amelia rewinds the kangaroo, puts it on her head, feels it trying to kick its way out of her curls. It falls out onto the floor, and she picks it up, rewinds it once again, and puts it on Darren's tighter, closer curls, where it successfully does a flip before sliding down behind his ears. Then she screws up her own face in imitation of the plastic snout, raises her hands into the position of the kangaroo hands, and gives a bound off the floor. Looks sideways at Darren, sees him trying to suppress a giggle. So she puffs out her cheeks and then pokes them in, hard, with her index fingers, pushing the air out through pursed lips to make a Bronx cheer noise. This never fails with Alexander, and it does not fail with Darren, who distinctly snickers.

Alexander, with that innate wisdom of childhood, picks the Star Market to ask his question; Amelia waiting in line at the deli counter for sliced turkey breast for his lunches, Alexander asks her, "Are there ever any babies at the hospital who don't get better?"

She has been telling Alexander about the babies-at-the-hospital for years; they are the reason she sometimes has to stay out late, or go to work on a weekend, the reason she leaves before he wakes up, the reason she wears the beeper. Alexander has been to the hospital, has been allowed into the special-care nursery, wrapped in a sterile gown, to see the babies, has prowled down the halls on the wards, never the least bit discomfited by IVs, prostheses, wheelchairs, what have you.

"Yes," Amelia tells him, looking down at her deli number, 77.

"Are there babies who die, ever?"

"Yes, there are babies who die sometimes." Why has he never asked this before?

"They are so sick that you can't make them better, right? So they die."

"Right. But most of them do get better."

She gets her turkey breast and wheels the cart off to stock up on canned tomatoes and tomato paste, wondering if the subject is closed, wondering what else she might have said. She lets him choose among the noodles, and he chooses shells and wagon wheels. As they round the corner into produce, Alexander contentedly eating out of his ritual box of animal crackers, he asks her, "Are there ever big kids, like me, who die sometimes?"

Before she knew Matt's mother well, Amelia was deeply respectful. Unfamiliar with all the jokes about psychiatrists-as-parents, about shrinks and their crazy children, she assumed that his mother possessed some professional wisdom, some understanding of what lay behind the surface conflicts of family life. Nowadays, she enjoys watching Matt with his mother, because it offers a rare opportunity to see him drop the sweet-tempered, easygoing small-town-boy stuff and behave like a tense, touchy son of a psychiatrist. Carol Markovsky is a small and elegant woman, very energetic, very ready to take over and do things the right way. At Thanksgiving, she spends most of her time smoothing her husband's path, since he is away from his own home, in unfamiliar surroundings, eating unfamiliar food, and therefore he is in constant turmoil. He is a big, tall man who looks disconcertingly like Matt, the same very dark eyes, the sharp nose, the cleft chin. Matt, however, has a dimple, and it pleases Amelia that his father does not.

"Carol, taste the pumpkin please, there's something red in it, some kind of spice." Harry Markovsky sounds nervous; everywhere there are people trying to poison him. A man has to protect his gastrointestinal tract.

"What spices did you put in the pumpkin, dear?" Carol addresses herself to Amelia, but before she can answer, Matt cuts in, a little bit too loud.

"I made the pumpkin, Ma. It's curried, it has a lot of different spices in it. But I didn't make it very hot."

"It's very interesting," his mother tells his father, "and it isn't sharp at all."

"I'll have the turkey."

Carol is alert, constantly, for hazards, trying to spot them before her husband does. She is over at the dining-room windows, checking to see whether they are closed tightly. "Dear, it might be a little bit drafty in here, I mean for Alexander," she tells Amelia; Harry has been known to get a stiff neck in a drafty room, and it can last him for days. Amelia turns up the thermostat a token three degrees.

Harry is dissecting his stuffing, a look of muffled disgust on his face. "Did you make the stuffing, too?" his wife asks his son, anxiously.

"The stuffing comes out of a *package*, Dad. It's breadcrumbs."

"But I taste something else here, something besides bread."

"Maybe it's the giblets, Harry, the liver, you know I always cut those up and put them in when I stuff a chicken. You like those."

"I didn't put the giblets in." Matt takes more curried pumpkin onto his own plate.

"It really has a very nice flavor," Carol goes on, speaking to Amelia. "Actually, I'm surprised to hear it comes from a package."

"Ma, I wish you would just sit down and eat, you keep getting up."

"I'm just going to get your father an extra napkin."

With her grandson, Carol Markovsky assumes a professional manner. Her voice pinches up into sweetness and understanding, and she nods too much. In everything she says to Alexander, Matt hears criticism. "Oh, yes, I like that very, very much," Carol tells Alexander. "Did you make it in nursery school?"

"In *day care*," Matt and Alexander say in unison.

"Yes, in day care. Isn't that nice, that you made such a nice picture. Now, tell me, who is this man up here in the corner?"

"That's not a man. That's a little kid, except he has a machine gun."

"And do you think he is going to shoot somebody?"

"He *already* shooted somebody. Can't you see, all the dead bodies are here at the bottom. But that's okay, because they were all the bad soldiers, and now they can't kill anyone anymore."

"What made the bad soldiers so bad?"

"Because if he didn't kill them, they might kill the kids!"

"Carol," says her husband suddenly, urgently, "did you remember to bring my decaf?"

"Yes, sometimes big kids die too."

"When they're *really* sick, and you can't make them better."

"That's right." She wants to say, but nothing like that could ever happen to you, my darling—but then, surely, he would say, how do you know?

"What makes them die?"

"People die for all different reasons, depending on what kind of sickness they have. But most children, when they die, die because they can't get enough oxygen to breathe."

Alexander thinks this over. "But usually, when most big kids get sick, you can save them, right?"

"Right." And nothing like that could ever happen to you, my darling.

Sara Blake's initial lab tests are all normal. Surprise. Her father has been calling the hospital number and paging Amelia, faithfully, once a day. He seems to feel that since she is now in charge of his daughter's case, he ought to check in with her frequently. Anything back on the lab tests yet, Dr. Stern? Any idea when you'll be hearing? And just why does it take so long, anyway? And what are you planning to do next if these results are inconclusive?

So since these tests are all normal, what now? Have you planned out an order for tackling all these other possible diseases? Could you give me a timetable? I mean, after all, I'd like to have some idea of what we're up against here. Cardiac disease, that's been on my mind. Can we be sure she doesn't have cardiac disease? Is it safe to wait around on something like that, without knowing for sure?

Amelia has talked on the phone with Dr. Sullivan. They went over Sara's medical history, what had been done, what needed to be done next. Tell me, Sullivan said, casually, do you do AIDS testing on these kids nowadays? Sometimes, Amelia said. Depends on the situation, but yes, AIDS does often present as failure to thrive, in children. Well, said Sullivan, I'd think about doing it here. There's something fishy about this family. I don't know exactly what, but they're awfully touchy, and I never really thought they opened up with me. And that father—he strikes me as the kind of guy who might have a secret.

I'll think about it, Amelia said. I'll have to get to know them a little better. Don't get to know them too well, Sullivan said. They're a pain in the ass. That guy got hold of my home phone number, and once or twice he woke me up at night, all because the little girl had coughed a couple of times, so maybe I wanted to check her out for lung cancer, or once she had a loose stool, so I needed to work up her bowel, right away, because here was the clue, at last. This is a family to keep at arm's length, he told Amelia. Watch out for them.

Amelia sits reading the death scene of little Eva, thinking, inevitably, of Darren, home for whatever Thanksgiving his grandmother wants to muster. This is how Eva dies:

"A bright, a glorious smile passed over her face, and she said, brokenly,—'O! love,—joy,—peace!' gave one sigh, and passed from death into life!"

There is a certain motif here which also hovered over Beth's death: life, specifically illness, is the state to escape; death is the passage to paradise and health.

But when you come right down to it, it is not Topsy, the battered, beaten, overworked and undernourished child, who dies. Topsy is surely statistically the child in that book who should not have lived to grow up, but then, can you imagine Topsy in that death scene? Topsy is too bad to die; she lies and steals and could not be presumed to be going straight to heaven. So she beats the odds, Topsy does. One child will walk away from that face-to-face moment, "Eva stood looking at Topsy." One child will survive, but not the one who has every reason to—good food, medical attention, love and gentleness surrounding her. That one will die.

"Has there ever been a child like Eva? Yes, there have been; but their names are always on gravestones, and their sweet smiles, their heavenly eyes, their singular words and ways, are among the buried treasures of yearning hearts."

Later that night, home from the Star Market, Alexander looks up from his arms-and-armor coloring book.

"Do I need oxygen too?"

"Yes, you breathe in oxygen every time you take a breath."

"What makes kids so sick they can't get enough?"

"Some very bad sicknesses. Nothing you need to worry about."

"Are they from the very baddest germs in the world?"

"Some of them."

"But *I* have lots of oxygen."

"Alexander, there's oxygen all around you, in the air. And you are very healthy, and you get all the oxygen you need."

"But some kids don't, and then *they* die," he says, not without a certain satisfaction.

CHAPTER IV
THE DUMB WOMAN BUILDS HER HOUSE UPON THE SAND

Sara Blake goes into the hospital on a cold and unpromising December morning, and Amelia comes around to see her later that day. Sara, wearing a pink terrycloth stretchie, is romping around in a large hospital crib, a monkey in a cage. A completely adorable tiny little thing, making faces through the bars. Her mother, dressed formally in a dark red suit, a gray blouse with a businesswoman's bow at the neck, sits statuesquely in the bedside chair, and an intern is interviewing her. Amelia stays only long enough to say hello. The intern is Greg Murphy, a wiry, serious young doctor who is, according to hospital scuttlebutt, a little in over his head. Not one of the stellar interns. He is taking, seriously and slowly, a very complete history from Geraldine Blake. As Amelia leaves, he takes up his line of questions again. "Her brother is three now," Mrs. Blake is saying. "He's always been just fine. I mean, no problems of any kind. He always ate, and he always grew. So I don't see how it can be something *we're* doing wrong with Sara, since there was never any trouble at all with Jonathan."

Food in families, a fraught subject. Take Matt's mother's goulash. When Amelia and Matt were first going out, before he gave up his premed studies, Matt brought her home with him one

Christmas vacation for a weekend. His parents were happy to welcome her, and put her in Matt's sister's empty room, right next to Matt's, apparently expecting some sneaking around at night. His mother served a goulash dinner, and it was clear that the goulash was a specialty of the house. Amelia went for broke, praising it, eating three helpings, never had she tasted such a dish. Well, it really was very good goulash, but she also did want Matt's mother to like her; she was beginning to suspect, just suspect, that Matt was going to be important in her life, maybe for a long time. And out of that first visit grew the myth of Amelia and the Goulash: the best thing I ever ate, the most amazing dish on earth. It was produced for her every time she visited Matt's parents, and after her marriage, Matt's mother solemnly offered her the recipe, now that she was legally part of the family. But Amelia had no real urge to make that goulash, with all its overtones, and it turned out to be a lot of trouble, involving a homemade brown stock and an intricate deglazing process. So it came to be understood that of course Amelia was too busy to make the goulash properly, and perhaps by implication that she was too busy to care for Matt properly, and Matt's mother, whenever she comes to visit, brings along a tub of goulash, for the freezer.

After Thanksgiving, there is a tub of goulash in the freezer. Amelia sees it whenever she goes for ice cubes, or for Alexander's popsicles. Inevitably, there will be some night when there are no groceries, when she and Matt are both tired, and the goulash will get defrosted under hot running water, crash in one chunk out of the Tupperware tub into a pot, and melt slowly on the stove, and they will eat it. Inevitably. They will not lovingly plan a special dinner around it, with parsleyed potatoes and a homemade torte for dessert. It is an intrusion, that white plastic tub of goulash sitting in the freezer. It is ostensibly an emissary of good wishes but actually a messenger of criticism, that most elemental complaint, You can't look after him the way I looked after him, you can't look after your own son as I looked after mine. A reminder that Matt's mother managed her psychiatry practice, at certain rigidly restricted hours, out of an office in her own apartment, and her M.D. never meant that her husband was inconvenienced. Organization. Devotion. A servant or two. A part-time practice. And thus you have the time to make goulash properly. It's an attempt to influence the daily life in Amelia's home. Like a missionary who pretends to offer education and health care but actually wants only to replace the native culture with his own.

What a cruel, stupid way of looking at a tub of frozen goulash. Matt's mother loves her son, her grandson, maybe even her daughter-in-law, she is a woman who cannot easily express love and approval, and so she cooks for them, brings her love to Boston in frozen form and leaves it behind, hoping that when it is thawed and enjoyed, some of the original flavor will still be left, the hours spent making the special stock, the careful chopping and stirring.

Or take the dinner that Matt and Amelia and Alexander are served by friends, the parents of Alexander's friend Jeremy. When you have a child, of course, you try hard for these matchups, the child who gets along with your child, whose parents are good adult company. You do not force your child to be friends with the children of your own friends, because how many of them have children the right age, and who can force a child to do anything, anyway? Instead, you sort through the children your own son picks out at day care, and you settle on the parents who seem acceptable. Jeremy's parents, Diana and Luke, are acceptable.

To tell the truth, for some time now, Amelia finds, she has been liking Diana less and less. Diana is so damn smug, and she is such a terrible cook—food again. Diana's cooking is intermittently inspired, but most of her brave experiments come crashing down, and everyone is expected to be charmed. At this particular dinner party, paying back Matt and Amelia for a dinner at which they served a really excellent sausage lasagna, Diana has produced a fish vindaloo, made, she says, from a recipe clipped from the newspaper, made by her for the first time, of course. Madcap Diana, why *not* try out new recipes on company? And why not screw up and put in so much cayenne that not one of the four adults, all of whom like spicy food, is able to eat a single mouthful? Ha ha. The rice is glue, the green beans are mush. Altogether one of Diana's most complete washouts. So with a shrug and a laugh, she goes to the refrigerator, produces a jar of fancy cornichons, a package of sharp cheddar, and some Hebrew National franks. How tremendously amusing, the adults telegraph to each other, eating their hotdogs. Good old Diana, giving a dinner party of hotdogs and pickles. Amelia is somewhat unamused; she gets enough hotdogs at the hospital, and if she goes out for an evening, making herself presentable and conversational after a long day's work, giving up the peaceful hours at home, she expects to be served grown-up food.

Diana is as thin as a spike, but her husband, Luke, has a little potbelly. Does he gain weight disposing of Diana's kitchen failures? Potbelly or not, Amelia rather likes his looks; he has thick dark hair, an unkempt beard, and bright blue eyes. In a good light, he looks like a rather domesticated gypsy. Amelia goes into the kitchen to help Diana wash up, and ask politely after the well-being of Diana's craft gallery, now gearing up for its big Christmas-present season. The gallery is actually full of lovely things; Amelia has been in, once or twice, to buy a gift and say hello to Diana (who does not give discounts to friends, not that Amelia would dream of asking), and has seen many things she would like to own.

But no, maybe she doesn't really like Diana. She would rather be back in the living room, with Matt and Luke. If she had sat still a minute longer, actually, Matt would have gotten up and gone into the kitchen to help, and then she would be in the living room with Luke, an appealing thought. She pictures herself sitting next to Luke on the couch, and then, oh my goodness, smooching with Luke on the couch. She has never imagined kissing Luke before, but it's a powerfully attractive idea. She must have been watching him all evening without realizing it. In her fantasy, the two of them announce to their spouses, busy in the kitchen, that they are just running out to the bakery to buy a wonderful dessert (Diana's apple pie has burned), they go outside, get into Luke's car, and end up making out in the front seat in front of the nice sturdy house where their families wait. She would love to kiss Luke. She was watching the messy way he ate, the way he scattered crumbs and licked his fingers. He probably kisses like a demon. So much for Diana and her lousy food. So much for Matt. Amelia nods, closing off the fantasy, slightly astonished that it hit her at all.

For someone who runs a gallery full of handthrown pottery,

handwoven towels and tablecloths, carved boxes, and stained-glass window ornaments, Diana has an aggressively plain kitchen. The plates are standard-issue wedding china, uninterestingly floral, the dishtowels blue-checked, the walls decorated only with a framed picture of Jeremy, aged perhaps two, surrounded by grandparents. And there is no real function for the dishtowels, or for Amelia, since Diana is efficiently loading up her dishwasher.

Amelia and Diana make conversation: Where are the boys, probably up to no good, yes, but don't you love it when they're out of sight? Then Diana asks her, Are you thinking of having another soon, and Amelia, who has just, to her own amazement, been idly imagining herself in bed with Diana's husband, takes a minute to switch gears and get her answer out. Someday, she says, someday soon. But we finally have a little bit of breathing space, just the three of us, and I want to enjoy that before we go and complicate things with another baby. Amelia wonders whether this is really true; is there any reason not to go ahead and jump back into the messy milky closeness of infancy, herself and Matt, Alexander too, all in the damp bed cuddling together, her nightgown unbuttoned for nursing, giving Alexander a try if he's interested, giving Matt a try, privately. What is she really gaining in this breathing space? Life is less frantic, getting to work on time is easier, her sleep is not interrupted, but isn't she just sliding farther and farther away from Matt? Would a new baby cure what ails them?

Why has she never noticed before that Luke is attractive? Did he smile at her in some special way over dinner? Sure, she likes Luke, has always liked Luke, but liked Luke and Diana, the parents of Jeremy, a unit. Now she is deliberately mortifying herself, hanging out here in the kitchen, aware that what she really wants is to rush back into the living room and look Luke over more carefully. Astonishing.

What is actually astonishing is this: I can't remember the last time I felt that kind of attraction, that dangerous possibility, that awareness of a man who was not mine, but was not far away. Is it with pregnancy that I ruled myself out so absolutely, or does it go farther back than that? Or is this just some kind of inevitable brain rot that sets in when you find yourself out on the young-couples-with-children circuit; eventually, out of sheer boredom, you start coveting other husbands.

Diana and I left the kitchen and drifted up the stairs together, searching out the boys. We could hear them, and paused in the hall; Jeremy was explaining to Alexander how to use a shield. I peeked in the door; Jeremy's shield was round and blue, plastic, with an eagle's head dead center. Jeremy was demonstrating the way to put his arm through the straps in the back. "And if someone tries to get you in the head, you lift it up. And if someone tries to get you in the legs, you put it down here like this."

We tiptoed back down the stairs to the husbands, took our proper places, Diana on the couch leaning very slightly against Luke, which set me wondering whether they had a very rich, exciting sex life, me in an armchair next to Matt, who sprawled on the floor and did not lean against my legs. One reason this friendship works is that Matt likes Luke. Luke works in a university library, he's in charge of the preservation and restoration of rare books and old documents, and he and Matt find some kind of common ground in the painstaking detailed work they do, restoring crumbling houses, preserving broken books. We sat, the four of us, and talked about the summer house Luke and Diana hope to buy on Cape Cod, and I wondered, as I have before, where their money comes from. Is her gallery really as successful as all that, or do their parents give them money?

A few minutes later, the little boys came charging down the stairs to show us their finery: Jeremy had the shield, but he had lent Alexander his second-best sword, and also a realistic little knife, made of rubber, that retreated into its handle when stabbed against something solid, and gave quite a good imitation of sinking into flesh.

"Look," Alexander announced to the assembled grown-ups, "I can smote two enemies at once."

Families and food, what a tangle. Amelia runs into Geraldine Blake when she is buying herself a cup of coffee and a slice of chocolate mousse cake at a genteel little bakery near Harvard Square.

Amelia is indulging herself; when is she ever alone and with time to spare in such a place? Most of her meals away from home are in the institutional cameraderie of the hospital cafeteria, or else a short walk away, in the nearby sub shop, or the deli, with a hospital friend. She is in Harvard Square, though, her errands finished, and because her last two patients canceled, she has almost an hour before she goes to pick up Alexander.

She is not thrilled to see Geraldine, whose daughter she stopped in on earlier in the day. Geraldine is looking even more polished than usual, dressed up in a very expensive-looking dress of dark green wool, high brown suede boots, and a matching wide belt around her willowy waist. What a beautiful, graceful woman; surely everyone in the bakery is admiring her. On her little tray are an espresso and a dainty bowl of fruit salad. Amelia has in her shoulder bag a new issue of *People* magazine, bought at the newsstand as part of her treat, and she wants to eat her chocolate mousse cake with Princess Diana and Cher, not Geraldine Blake. But there is something in the other woman's eyes that makes it impossible to turn away, some appeal, some recognition that they are, after all, two busy mothers snatching a moment in a coffee shop, two members of the same social class, proper company for one another. Amelia sits down and glances invitingly at the other chair; Geraldine Blake takes it.

Defiantly, Amelia begins to eat her cake. Daintily, Geraldine nibbles her fruit salad. Each makes an insincere little comment: how good that looks. They chat about how rare it is to snatch such moments for themselves, about work, husbands, children. Amelia is mildly, not unpleasantly, bored, wondering whether she may in fact escape any outpouring of misery from this lovely woman.

But Geraldine (and they are now using first names) steers the conversation inexorably toward Sara, off in her hospital crib. Initially she excuses herself; she's been spending every night in the hospital, today she had to see a client in Cambridge, she never got a chance to eat lunch, she simply had to take a break. Amelia is preoccupied with a side issue: does Geraldine emerge each morning from the hospital bathroom this perfectly groomed? It seems unlikely; herself, if she had to stay overnight with her child (knock on wood), she would probably live in sweatpants and never comb her hair.

"I know I shouldn't ask you this, I shouldn't intrude business on you when you're off-duty," Geraldine says, smiling apologetically, as one who has every intention of doing just that. "But how do you think Sara is doing?"

Amelia is not actually a prig about on-duty, off-duty. How can you expect people to leave their children behind them, after all. "It's obviously very hard to feed her, though I still don't know whether that's the cause or the effect of her failure to thrive. The nurses are getting adequate calories into her, as of yesterday, with the new supplements, and we'll just have to see. It's a tough problem."

Geraldine, across the table, is weeping into her espresso, though her back is straight and the hand holding the cup to her lips doesn't shake. "Everything was going so well. You can't imagine how well. You look at me now and you think, There's a woman who couldn't manage to nourish a child. Teenage mothers do it all the time, people with IQs of 70 do it, and here's this woman who let her baby starve. You have no idea, my first baby never gave us any trouble at all, he grew and did everything right on schedule. And then everyone says the second one is supposed to be easy, the second one sleeps right through the night, the second one you just take in your stride."

Amelia has questions, of course. She could ask for more details about Sara's delivery, infancy, look for roots of difficulty between mother and baby. But she wants to eat her cake, and she knows that in fifteen minutes she will have to get free and go pick up Alexander. "Failure to thrive is a syndrome we don't understand very well at all, but we do know that it happens to all kinds of people, all social classes, all backgrounds." Her didactic sociological tone floats out into the air like frozen breath.

"Like wife-beating." Geraldine dabs at her eyes with a napkin.

Amelia wonders whether Frank Blake beats his wife, his children. Is something else wrong in this pretty family? And when is she going to discuss with them the need to test Sara for AIDS, which is now statistically on the increase (rapid) as an etiology for

FTT. Oh, they will just love that, Frank and Geraldine, love the suggestion that maybe one of them has been screwing around, or screwing around with drugs. Still, the suggestion will be made at their next conference, part of the next list of diagnostic tests she goes over with them.

"This is kind of like some baby version of anorexia," Geraldine says. "Why is this happening to us? It's like some kind of punishment for thinking you have it made, nice jobs, nice family, nice house, then boom, sock, pow."

This thought has actually occurred to Amelia, too, but it is automatic with her to discourage parents from blaming themselves, for this or anything. "It's not a punishment. It's a bad thing that is happening to your daughter and to you."

"And so you believe that bad things do indeed happen to good people?" Geraldine is fully in control of herself once again, straight-backed and dry-eyed. Amelia is conscious of crumbs on her own shirt.

"I believe that bad things happen, period. In my job, I get to see a lot of them. And I don't think there's anything to be gained from looking at them as punishments. Look, we've all done things for which we deserve to be punished. And we've all had rewards we didn't deserve—just think about our children. Even think about Sara."

"Thank you, Doctor," says Geraldine, and Amelia watches her as she leaves the bakery, tall and straight and walking proud, off to her daughter who does not eat.

Alexander and food. Well, Twinkies, of course, and frozen corn. And hotdogs, too, though he has been sheltered from McDonald's, raised instead on peking ravioli and roast pork lo mein, his two favorite meat-and-dough combinations.

Alexander sitting at the battered butcher-block kitchen table, staring into space, above his plate of Sixty-Minute Gourmet paella. Alexander likes paella fine, likes shrimp and scallops and rice. But Alexander comes home from day care and burrows into his lunch-box, digs out the morsels left at lunch and now well seasoned, aged, in his cubby. Happily, he chews his half sandwich, his now doubly leftover roast pork lo mein, his grapes (no white sugar!). By the time the paella's sixty minutes are up, the edge is off Alexander's appetite. Amelia and Matt both eat hungrily, but Alexander is off in space. Doing what? Amelia assumes that he is somewhere, eight feet tall, armed with a shining gold sword, smoting his enemies. Boys are so mysterious, so drawn, for whatever reasons, to the things that draw them, so aware that the world will attack them with deadly weapons. You have to be a pirate, a knight, a cowboy, you have to be armed. You need power. Which is of course quite legitimate fantasy material for a group of beings dominated at every turn by adults, who rule by virtue of superior size and strength. At the day care center, there are those who believe that if we handled the boy babies differently, more gently, if we took them off to a verdant peaceable kingdom and raised them in the midst of only tenderness and vegetarian coexistence, they would grow up not wanting swords. Or would they still see through us, through our adult power, as we pushed them around, made them eat their nice breadfruit and play their noncompetitive games?

Funny, before Alexander was born Amelia had vaguely wanted a girl and felt no particular connection with little boys, had wondered what Jo March saw in them. Now, of course, her heart is with the little boys, with Alexander and Jeremy and the others as they tear hectic through life and make each other hysterical with their endlessly repeated jokes, "Hey, over there with the poopy hair!" The girls at the day care center often seem to her a rather mimsy group, careful of themselves, conscious of who is sitting next to whom, who is whose best friend—and yet, the girls will probably grow up to be a group of people she will like better than the boys. And perhaps someday she will have a daughter of her own, and learn how to look at little girls.

"Alexander, eat some of your paella."

Dreamily, he picks up a shrimp, scattering yellow rice onto his lap; dreamily he puts it into his mouth and chews. Amelia watches, so does Matt, and it becomes one of those moments when they are watching him without him aware of them, but aware of each other, of each other's appreciation, how beautiful he is, how sweet, how perfect, how inadequate words are to describe what both these parents are feeling, across their kitchen table, watching their four-year-old chew.

Sometimes when he is about to taste some food that he cannot remember having eaten before, Alexander will ask them, Do I like this? Amelia thinks of this inquiry, of its mixture of trust and suspicion, the suggestion that Alexander knows the world is full of foods he doesn't eat, and knows that his parents are always trying to expand his repertoire. But the thing that really makes it touching, that question, is the implication that already, at four, his experience is too varied and complex for Alexander to track by himself. His head is too full of whatever is in there, swords and battles, the tangle of the letters, just beginning to make sense, grandparents and birthdays, the children at day care, Dr. Seuss. How can he track what he has and hasn't eaten? It would be like asking him to list his T-shirts, to tick off the dinosaur shirt, the Boston Aquarium shirt, the Pirates of the Caribbean shirt, the New York Museum of Natural History and the Shakespeare Festival shirts, gifts from Amelia's mother—Alexander likes the pictures on the shirts, likes choosing one to wear, but they are for someone else to keep track of. He has other things on his mind.

Food and love, food and sex. Amelia, since that dinner party with Jeremy and his parents, has begun to imagine an affair with Luke, imagine it in great detail. She has stopped worrying over the initial encounter, the dropping of the barriers, the transition from being parents of two kids who are friends to being Man and Woman. Why bother making that up? It's never going to happen. She has skipped to their afternoon assignations (which are never going to happen either, for Christ's sake; everything else aside, who the hell is free in the afternoon?), which take place in a cheap motel room on Route 1, thus adding another element of improbability to the scenario, since who on earth would take the trouble to fight Boston traffic out to a motel on Route 1? Surely there are places closer by.

But nevertheless, Route 1 is where it happens; she must have taken note of the motels on some family trip (coming back from Crane's Beach, maybe) and had them in mind as the place to go. In this sleazy room, Amelia and Luke claw at each other, ripping clothing in their haste. They hump against the composition-board walls. They do the things that people do in trashy novels about sex and success, swept away by their lust, their panting, their insatiable hunger for each other. Interestingly, these fantasies are what you might call anatomically correct (an expression used to refer to wildly expensive imported dolls for little boys, made with little plastic penises rather than the usual egg-smooth groins). In the past, when Amelia had fantasies, your casual postmovie roll in the hay with Paul Newman (she has not made the transition to the younger movie stars, by and large), the Amelia of her fantasies had full high breasts, a flat stomach, as the movie star lovingly stripped off her clinging garments. But when she thinks about Luke and herself, she sees them as they are, or at least as she is, as she imagines him to be. Bellies and love handles and all. No matter. His hand squishes against her soft stomach as he turns her over on the bed, drives into her from behind. Porn for the paunchy. She makes fun of it even to herself, but also thinks about it, sometimes obsessively. Finds herself alone in an elevator at the hospital, and it rushes over her, the motel room, Luke, his hands, his mouth, his penis. Anatomically correct.

To tell the truth, Amelia cannot really believe that it will ever affect anything, whether or not small boys play with guns. She cannot take it seriously—but then, she cannot take the nuclear freeze movement seriously either. Matt's obnoxious brother, who since the age of fourteen has been declaring himself a neoconservative, with his copies of Commentary and his loud ambition to move to Israel and settle the West Bank, is fond of the term "fuzzy-headed liberal." And though she dislikes Matt's brother and is very bored by his politics, Amelia would grant that, politically, that is what she is, fuzzy-headed. And a liberal, too, of course; she believes in public assistance for the poor, and equal opportunity and affirmative action; she never looks at her son and worries that some minority child will cheat him out of a place—there are certain things it would be just too obscene for Darren's doctor to worry about. She believes that countries should destroy their nuclear weapons, but not that she or anyone else can make them do it. She maintains vague (yes, fuzzy) liberal positions on just about any issue you can name, all without any interest in actually being well-informed, in reading up on what the liberal position really means, in knowing the facts and the figures. She keeps track of medical issues in that other, more thorough, way, but she lets the great world go where it will. She would rather read *People* magazine.

Ask Amelia about world affairs, proselytize at her about boycotts and freezes and referendum questions (which in Cambridge, Massachusetts, typically involve meganational issues), and she is polite and liberal and conscious that it behooves her to have an opinion and some information. But inside her head she is thinking with scorn that some people certainly have a lot of time to waste, and thinking most of all that all political activists, all people putting their time into Causes, left or right, should be forced to put that same time and energy into taking home one baby with AIDS, caring for it and learning to love it properly. Then all that misdirected energy that goes into editorials and petitions and door-to-door canvassing would go where it counts. So much for Amelia's trivial world view.

Does she worry that one day the bombs will fall and wipe everything out? Sometimes—after all, she does have a child. But this subject is one she does not choose to think about very much, and the truth is that somewhere in the depths of her self-deluding soul she cherishes a mild hope that when judgment day comes and the men in business suits push all the buttons, maybe it will turn out that the machines don't work. Thus the fuzzy-headed re-create the world in their own image.

So while Amelia and the other people whose lives she understands are taking care of sick babies, what if the men in business suits blow up the world? Well, let Alexander get in all the fencing practice he can; after the deluge it might come in handy.

Amelia at work, dressed neatly, good navy blue skirt, heavy cardigan made of dark gray yarn, wool and silk, expensive. Neat pumps. She looks like someone who belongs in the hospital, like a doctor. Like a doctor. Her offspring safely in day care, Amelia in the hospital. It is good to be in control. She is checking on a little girl named Ashleigh Dugan, whose pediatrician is one of the residents in the clinic Amelia supervises. Ashleigh is a year and a half old and generally healthy, though she is one of the largest and fattest babies for her age that anyone can remember. She is pink-and-white behemoth, with golden curls and the disposition of Genghis Khan, doted on by her proud parents. The resident who takes care of her was afraid she would never learn to walk, that her legs wouldn't bear her up, but she walked on schedule and went running around the clinic like a loose tank, mashing smaller, older children down before her. Anyway, last weekend Ashleigh got a cold, and the cold turned into croup, and advised by the resident, her parents spent a night treating the croup at home. They put a vaporizer in the baby's room, and when the cough got worse they took her in the bathroom and turned on the hot shower, but with all the steam, she coughed more and more, and finally ended up in the emergency room, where Ashleigh was observed to be pulling her chest wall all the way in toward her backbone with every breath, and going into lengthy coughing fits, during which she barked like a seal and her pink face got a little dusky. And she spent the day in the hospital, in an oxygen tent, and then night came and the croup got worse, as croup usually does at night, and two days ago the poor baby ended up in intensive care, intubated.

Amelia visited her there, spent some time with her terrified parents. This can't just be croup, Mrs. Dugan kept saying. Everyone gets croup, croup doesn't kill you. Amelia didn't say, Well, actually babies have often died of croup, and Ashleigh would probably have died of hers a hundred years ago. That is not the way to comfort. Instead she said, Ashleigh's going to be just fine, wait and see. And today here is Ashleigh, the tube out of her throat, back out of intensive care. The viral infection that caused the croup, the swelling in her airway, has gone away. She still has a runny nose and an occasional cough, but that's about it. She's perched massively on her mother's lap, wearing ruffles, with her father spooning red Jell-O into her. Probably her parents are worried that her day of not eating in the ICU has left her malnourished.

"What a lovely dress," Amelia says. "I love those matching panties."

"It was going to be her Christmas dress, but my mother just called up and said she's making one for her out of red velvet," says Mrs. Dugan. "So now it's her getting-better dress, cause she's going home tomorrow."

"I'm sure you folks will be glad to get out of here."

"We'll never forget what you did for us, Doctor. We're going to tell our little girl, too, so she'll always know how lucky she was."

Amelia nods, accepting credit on behalf of the hospital, the profession. The nurses, the anesthesiologists, the residents, the hospital kitchen where the red Jell-O was mixed up. And why not? Here's a healthy eighteen-month-old who had a virus inflaming her respiratory tract, and the swelling got so bad it almost cut off her air supply, and instead of being dead, she's going to go on home and live another seventy or so years. So even if Amelia didn't personally have anything to do with saving Ashleigh's life, still, thank you very much, think nothing of it, all in a day's work.

The songs that Alexander brings home from day care have progressed, over the years, from "Twinkle, Twinkle" to "Dinosaur Rock." This new one, though, is something of a departure; it takes several renditions before Amelia realizes that in fact it is a hymn of some sort. Alexander likes it very much and sings it with great emphasis:

"The dumb woman builds her house upon the sand,
The dumb woman builds her house upon the sand,
The dumb woman builds her house upon the sand,
And the rain came tumbling down!
The rain came down and the floods came up,
The rain came down and the floods came up,
The rain came down and the floods came up,
And the house on the sand went ker-splatt!"

Alexander is in a cuddly mood, happy to sit in his mother's lap, his eyes maybe a little bit shadowed by fatigue. An especially active day sometimes sends him home like this, needing a little rest before the action of the evening. Amelia, also tired from her own day, treasures him up, strokes his head, kisses the back of his neck. She tells him she loves him, just for the pleasure of having him say, irritably, Why do you always keep *saying* that. Because it's true, she tells him, I love you once, I love you twice, I love you more than beans and rice. Alexander begins to sing again, poking at the couch with a Tinkertoy stick to keep time.

Amelia's beeper goes off, calling shrilly to her from her pocketbook, and she dials into the hospital phone system, hoping it is not Frank Blake. It is Frank Blake. He apologizes for disturbing her, but not as if he means it. He's been meaning to call all day, he tells her, but he's had a busy day at the office. He wanted to ask her, he was reading something in the newspaper the other day, reading an article about some of the less-well-known inherited diseases. And they mentioned various kinds of dwarfisms—now, no one has suggested so far, says Frank Blake, that maybe Sara isn't growing because she's some kind of a dwarf. Does that need to be investigated?

When Amelia finally gets rid of him, she comes back into her living room weighted down with the feeling that this frantic man hangs over her own family like a curse. The perfect Blakes and their perfect daughter, who cannot grow.

"The dumb woman builds her house upon the sand,
The dumb woman builds her house upon the sand,
The dumb woman builds her house upon the sand,
And the rain came tumbling down!
The rain came down and the floods came up,
The rain came down and the floods came up,
The rain came down and the floods came up,
And the house on the sand went ker-splatt!"

Irresistibly, Amelia is thinking not of her own house but of the house Matt and his partner bought to restore, five blocks away. Alexander is still singing, still beating time.

"But the smart woman builds her house upon the rock,
The smart woman builds her house upon the rock,
The smart woman builds her house upon the rock,

And the rain came tumbling down!
The rain came down and the floods came up,
The rain came down and the floods came up,
The rain came down and the floods came up,
And the house on the rock stood firm!"
Yes, definitely some kind of hymn.

The last time that Amelia was prey to such obsessive sexual fantasies, actually, was when she was pregnant with Alexander. She does not cultivate the memory, because it embarrasses her. Oh, of course she had read the politically correct chapters in the politically correct manuals of pregnancy and childbearing: You and your sensitive supportive husband can enjoy a thrilling sex life together right through the pregnancy! Don't fall prey to old-fashioned taboos! Get on top of him when your belly gets too big for him to get on top of you! Prop your bottom up with pillows and have him kneel between your legs! And what about doggy-style? Not that they called it doggy-style. And not that she and Matt didn't occasionally do one or the other of those things. Still, she hardly felt at her most graceful, and there was something a little silly about bothering to maneuver her bulk onto Matt's thin body, and she was exhausted all the time, and to be honest, Matt didn't seem any more interested than she did in setting any records. Toward the end of pregnancy what you really need is cuddling, so they cuddled.

But Amelia had a secret life, starting somewhere in her second trimester, a secret and profoundly embarrassing haze of fantasy and masturbation (all those afternoon naps!). She attributed it to some hormonal imbalance of pregnancy, and indulged herself, and expected it to go away after the baby was born, which it did. And talk about politically incorrect. She was having, there is no other word for it, bimbo fantasies. Fantasies in which she had the body of some pneumatic little beach bunny, in which lecherous, mildly brutal men encountered in one or another soft-core setup pulled her clothes off and ravished her. The secretary and the boss. The cocktail waitress and the traveling salesman. And even, God help us, the beach bunny and the lifeguard (behind a dune!). As the pregnancy progressed, she got younger and younger in her own private blue movies; the sultry high school student and the stern teacher, the baby-sitter and the groping father (in the car, driving her home). Embarrassing to remember, and usually she doesn't but at the time she allowed herself the indulgence as she allowed the other indulgences of pregnancy, ice cream for calcium, hot baths for aches and pains, afternoon naps. And if sometimes she came downstairs after a particularly humiliating and passionate afternoon nap, all alone with her cheap thrills, she always felt refreshed, relaxed, and rather pleasantly naughty. But those fantasies went away, not to be remembered, after Alexander was born, and they are now a distant, guilty memory, embarrassing, politically incorrect, and more than a little bit ridiculous. Now she has respectable married-woman fantasies about her son's friend's father, realistic and theoretically attainable fantasies; she will never be a provocatively buxom baby-sitter, doing it in the car with a horny drunk daddy, but theoretically she could find her way to a motel with Luke. That is the sort of thing that happens, isn't it? Therefore, these new fantasies must represent maturity, emotional growth, and increased sophistication. Right.

Sara Blake's blood has been drawn out, plugged into every kind of tube, red top, blue top, green top, and sent to every kind of lab. Here are some of the things that are not wrong with this child: her body chemistries are not out-of-whack; her blood contains the proper amounts of sodium and potassium and chloride, and the right proportion of acid. So no reason to suspect an inborn metabolic error, short-circuiting some biochemical reaction and letting molecular garbage pile up in her bloodstream. Her kidney function is fine; all the waste products are promptly cleaned up and peed out. She is only mildly anemic, which is to be expected in her malnourished state, and she shows no sign of any malignancy, nor of any chronic infection. Her liver seems to be working perfectly. And on and on and on. Amelia could have told you all this before any blood was drawn. Probably, if Sara were some little child of poverty, the product of an obviously chaotic and destructive home,

Amelia would not have allowed all these blood tests in the first place. Just feed the kid and see if she grows before you get all carried away, she would have said to the intern.

But the Blakes are here for tests, the Blakes want a medical diagnosis, and the intern half does too, just because it's hard to look at Sara and her parents and think, Oh yes, psychosocial. So when Greg Murphy comes up with one more list of things he wants to rule out (Could she have congenital heart disease? Could she have chronic sinusitis? Could she have a malabsorption syndrome?), Amelia shrugs and lets him schedule the tests. If nothing else, they keep the Blake parents happy.

And of course the electrocardiogram is normal, the sinus x-rays are clear, the malabsorption tests are negative. Meantime, it is a little hard to feed Sara properly; she is always sleeping off the sedative from one test, or else restricted to IV fluids only, to prepare her for the next. It's a little ridiculous: here is this little girl whose whole problem is probably that she doesn't eat enough, and day after day the intern writes orders making her NPO, nothing by mouth. Have to keep her stomach empty so she can get her malabsorption test, have to clean out her bowels so the barium x-rays will be easy to read. Amelia lets it go on almost a week before she puts her foot down, firmly, on Greg Murphy. He is the type who was probably an ace medical student; he has an awesome capacity to memorize lists of possible diagnoses, and an equally awesome tendency to fixate on the least likely. He wants to rule out histoplasmosis now, and diencephalic syndrome. And furthermore, every time he comes up with another possibility he lets Sara's parents in on the news, and they fixate on it too, and then there is no getting out of sending the tests.

Somewhat apologetically, Amelia squashes him: Please don't suggest any more diagnoses to the parents without discussing them with me first. Please remember that this child has shown us no evidence of any organic disease whatsoever, please remember that most failure to thrive is nonorganic. Please make feeding Sara the priority; the most important piece of information we need is whether she gains weight with adequate caloric intake, and I don't want to come back here tomorrow and find she's NPO for another upper GI series. Yes, I know we could still be missing something, but there'll be time enough to worry about that if it turns out that good calories don't do anything for her. Amelia sees the rebellion in Greg's intent eyes; he says nothing further, but she knows she has made his fascinating differential diagnosis into a social problem, and everyone hates a social problem. No medical fireworks, no fascinating biology. Even Amelia hates a social problem, to tell the truth—frustrating and hard to treat. But it's too late in the hospital year for Greg to be this thick about these things; failure to thrive is a common problem and he seems to have no clinical judgment whatsoever to bring to bear on the case. She supposes she should have a little talk with someone, pass on a message to be passed on eventually to Greg, wake up and smell the Betadine, but she knows she never will. Greg is somewhat irritating and, God knows, not the intern she would choose to handle the Blakes, but he is still an intern and downtrodden and she doesn't need to add to his problems.

Meanwhile, what have they done to poor little Sara Blake? Sometimes when you take a child out of a truly awful family situation and plunk it down in the hospital, the child blossoms. From being ignored, being abused, the child moves to conscientious nursing care, regular meals, the trained attention of the play therapist, the age-appropriate toys in the playroom. Sometimes you get a child who tells you, I don't ever want to go home. I like it here. Sara Blake, who of course cannot talk yet, is not saying this. Too many tests, maybe. Sara refuses to settle down to sleep unless her mother is with her, and several times a day she gives way to fits of hysterical screaming, which Amelia suspects she enjoys. The nurses feel particularly bad, since everyone agrees that Sara did not behave like this at the beginning of the hospitalization. And of course it makes her even harder to feed; at the beginning of the hospitalization, the nurses found that feeding Sara was very much what her mother had described: she giggled, she squirmed, she took food into her mouth only to hiss it all out between her teeth, she stood up in her high chair, she overturned the spoon, or the bowl, she looked everywhere but at her food. Now, after a week in the hospital, instead of being mischievous and difficult at mealtime, Sara is frequently furious, screaming, banging her hands on her high-chair tray. She does slightly better when her mother feeds her; so much for the idea that competent nurses would take over and really get good calories in. In order to help overcome Sara's mealtime difficulties, new and old, Amelia has asked Greg to consult a number of people, and Sara is now the subject of extended scrutiny by the behavioral medicine team, the pediatric psychiatrist, and the nutrition nurse. Additionally, the nurses have called in Social Service to "help the family cope with the stress of the hospitalization," and Amelia finds out about this one afternoon when she stops by to see Sara and finds Geraldine being icy and patronizing to a social worker. Amelia starts to excuse herself, but Geraldine dismisses the social worker instead, and turns on Amelia, demanding why should she be subjected to social workers, and how dare they tell her that her daughter has a behavioral problem, when it's the hospital which has done all the damage, and is this usual procedure when the hospital staff can't feed the baby, to unleash a social worker on the mother?

Amelia has a strong sense of sympathy; one of her private nightmares is the idea of a social worker prying into the details of her own life, her own family. And if history is now being rewritten so that all Sara's tantrums are being attributed to a "dysfunctional family" rather than to the effects of hospitalization and separation from her family, then Geraldine is right to be angry. But Amelia deflects the anger, talks instead about how she needs to meet formally with both parents, discuss what to do next. Then she goes in search of Greg Murphy.

Finds him sitting in the doctors' conference room, talking on the phone. Waits patiently till his call is over, then, as tactfully as she can, suggests maybe we can wait a while on social service, maybe we can humor these difficult parents. "Difficult" usually means upper-middle-class; the euphemism is "entitled," the acronym is PWS, for Privileged White Syndrome. It's perfectly true; if Geraldine were a poor, black, single mother, she would probably accept the appearance of the social worker without asking questions; if you live a certain kind of life, social workers just show up every now and then. Still, Greg, could we just concentrate on feeding the child, which we still haven't done adequately, could we document what happens with several days of good calories, and then go on from there? Draw tomorrow's panel of labs, then no more tests for a while.

Greg's face looks pinched and tight. He works hard, he is there all the time, he takes endless trouble with his patients, frequently to very little effect, and writes long illegible notes in their charts. And Amelia breezes in and tells him he's doing it all wrong.

"Are you going to ask them about HIV testing?" Greg asks, his tone suggesting that Amelia is going to wimp out again here.

"I'll mention it at our next meeting with the parents, Greg. I don't think it's highly urgent that we do it now, since we don't have any other signs pointing us in that direction."

"She's got some neck nodes."

"Well, lots of kids have a neck node or two. But I think we do need to bring it up, just in case there's something the parents aren't telling us—they need to know why we need to know if there are any risk factors."

"So, another megameeting."

"That's what these cases are like, Greg."

Listening to him, Amelia knows that he spends his time complaining about her to the other interns; she pushes him around, she interferes between him and the parents, she doesn't know what she's doing, she has no coherent approach to the diagnosis. She can just hear his self-satisfied whiny voice going on and on, and the thought of it irritates the hell out of her. Maybe she will go complain about him after all.

The hospital rule is, painful procedures happen in the treatment room, never in the patient's bed. Children need to feel safe in their beds. So it was wrong this morning, when the blood-drawing tech came through, for her to take blood from Sara Blake in her crib, but the tech was in a hurry and the parents were out of the room (changing of the guard; Geraldine had left for work and Frank had not yet arrived for his morning visit) so she went ahead and drew the next few tubes of blood. So Frank Blake is storming through the corridor in a fury when Amelia arrives, paged to come soothe him. Frank Blake, who knows little or nothing about medicine but is so profoundly indignant about this breach of hospital policy that he backs Amelia up against the wall, shaking his finger in her face.

"What do you think then, *Doctor,* of someone who would walk into a room and see an innocent child lying there and just go ahead and stab a needle into her, in the crib that's supposed to be safe? Just go ahead and torture her, even though her parents aren't there to comfort her?"

"Mr. Blake, I think we should go sit down somewhere and talk about this." Amelia shakes her head no at the nurse, standing behind his shoulder and mouthing the word "Security?" Security is no use unless you actually want a violent parent led away by force.

"What do we have to talk about? About this splendid pediatric ward where you go to so much trouble to give children a sense of security? About the splendid medical care our little girl is receiving here?" But he allows her to lead him down the hall, sit him down in the claustrophobic little parents' room.

"Now, I'm sorry that Sara's blood got drawn the way it did, and I'll make sure the techs get reminded about always using the treatment room. But you know, Mr. Blake, hospital policies are designed in a best-of-all-possible-worlds framework. If we could, we would always do everything painful in the treatment room, but sometimes that doesn't work out—"

"It doesn't work out because your goddam Nazi employees enjoy torturing children. Just walk in and stick needles in her when there's no one there to comfort her, just don't give a damn, just laugh at her when she cries, poor little sick kid. You know, I never understood Auschwitz before, how they could take children and just throw them into those ovens . . ." Incredibly, he is crying, he has choked on his tears.

Amelia is floored, dazzled by the magnitude of the rage he has channeled at her, offended, angry, and at least a little bit sympathetic, especially to see him crying, to imagine the level of strain he must be under if he is willing to let her see him cry. She is trying to think of her next line when Mr. Blake suddenly gets to his feet and walks out of the room, slightly unsteady, heading back to his daughter's bedside.

"The dumb woman builds her house upon the sand,
   The dumb woman builds her house upon the sand—"

"Alexander, do you think you could sing something else for a while?"
"What do you want me to sing?"
"Any other song."

"But the smart woman builds her house upon the rock,
   The smart woman builds her house upon the rock,
   The smart woman builds her house upon the rock—"

"Alexander, that's the same song, it's just another verse. Please sing something else."

I was reading a collection of short stories by Elizabeth Gaskell, who is notable among the nineteenth-century British women of letters in part because she had a successful domestic life as the wife of a clergyman and the mother of five children. On some of her books, she has no first name; she is just listed as Mrs. Gaskell, as if Mr. G were so famous that anyone could instantly be identified by relation to him. Actually, Elizabeth was quite celebrated as a writer, and wrote often for Mr. Dickens's periodicals, and traveled abroad and met the famous, and so on. Meanwhile, according to a new biography I leafed through in the bookstore, Charlotte Brontë died of hyperemesis gravida—I had always assumed tuberculosis; it seemed to go with the legend. But no, the author of *Jane Eyre* actually died because she was pregnant and vomiting too much. This information will not be found in Elizabeth Gaskell's most famous book, the biography of Charlotte Brontë. What I really like about Elizabeth Gaskell is that she was the only Victorian, as far as I can tell, who actually liked writing short stories.

"But what should I sing? I don't know what to sing."
"Sing 'Puff.'"
"I don't know all the words, you have to help me."
"Sing 'Oats and beans and barley grow.'"
"That's a baby game."
"Sweetheart, let Mommy alone, she's tired and she's reading."
"What are you reading?"

"A book, a snook, a crook, a dook, a mookitymookmook. Now
let me read it."

"The dumb woman builds her house upon the sand,
The dumb woman builds her house upon the sand,
The dumb woman builds her house upon the sand,
And the rain came tumbling down."

The story I was reading was "The Three Eras of Libbie Marsh,"
about a plain and unmarriageable seamstress in Manchester who
sees out her window the life of the little crippled boy next door.
Doctorlike, I could not help wanting a diagnosis and was not satisfied by what the story offered: "'Summut's amiss wi' his backbone, folks say; he's better and worse like.'" Libbie's heart is
touched by the poor child's sufferings, and after watching the pleasure he takes in a small bunch of flowers, she conceives the idea of
buying him a canary. My heart was touched too, somewhat, by the
pleasure that the child took in the bird, and I admit I hoped it was
not the author's purpose to kill the canary off so as to demonstrate
the harshness of this world, or even the inhumanity of men. But in
the nineteenth century, no writer needed to settle for bird deaths,
and the canary outlives his little master, whose death is described
by a series of images passing through Libbie's memory: "of the
fevered moaning slumber of exhaustion; of the pitiful little self-
upbraidings for his own impatience of suffering (only impatience to
his own eyes,—most true and hold patience in the sight of others);
and then the fading away of life, the loss of power, the increased
unconsciousness, the lovely look of angelic peace which followed
the dark shadow on the countenance,—where was he—what was
he now?"

"The rain came down and the floods came up,
The rain came down and the floods came up,
The rain came down and the floods came up,
And the house on the sand went ker-splatt!"

Mind you, of the various people who manipulated dying children in their fiction in the nineteenth century, Elizabeth Gaskell
was one of the ones who actually knew whereof she wrote. Her

only son died at the age of ten months, and she also lost a newborn or two along the way. That did not stop her, as you see above, from buying in most thoroughly to the Victorian ideal of the dying innocent, which perhaps goes to prove that bereaved mothers most of all needed to believe in that angelic peace which claimed their little ones.

"But the smart woman builds her house upon the rock,
The smart woman builds her house upon the rock—"

"Alexander, stop singing that song, right now, or I will tape your mouth shut with Scotch tape."

"If you do that, I will kill you with my gun."

"You don't have a gun."

"Yes, I do, I made one out of my Legos, and I hid it so you don't know where it is."

"Alexander, come lie on my stomach and kiss me on the nose."

"Okay, in one minute. If you will stop reading."

"The dumb woman builds her house upon the moose,
The dumb woman builds her house upon the goose,
The dumb woman builds her house upon the juice—"

"Stop it, Mommy! That's wrong, you're singing it wrong."

"I will stop it as soon as someone kisses me on the nose."

"Well, here I come, so don't sing it anymore. You mixed it up."

Ashleigh Dugan has gone home, and Amelia reminds the resident who sees her in the clinic to bring up the subject of overfeeding yet again at the next visit. They had hoped that with the extra exercise of walking, Ashleigh would stop gaining so much weight, but that hasn't happened. Sara Blake is now subjected to a rigorously implemented feeding program worked out by a behavior-modification specialist; she is fed at set times in a small undecorated room, forced to stay in her high chair until she has consumed the proper amount. All distractions are forbidden, and the feeding is done either by the behaviorist or by one of four specially trained nurses. Sara's parents are not allowed to be in the room at feeding time.

Sara is getting good calories now, finally. This brings Amelia an almost physical relief as she checks the nutrition charts on Sara, seeing how many mouthfuls she has finally, resentfully, taken in, shut up with her nurse in her distraction-free eating environment.

"It must be my ethnic heritage," Amelia says to Greg Murphy, who blinks at her, not understanding, still maybe a little resentful. "I feel better when people are fed," she explains, then gives it up.

Talk about using a child's death as a plot convenience—there's one Elizabeth Gaskell story which is the most egregious example of that I have ever come across. The story I mean is a bizarre little piece of gothic horror called "The Doom of the Griffiths," rather heavy on Welsh background, scenery, names like Glendwr and Augharad. The story is about the curse that is laid on this family, that after nine generations the family will dwindle away and the last male will kill his own father. Now, in order to provide that ninth-generation Griffith with a motive strong enough to make him kill his own father, Mrs. Gaskell goes to the trouble of marrying him off to a village woman too lowborn for said father to approve, and then they have a son, and from the first description, you know this child is in trouble: "The boy . . . was as lovely a child as the fondest parent was ever blessed with, and crowed with delight, and clapped his little hands, as his mother held him in her arms at the cottage door." Poor baby. Sure enough, the father (the Squire) bursts in on the domestic happiness of these three, denounces his son as a fool, the wife as a harlot, the child as some other man's bastard. And then, when this is not enough to bring on the curse, the Squire "snatched the poor infant from the loving arms that held it, and throwing it to his mother, left the house inarticulate with fury." So then the mother, who went by the name of Nest, "opened her arms to receive and cherish her precious babe; but the boy was not destined to reach the white refuge of her breast. The furious action of the Squire had been almost without aim, and the infant fell against a sharp edge of the dresser down on to the stone floor." And what do you know, the plot must go on. Sure enough. The baby's eyes roll and his lips ("yet warm with kissing," Mrs. Gaskell tells us) quiver one last time. And thus the Squire, in his fifteen-minute visit, leaves only death and tragedy behind. "And that poor desolate husband and father! Scarce one little quarter of an hour, and he had been so blessed in his consciousness of love! the bright promise of many years on his infant's face, and the new fresh soul beaming forth in its awakened intelligence. And there it was: the little clay image, that would never more gladden up at the sight of him, nor stretch forth to meet his embrace; whose inarticulate, yet most eloquent cooings might haunt him in his dreams, but would never more be heard in waking life again!"

This makes me so mad. She had no right to use that baby that way. Scarce one little quarter of an hour indeed; she created a happy beautiful bright baby just so she could casually murder him so that, at much greater length and with much more drama, the last Griffith male would have a motive to hunt down and murder his own father. What a waste of a baby. What a cheap way to push the buttons, what an easy way to throw in some easy sentiment. Write a baby, throw a baby, kill a baby. And the worst is that it gets to me. I think it's a real throwaway from the writer's point of view, no pun intended; it comes and goes in a single page, but those lines about the little clay image stay with me, probably with any parent. Scarce one little quarter of an hour. I tried to think about which disasters send parents into the hospital with that sense, that one little quarter of an hour. The toddler who suddenly runs into traffic, or manages to fall out a window? But I'll take a random accident any day over a manufactured plot twist. The children of nineteenth-century literature really ought to strike for safer working conditions.

Amelia lets Greg Murphy explain to the Blakes why they want to do the HIV tests. She sits by quietly while he makes the case, trying to be as reassuring as possible. Because failure to thrive in children is now one of the standard presentations of AIDS. Even if there are no known risk factors in the family, still a good idea to be sure. Get it out of the way and never worry about it again. Can't test a child as young as Sara reliably, so we test you. If the mother's negative, then you know the baby has to be negative.

Amelia herself, mind you, would probably have been less embarrassed, would probably have said to them, straight out, Listen, unless you know for absolute sure that all your sexual partners for the past ten years, and all the sexual partners of your sexual partners, were absolutely risk-free, then there's some small chance. And that includes almost every one of us. So let's not chase down risk factors, let's do the blood test and stop worrying.

"I've had a transfusion," Geraldine Blake says, looking stricken. In fact, both she and her husband look as if the bad news has finally hit. The explanation! The disease! The doctors gave Geraldine a blood transfusion in 1982, when she had an ectopic pregnancy. Obviously, the doctors gave Geraldine AIDS, and she infected Sara, and probably by now the whole family is carrying the virus. Amelia can see the scenario write itself across Frank Blake's face. He is ready to initiate the lawsuit, there and then.

Both parents are eager to have their blood drawn. Geraldine looks sick and guilty, but Frank looks avid. This is it, Amelia thinks of him saying, this is where we prove that I was right and Sullivan was wrong. My little girl is sick, my wife is sick, and it's all someone else's fault. I've been telling them and telling them and telling them. Finally, the right blood test. Finally, the answer.

In the bathroom of a sleazy motel room off Route 1, in the shower stall. Amelia rubs her hands through her curls and imagines the water falling down on Luke's back as he presses her against the cold tile wall, insistently washing her breasts over and over again, till finally she drops down on her knees and takes his penis in her mouth, the shower now cascading over her head, soaking her hair. She can imagine the exact temperature of the water, the exact taste of Luke. And then, no doubt, Anthony Perkins barges into the bathroom with a knife. Sit up straight, Amelia, write up your clinic notes, and go home.

In the car, driving back to Cambridge, she imagines that she and Luke are back in the double bed; she is sitting on top of him, the way the books say to do when you are pregnant, bouncing up and down on him, driving him out of his fucking mind.

The little house that Matt and his partner bought is too small for a family. Two downstairs rooms, two upstairs rooms. A couple could live there, or a single person with money. The house will cost a tremendous amount when Matt and Marco finally put it up for sale—if they ever do. They have been working on the house for over a year, and it is nowhere near done. Will it ever be done, will they ever be able to give it up? It's a late-Victorian gem, built for the spinster daughter of a Harvard philosophy professor—Matt has gone so far as to hunt down his one book, which has not been taken out of the library in eighty years. He was from a good Boston family and had lots of money and apparently built his daughter this little house when it became clear she was not going to marry herself off his hands. She herself was an avid amateur herpetologist and also an insanely productive painter of watercolors, many of reptiles, all quite bad, in what seems to have been the family tradition of earnest but trivial scholarship. But the little house her father built (did she have a hand in the design?) was a monument to late-Victorian ornamentation; there was decorative woodwork everywhere, there were built-in curio cabinets and whatnots, and every room had molding of a different pattern. Unfortunately, after the lady's death in 1926, the house was rented to a series of struggling young academics, then graduate students, and most recently a group of four undergraduates, one to sleep in each room. It got very shabby, and its inmates fixed it up according to their various lights; some vandal, at some point, painted all the wood floors electric blue, others painted the walls and woodwork. When Matt and Marco first saw it there were big holes in the plaster, one ceiling was coming down, and someone had tried to enlarge an existing window by cutting a semicircular hole in the wall above it; the attempt had failed, but the scars remained. Matt and Marco bought it cheap, from the elderly lady who was the original owner's great-niece, who lived in a nice house in Winchester and didn't want to be bothered with collecting the rent anymore.

Amelia runs hot water over the bottom of the goulash tub, the phone squeezed between her ear and her shoulder. Frank Blake showed up at the hospital for his evening visit and found that Sara had actually lost twenty grams. How can this be, if she's getting the right number of calories? You say the scales may not be perfectly accurate—well, for heaven's sake, then the hospital needs new scales. What if she's lost weight again tomorrow? Have you simply given up on my daughter, have you decided that there is nothing wrong with her? Maybe you think it's all in our heads, that she doesn't grow. And by the way, when do you get those AIDS test results back? My poor wife is getting more and more worried about that transfusion. Dr. Stern, just between you and me, what exactly would be the probability that one blood transfusion in 1982 would give you AIDS?

She puts the frozen block of goulash into a pot, turns on the stove, and takes the phone out into the hallway.

Now, if my wife did get AIDS from that transfusion, what would the odds be for our older child? He hasn't had any problem growing, you realize that? Would it be worth bringing him in, though, and getting him tested? And come to think of it, are any of these other diseases things we should worry about in Jonathan? Do we need to have his kidneys looked at, or his heart? I mean, just suppose one of those things really is wrong with Sara, and you guys have just failed to pin it down—shouldn't we be checking out Jonathan?

It is getting harder and harder to get him off the phone. Of course, she generated this particular spate of anxiety, she asked for the HIV test. And it is surely not true, her sense that Frank Blake would rather see his wife and daughter test positive for HIV than continue with the "inadequate caloric intake" diagnosis. He is just an anxious father who likes to be in control, and he has no control at all. She can sympathize, if she really tries.

When he has finally hung up, she goes back into the kitchen. She will make egg noddles to eat with the goulash. She will open a bottle of wine. She will insist that Alexander try at least a little gravy on his noodles, and she will tell him, Your grandmother made this, your Grandma Carol. It's a very special stew, called goulash, and she makes it better than anyone else in the world.

CHAPTER V
NO APPARENT DISTRESS

Amelia calls Roberta Wilson once a week, asks how Darren is doing. Roberta Wilson doesn't really want to talk to her, doesn't really want to be asked questions that remind her of Darren's illness. To be honest, doesn't really want to bring him to the clinic to see his doctor, not even once a month, the compromise she and Amelia settled on between the every two weeks Amelia wanted and the every six months Roberta imagined appropriate. But she brings him; Roberta Wilson, Amelia imagines, has never been five minutes late for a doctor's appointment in her life. It would be rude to keep the doctor waiting, though the doctor often keeps you waiting. Amelia calls once a week, and of course she gets regular reports from the visiting nurse service and the physical therapists.

At Darren's December clinic visit, the first visit after discharge, he has gained a pound and a half. He sits on his grandmother's lap and clings tight around her neck; he has clearly not forgotten Amelia and her hospital, he knows he is in danger. But he looks almost like a well child, clinging so tight, not lying passive in a hospital bed waiting for unnatural things to be done to him. He is trying, weak though he is, to defend himself, which means he has found some hope.

All this Amelia tells herself and obviously wants to believe. She wants to see a spark in Darren's eye, a slight increase in the circumference of his limbs, a vigor in the way he tries to escape when she looks in his ears. And surely all of that is there. His grandmother speaks with pride of his appetite, of how he now sleeps soundly through the night, untroubled by the little aches and the small terrors of the night that at first had him waking and whimpering every couple of hours.

"What about his skin, Doctor?"

"Does anyone else in the family have eczema? Dry skin problems? How about his mother?"

"No, Doctor, no problems with her skin." Remembering the rashes of a small child now grown up and dead.

"Eczema is a very common skin problem, lots of kids have it. It does sometimes seem to be more common in kids with AIDS, though."

Why did I do that? Have I made a resolution that at every appointment I will name the disease once, keep her from being able to forget what Darren's diagnosis is? What a cruel pointless service that would be. If she can deny it all and buy herself even a few weeks, let alone a few months, of pretending he's going to live, whose business is that? I don't want her hypervigilant, after all, do I, the last thing I want is her bringing Darren in to me for every little cough. I already settled this with myself, didn't I, what I want is really for Darren to die at home, to escape another hospitalization. So let her ignore it if he has a little fever or if he breathes a little hard.

UPDATE: Darren is a three-year-old boy with AIDS, status post a prolonged hospitalization for fever of unknown origin and nutritional debilitation. He has been home for almost a month, doing well, though he continues to have problems secondary to poor food intake and generalized weakness. However, he has gained almost eight hundred grams since discharge, and his grandmother reports that his appetite is improving. He has had no intercurrent fevers, upper respiratory symptoms, vomiting. His stools are loose but occur no more often than twice a day. On physical exam, he is a small-for-age somewhat cachectic male, fearful but consolable, in no apparent distress. Examination of his oropharynx revealed normal tonsils and no thrush. His skin exam was notable for dry scaling eczematous patches in his axillae, his elbows, and behind his ears; all bore marks of excoriation. His neck was supple, with pea-sized lymph nodes palpable bilaterally, which is his baseline. His chest exam was normal, with no wheezes, rhonchi, or crackles heard, and his cardiac exam was also normal, with no murmurs. On abdominal exam, his liver was found to be somewhat enlarged, palpable at three to four centimeters below the right costal margin, and his spleen tip was just palpable. Neurologically he is obviously somewhat delayed, but his exam was without notable spasticity. He responded to verbal suggestions from his grandmother and though he did not speak himself, his grandmother reports that he is making two- and three-word sentences at home. In summary, Darren seems to be doing well; both his lymph node swelling and his enlarged liver are old findings. Hydrocortisone cream was prescribed for his eczema, and the possibility of high-calorie supplements was discussed with his grandmother. She prefers to continue a regular diet with him, explaining that his caloric intake has improved steadily since discharge.

So there is this little house that Matt owns, along with Marco, and the two of them like to go over there in the evening and put in a little time on the ridiculously ornate woodwork screen that separates the dining room from the central hallway. A labor of love should not be hurried. Someday they will finish the house, and then, if they can bear to, they will put it up for sale. Disturbingly, Amelia pictures Matt moving out and then moving in to that small house, so perfectly sized for one man who loves Victorian detail, so tenderly restored and polished, so free from all the miseries of home.

What fucking miseries of home? Say what you like about Matt, suspect him of any infidelities you please, but uxorious he is without a doubt.

Amelia comes home from work as Matt and Alexander come in

from day care. Alexander is in tears and his face is smudged and dirty, his voice somewhat weakened, as if he has been crying a long time. He runs to his mother and she gathers him up, enfolds him, hugs and promises and kisses, though wondering cynically if he has turned on the faucets anew at the sight of her in hopes of a fresh wave of sympathy.

Matt explains. Alexander explains too. Brandon cut me with some scissors, here on my finger. The cut, on the one carefully washed finger, white next to the other four brown ones, is minuscule. However, Amelia is very glad to discourage any friendship between her son and Brandon, since she herself dislikes both Brandon and his mother. Therefore she hugs Alexander tight and tells him, "That bad Brandon. He hurt you, so I don't like him, not at all."

"He's very bad," says Alexander, somewhat gratified to be thus passing judgment.

"He's so bad, I don't ever want you to play with him again," says Matt, going a little overboard.

The truth is, for the past couple of months, Mr. and Mrs. Brandon have been calling, inviting Alexander over to play, suggesting that it would be great to get the kids together on the weekend. Matt and Amelia have fought these suggestions unrelentingly, always too busy, always saying with false regret, Well, they'll see each other in day care, anyway. Never telling Alexander, who would probably be perfectly happy to go over to Brandon's house and explore a new hoard of toys.

"I don't ever want to play with Brandon, because he hurt me." Alexander sounds good and smug.

"And besides," says Matt, who doesn't know when to stop, "he's an evil and disgusting child."

"You can go to Jeremy's house again this weekend," Amelia says. "Jeremy is a nice kid."

Most of the kids in the center are nice kids; Brandon is the only one Amelia would actually like to eliminate, along with his parents. Jeremy is Alexander's best friend, but Alexander also gets along well with Nicholas, and for that matter with Emma and Kristen. He is a sociable little boy, after all these years of day care, and

134 • PERRI KLASS

his idea of a really great Saturday afternoon is to be at Jeremy's house, both of them pretending to be the G.I. Joe dolls they are not allowed to have. "G.I. Joe!" they shriek triumphantly, rampaging through the halls with plastic swords and guns, jumping from the fourth step up. "G.I. Joe!"

Jeremy, Amelia knows, is slated to go to the Conservatory School. His mother went there when she was a girl, and has been donating assiduously to the alumni fund ever since Jeremy was born. Brandon will go to public school; his parents live in a house they selected for its proximity to the best Cambridge elementary school. So this year should be the last one that they see anything of Brandon, but maybe, with luck, Alexander and Jeremy could go on together. As long as Alexander gets in, first and foremost, Amelia is happy to hope Jeremy does too.

In other day care center news, it is December, so the annual holiday ethics discussion has to be held. Amelia attends the meeting and sits next to her crush object, and spends the hour storing up details of his physical appearance (his motheaten navy blue shetland sweater, his rumpled gray wool pants) for illicit use later on, rouses herself only when Mr. Emma gets carried away with his anti-Christmas speech.

Every year, every single year, we have to go through this shit. And Mr. Emma is always the ringleader. No Christmas celebrations in the day care center, my precious darling daughter of Israel must not be exposed to Santa Claus, or cookies shaped like Christmas trees, or "Silent Night." "I don't want her to feel like a religious minority."

Matt is the bravest of us all, Matt says what surely everyone is thinking. "Oh, come on," says Matt. "How is she gonna feel like a religious minority when more than half the kids in the center are Jewish? How come half the story books in the center are based on Native American legends, when there isn't a single Indian kid here, and African arts and crafts are totally cool, but Santa Claus is out because it might make one of the Jewish kids feel funny?"

Dead silence. A group of Cambridge academic-professional white upper-middle-class Jews and Protestants, brought face to face with the fact that they are not native Americans. Or something. What Matt says is perfectly true; they are always reading some instructive little children's book to Alexander about Swift Eagle's Big Adventure, or A New Gourd for Ashanti, complete with colorful illustrations that draw on age-old artistic traditions. I don't see why Santa Claus can't get equal time with the Wise Woman of the Iroquois. Alexander is interested in Santa Claus.

Mr. Emma, on the other hand, is obsessed with Santa Claus. Clearly, Mr. Emma believes that if his little flower is exposed to a fat man in a red suit handing out gifts, she will never get those fabulous SAT scores that ought to be her ethnic birthright. Mrs. Mark, a quiet woman who is just a little out of her depth here and rarely speaks up in meetings, is now saying that she had been thinking of baking Christmas cookies for a special project, since Mark always enjoys that so much, but if it would be disturbing to the Jewish children, of course she won't. Another battle fought and won by the self-righteous forces of Raising Children the Right Way.

In Amelia's clinic, the babies mark off the passage of time. Two-week visit, two-month visit, four, six, nine months. Amelia remembers Michael as an exceptionally beautiful newborn baby; now Marcelle brings him in for his two-month checkup, and he looks completely different. Healthy and thriving, but he has lost that downy newborn look, and with it also most of his character; he is a fat little piglet, all chubby thighs and yellow hair and drool. Not one of the baby types Amelia admires, though there are plenty of people to call him cute; he looks like a baby in an ad. No soul to him, really.

But thriving, unquestionably thriving. Amelia plots out his gains in weight, length, head circumference, on the blue-background graph (the pink one is, naturally, for plotting out girls' growth) and shows Marcelle, who has herself made slow progress in the other direction and is today zipped into a pair of blue jeans and a clinging ribbed cotton shirt. See, Marcelle, what a good job you're doing. How he's growing. It's important to reassure teenage mothers, to validate them, to support them, to reinforce them, as the social workers say. Marcelle does not seem particularly interested in the graph, but she is clearly proud of her piglet and handles him competently, his puffy blue snowsuit bundled into a blue baby bag replete with extra bottles and diapers.

Amelia checks him out, and he's fine. He can do the little things that a two-month-old should do—fix and follow, support his head a little—and there's nothing remarkable to see anywhere, except those deep thigh creases, which will blossom forth with heat rash next summer. So she goes and gets a little plastic ampule of pink liquid out of the med-room freezer, fills a tiny syringe with half a cc of DPT vaccine, and marches back in to do the permission-slip routine. Nowadays you have to get informed consent before you give vaccinations. In practice, this means advising parents that there are rare allergic reactions to this and to that, and then, when you get to the DPT shot, you have to tell them about the rare, but not rare enough, side effects. Yes, one child in so many hundred thousand will develop seizures, permanent brain damage. There is no way to smile reassuringly while explaining this. You can gloss it over, just mutter something about rare side effects which needn't concern us now, hand the partially literate parent the form to read—but somehow, even though she thinks it's crazy to terrify every parent this way, Amelia has scruples about this. Informed consent is informed consent, and Marcelle is entitled to the same anxieties that Amelia went through when Alexander got his DPTs.

There sits Marcelle in the little clinic office, listening seriously to all the possible evils she is exposing her chubby son to by signing the consents. Amelia winds up her spiel with the usual, that the dangers of the diseases, diphtheria, pertussis, tetanus, are much greater than the dangers of the vaccine; in England, she tells Marcelle earnestly, they stopped giving the pertussis part of the vaccine because of the side effects, and there was an epidemic of pertussis, whooping cough, and lots of babies died—so it's safer to give the vaccine. Marcelle nods. Actually, this is specious logic; it may make sense from a public health point of view to vaccinate all the babies in America against pertussis. But the odds that Michael will get that disease, living in a country in which most babies are vaccinated, the odds he would die if he did—possibly it would make more survival sense for any individual baby to ride on the herd immunity of the crowd and skip the pertussis shots. Amelia did in fact think about all this when it was Alexander's turn to get the needle, but having set it up that way, she could not let her child tag along as a parasite. Alexander got all his shots. And now Michael will get his. Marcelle signs in big round letters.

Lay the baby down on the examining table. Twist off the little plastic cap of the pink oral polio capsule, squeeze the pink sugar water into his mouth. Good stuff, he swallows it down enthusiastically. Make the usual rueful joke to his mother about how nice it would be if we could give all the vaccines this way. Then swab off his fat thigh with alcohol, grab a pinch full of baby, and jab. Too startled even to cry till the needle comes out, but as Amelia covers the pinhole with a round bandage, Michael gives an outraged scream. Pick him up, Amelia tells Marcelle, give him a bottle, comfort him.

What Alexander is most excited about these days is a spaceship they are building at the day care center out of a refrigerator carton and enormous sheets of silver paper. Amelia stares at it all through the meeting, all through the Santa Claus nonsense. The teachers have hung a hoop of wire from the ceiling, and the silver paper is suspended down from it in a great big cone. There is a little door cut in at the bottom, and the outside is decorated with construction-paper stars and planets made by the children. Except for Saturn, of course, it's hard to tell one planet from another, especially as represented by a lopsided circle of blue paper embellished with crayon stripes, so the teachers have labeled them, Mars by Kristen, Venus by Jeremy, Pluto by Emma. Alexander himself goes in for comets, carefully cut out of red paper with details done in black; there are several on the spaceship, and they look a little like big red spermatozoa. Every day, at morning drop-off and afternoon pickup, Alexander drags his parents over to see the spaceship, the new additions, the space map inside, the space helmets being constructed from supermarket paper bags. And, of course, his comets. They can never be admired too much.

Alexander has never been particularly interested in space before, but he can now recite the planets in their correct order, and he sings an irritating little song about blasting off and counting down. The song ends with a countdown, ten, nine, eight, seven, six, five, four, three, two, one, and then a "Blast off!" shouted as loud as possible. Amelia can remember staying up unusually late one night to watch Neil Armstrong walk on the moon. He said, "That's one small step for a man, one giant leap for mankind," and then after a little while the announcer came back on, and her mother said it was time for bed. Amelia waited for one of her parents to say something else, something that would recognize the momentousness of the occasion, but all they did was begin to joke about what were the other possible lines NASA had rejected for Armstrong to say. Hey, it's made of green cheese! Hello, down there! Hey diddle diddle. Amelia suggested he could just have said, "Well, here I am on the moon." Then she was sent to bed and in September in school raised her hand along with all her classmates when the teacher asked who had stayed up and watched the moonwalk.

The moving force behind the space program at Alexander's day care center is Amelia's favorite of the teachers, Doree. Doree looks like everyone's perfect day care teacher, tall and balletic and slim with long blond hair ponytailed down her back and Ivory Soap-ad skin. But she is the least politically correct of any of the teachers; she lives, she has confessed to Matt, on potato chips and 3 Musketeers bars, and she has a streak of physical rough-and-tumble about her that makes her the focus of all the most frenetic activity in the room. Out in the yard, one of the other teachers will be leading a docile group of children in a game of Mother, may I, but Doree will be the center of a brutal game of freeze tag, screaming in triumph as she unfreezes one child after another, taunting whoever is It to come and get her, he can't get her, he'll never get her. Alexander's usual greeting, when he sees Doree, is to take a running leap at her and cling on as long as he can, legs locked round her waist, hands clutching her shoulders. And Doree will buck around and pretend to knock him against the wall and wriggle her shoulders till he gives up and slides down to the floor. Doree has no ax to grind, no message to teach, no interest, if it comes to that, in child development. Doree, in the tradition of all brilliant teachers, seems to be a child herself, a four-year-old; she thinks their jokes are funny and their stories are interesting and their games are worth playing for hours on end. When Amelia and Matt talk about schools for next year, what one of them always says is But how can we leave Doree?

So now Doree is the space lady, and Doree is the one who found the luminescent paint so they could put glow-in-the-dark stars on the wall near the spaceship and then pull down all the shades and admire the glow, and Doree is the one who is helping them braid long ropes out of yarn to attach the astronauts to the rocket ship when they go on space walks.

I am no longer used to staying up all night. When I was a resident, I took for granted that certain nights you didn't sleep, you stayed on your feet. When I was a resident, I knew, I think, the hour-by-hour progress that fatigue made through my mind and my body: now it is ten o'clock, and if I eat supper I can keep going strong; now it is twelve but I'm on my feet and steady; now it is two and there is an emergency and I'm thinking straight; now it's three and the low point and I fall asleep over my notes, slump down onto the table, and the nurses take pity on me, so nothing wakes me till I jerk up, suddenly, with a pain in the side of my neck and my arms clammy from the tabletop Formica, not refreshed, a sick taste in my mouth. Wash my face, brush my teeth, and if I still have things to do, drink a cup of coffee with lots of sugar, for caffeine and energy and comfort, and go back to my work, somewhat refreshed, but now with that underlying buzz in my brain, telling me that I am crossing over the edge. Five o'clock and physical weariness takes over, not standing up anymore, feet hurting, moving slow. And then after six the tempo building till the new day officially begins at eight, with fresh new people, recently asleep between sheets, and me rumpled and dirty and eager to mumble my way through and let them take over. Nobody likes staying up all night, but I did it often enough, as did we all, and as I say, I was used to it. It was a fact of my life. But now every couple of months when my night in the emergency room rolls around, I feel my whole body protesting, How can anyone expect me to do this? *Me?*

The truth is, though, that while I grumble about this required ER duty, just like all the rest of the pediatric attendings who are pressed into service, I also secretly look forward to it—and so do most of the others, I suspect. They don't have to do this over at Harvard, we mutter. But actually, I like being reminded of what I know, I like the change in the tempo of my life—sometimes I even find myself pretending that I am still a resident, still on the front lines, that my life is without big choices, locked into a schedule too tight for luxuries. So I do my one night of student supervision in the ER like a stockbroker on a weekend camping trip, pretending to belong.

Usually, my job is fairly gentle. I supervise the medical students, help the interns if they need it, make myself available to see sick patients if things are really busy. The emergency room attending who runs the place usually goes to bed by two, and if things are quiet, that's what I do too, in the top bunk.

Sure enough, Mrs. Brandon calls again, Thursday night: Brandon was hoping maybe Alexander could come over this Saturday; he has some new video games he thinks Alexander would just love. No, says Amelia, firmly; I have to work all Friday night in the emergency room, so Saturday will be our family time. Mrs. Brandon bows to the importance of family time. Before she can suggest Sunday, Amelia hangs up, then wishes she had said, Besides, your loathsome little boy cut my son with scissors, and we hate him.

Alexander thinks that next Halloween, on balance, he might be a knight instead of a pirate. With confidence he tells me, You could make me leg armor and arm armor, and I could wear my sword in its scabbard, and I'll put my mace in my belt and in one hand I'll carry my battle-ax, and in the other hand I will carry a spear, you could make the spear because I don't have one, and I'll put my bow and arrows over my shoulder.

"How will you be able to use the sword if you're carrying other weapons in both hands?" I ask.

Alexander tells me patronizingly, I would use the spear to kill someone, and then when it was sticking in the bad guy, I would grab my sword.

A year ago, shortly after Matt and Marco had bought the little house, Matt brought Amelia over to see it one Sunday afternoon when Alexander was at the Children's Museum with a set of visiting grandparents. The house was dark and dusty, and the electric lights didn't work properly; Matt used a big strong flashlight to show her, the hideous electric blue of the floors, the gaps and crevices in the plaster. As his light moved across the abused walls, the blotched moldings, Amelia found herself frightened, as if her own protective shell were threatened. A house should stand strong against the world and protect its inhabitants; when it is gouged out from the inside, it is hard not to feel betrayed, unsafe, exposed. There were cobwebs floating from the ceilings, and dim unidentifiable bits of debris in the corners, and though the afternoon sun outside the windows was bright enough, Amelia felt she did not like the house, it was neglected and abused, and dead past resurrecting.

Matt was alive with the excitement of owning it, of showing her exactly where they would strip the paint, where they would rebuild the damaged cabinetry that had once lined the living room, replace the glass in the built-in china closet. The window frames and door frames were true mahogany here on the first floor, upstairs they were oak. Stripped and refinished and polished, each window would be a jewel, glass in a gleaming precious setting. Amelia, trying her best to be enthusiastic, followed him up the curved staircase, not wanting to see the upstairs rooms, thinking, in spite of her best intentions, of all the money that had gone to purchase this creepy piece of property, Matt's money, her money, Alexander's money.

The first upstairs room was the worst of all. Something had happened to the floor, so instead of the painted boards in the rest of the house, there was only an underlayer, beams and clumsily laid sheets of balsa wood. This was also the room with the hole in the wall, some vandal's attempt to enlarge the window. The ceiling dipped downward at the center, as though the walls of the room had been crushed together, and large flakes of plaster had chipped off, leaving a moon surface of craters and canals. The room smelled of mildew, and perhaps of something worse: rodents, or long-abandoned garbage, or just malignant decay. Amelia looked around the room and knew absolutely that no matter how it was cleaned and repaired and restored, she would never want to spend time in there. She shuddered and would not step on the ravaged floor, breathed through her mouth to keep the smell away.

It was that, the breathing through her mouth, which made her think suddenly of her own work, of the way she automatically shut her nose when she came close to a patient who was vomiting, or who was having diarrhea. She imagined herself leading Matt through a nightmare hospital tour, the smells and sights hitting him, room after room, without respite. He would hate it, he would be repelled and not the least bit fascinated. But was there in fact some hidden parallel? Never before had she looked at his work and considered the possibility that he was moved by some desire to heal wounds. And thinking of it again later on that day, she found the whole idea farfetched and foolish; repairing broken woodwork and repairing damaged bodies were not actually at all alike. But for a few minutes in that horrible room it seemed to Amelia she had grasped some serious truth, some connection hitherto unnoticed but essential, between Matt and herself. And as she tried to absorb the magnitude of this truth, as she breathed through her mouth and drew her body in tight, avoiding any brush against the doorframe, the walls, Matt took her hand and led her to the other upstairs room.

I arrived in the ER to find, to my displeasure, that the medical students were brand-new. They would require a lot of supervision, and they would ask the kind of naïve questions that would be hard to answer, and also the procedural questions that would slow everything down: how to stamp up labels, fill in lab requests, package specimens. There were two of them, eager to please in bright white jackets, pockets loaded with file cards and reflex hammers, pens and penlights, and those dense little manuals that promise to distill all medical wisdom into one pocket-sized reference—a reference that distends your silhouette, weighs down your jacket, but does indisputably fit into your pocket.

One was named Jasper Greenberg, formal in oxford shirt and tie, but a little blowsy, a little overweight. He had tightly curled blond hair and adolescent skin, and his nervousness was visible. His partner was Mark Gifford, and I wondered whether the two of them were alphabetically paired to wander together all through medical school. Mark was tall and jocky-looking, with big shoulders and an air of some self-confidence, whether because he knew what he was doing, or because he didn't care what I thought of him. I looked at him and thought, orthopedic surgeon, and as it turned out, I was right, that's what he was going to be. When I had my friendly little talk with them about what clinical work they'd done, and what they wanted to do, and how they were liking the third year of medical school, Mark informed me that he'd planned to be an orthopod ever since college. Jasper said he still didn't know, added nervously that he'd liked everything he'd done, was still making up his mind. Maybe pediatrics, he said, then seemed abashed; one popular medical-student sucking-up trick involves telling the pediatricians you're going to be a pediatrician, telling the surgeons you're thinking about surgery, et cetera, and he must have thought I suspected him of that particular childish behavior.

I went over the ER forms with them, but it turned out that had already been done; they had had a full orientation. So I checked the master board, where patient names were listed as the patients were put into examining rooms, and I found them each a nice straightforward not-very-sick child and sent them off to do their stuff, then retreated to the doctors' desk and sat down to wait. Your average third-year medical student takes a good forty-five minutes to do even the most straightforward medical history and physical, and though any doctor in the place could have done these patients in a third of that time, I didn't really worry that the children or their parents would mind. People mind waiting, in the waiting room, in the examining room. They don't mind a lot of protracted medical attention. As I thumbed through a bedraggled reprint on hydrocarbon poisoning that happened to be lying on the desk, I noticed that Christine was one of the interns working that night, and we greeted each other. I told her I'd seen Darren in clinic, that he was doing well at home, and she told me she was glad. I remarked that it seemed to be a slow evening in the ER, and she agreed, continuing to fill out her forms. We would later refer to that night as Hell night.

Amelia is rarely angry at Matt about Alexander; lately, though, she has been noticing, repeatedly, and always with irritation, that Matt is pushing Alexander, more and more, toward adult things, adult stories, adult conversation. Matt is easily bored; he likes some of the classic children's books, he likes the full-length Disney cartoons—but he would rather not go over and over *Bread and Jam for Frances,* or play the record of *Mary Poppins* five times straight. Here he has this intelligent child, almost five, eager to please and eager to understand anything thrown his way, so Matt has begun introducing real books, real music. Alexander has been hearing opera plots as bedtime stories, and no question, Matt shows patience and imagination as he plays selections from the record albums and carefully answers one question after another. And Alexander enjoys it too. But still, Amelia finds herself resenting it a little on his behalf; instead of relaxing and enjoying a familiar picture book, a story he can understand, told in words he knows well, with a comforting resolution, Alexander is performing for his father's approval, trying hard to keep up with jealousy and murder and betrayal, not to mention gods and goddesses, not to mention the different voices. Amelia will hear Matt playing the beginning of an aria, hear his voice asking, now, what kind of singer is that, and hear, or at least imagine, the anxiety in Alexander's voice when he answers, that's a soprano. And the relief on his face when Matt tells him, yes, very good.

Or Bulfinch. Alexander is suddenly interested in the Greek myths, which he persists in calling the Greek Smiths, and Amelia meant to go look for some large illustrated children's book to read him—she is just as eager for educational materials as Matt, really, she supposes, just a little more willing to pitch them lower. Anyway, Matt went out and got him *Bulfinch's Mythology* and has been reading through it with him, Hero and Leander, Ceyx and

Halcyone, as well as Hercules and Apollo and Theseus. And the language! Matt does not believe in simplifying, preferring, bravely enough, to read straight through and then answer questions, and so at story hour Amelia will overhear the death of Orpheus at the hands of the maidens of Thrace, inflamed by the rites of Bacchus: "The maniacs tore him limb from limb, and threw his head and his lyre into the river Hebrus, down which they floated, murmuring sad music, to which the shores responded a plaintive symphony." When Amelia reads the occasional chapter from Bulfinch at Alexander's request (he does seem interested), she cheats, smooths out unduly complicated sentences, reshapes the story slightly so her son can listen and understand. Which makes Matt the purist, the academic, and Amelia the adulterator, unwilling to trust her son to handle the real stuff.

Mark Gifford emerges relatively promptly from the examining room, reports a relatively straightforward history, tentatively suggests a diagnosis. Streptococcal pharyngitis, he says, and Amelia agrees that it seems likely, then goes back in the room with him, examines the child hastily, shows him how to take a throat swab, then how to label it, package it, fill in the slip, send it to the microbiology lab for strep culture. Laboriously, he writes out a prescription for two days of penicillin, and Amelia checks the dosage and signs it, and then sends him back to explain to the mother that if the strep culture is positive, the hospital will call, and the prescription will have to be extended for ten days; if the culture is negative, however, the sore throat is probably viral and the child can stop the antibiotics in two days.

Jasper Greenberg comes out a little later, flustered and frustrated by his own inability to see into a sixteen-month-old's ears and make the diagnosis of ear infection, which the child's mother has already made. "She says whenever he has trouble sleeping and pulls at his ear and gets cranky and has fever, it's always the same thing."

"Sounds like an ear infection," Amelia says, and leads both students back in, assigns muscular Mark to help the mother hold the child down, and then finds herself staring through her otoscope into a wad of earwax. Cleans it out carefully with one of the wire cotton-tipped swabs, the child's screams escalating, then presses the little black funnel back into the ear canal, finally, looking around more cliffs and crags of wax, gets a partial view of the eardrum. Which is bright red, no surprise, the way this child is screaming. But which does seem to be bulging out—Amelia has Jasper look through her scope, squeeze the little red bulb to blow air at the drum. He agrees, it doesn't seem to move the way it should—though she knows how hard that is to tell on a screaming squirming child. Resolutely, Amelia has the two medical students switch places and gives Mark a chance to look at the other eardrum, grateful that she doesn't have to dig the wax out of this ear too, another red drum, another probably infected ear. The eardrum, the tympanic membrane, is one of the body's secret places; you don't have to cut someone open to see it, the way you have to in order to see truly internal organs, but you have to pull on the earlobe, straighten out the curves of the ear canal, poke past the wax, to shine your light on that tiny hidden cave, that pearly lagoon. Compare it with the cervix, perhaps, or with the inside of the eye, other hidden destinations that doctors routinely pursue with their bright lights.

Poor Jasper came to grief on his second patient. I had seen only the nurse's note that it was an upper respiratory infection in a two-year-old, and the nurse had checked off "non-urgent" on the triage sheet, so I figured the kid wasn't too sick. Then I did wonder why Jasper was taking an hour to see a child with what his mother would have called a cold. In the meantime, Mark saw two more kids, one with a sprained ankle, whom we sent up for an x-ray and then taught how to do an ace wrap—this, after all, was right up Mark's future alley, and he had a good time teaching the boy how to maneuver on crutches. The other was a five-month-old with very mild diarrhea, and a fifteen-year-old mother who required a great deal of reassurance; Mark was less sure of himself here, and kept looking to me to provide absolute answers—how many bottles of what does the child have to drink, how many bowel movements a day would be cause for alarm.

Then Jasper emerged and "presented" the child with the URI to me in unbelievable detail, following all the forms: the age, the weight, the height, every detail of every sniffle. "Four days prior to this emergency-room visit, the mother first noted some slightly increased congestion, worsening in the evening. There was no associated rhinorrhea or cough, and no other symptoms at that time, including no fever, no vomiting, no diarrhea. The cough developed three days prior to this visit, and is described as dry, not productive of sputum." And on and on. And all I could think was here is this young man of normal intelligence, and his brain has been so bent out of shape that he is not capable of saying, "The kid has a cold." And really, when you come right down to it, it's kind of sweet that this activity, seeing patients, has such impact, such power to rattle him. I mean, here's this boy who's already spent two and a half years in medical school, taken a dead body apart piece by piece, day by day, busted his balls memorizing volumes of largely useless information. He could probably reel off the signs and symptoms of the major types of endocrine tumors without any trouble at all. And yet you throw him into a room where there is a toddler with a cold, a real live child with a real live mother, and his reason deserts him with a whoosh. He clutched his clipboard, the top sheet covered with minute chicken-scratch notes answering every question he had thought to ask. He told me which formula the child had fed on till the age of one, and he told me that the family history was negative for childhood deaths and disabilities, as well as for genetically transmitted diseases, and I swear to God, he told me that both maternal grandparents were alive and well, but the paternal grandfather suffered from hypertension and the paternal grandmother had died of stomach cancer. For a kid with a cold! But really, wasn't it touching that Jasper was so rattled by real live contact with patients; he had not yet lost his awe. In his obsessive attempt to capture every detail that might bear on this ordinary story you could still see some of the primitive power of the role he was being trained to play.

Anyway, he finally finished his dissertation and summed it all up: two-year-old female with upper respiratory infection, possibly with some reactive bronchospastic component, presenting now with mild exacerbation of symptoms. I nodded at him, too exhausted by his thoroughness even to comment, and let him lead me back into the examining cubicle. There sat a very large woman wearing a shamrock-green sweatsuit. Her straw-blond hair was braided into two tight braids, hanging down her front to the top of her massive bosom, and she wore thick glasses with heavy black rims. She was reading a Little Golden Book aloud to her daughter, who lay quietly on the examining table, wearing only a paper diaper.

To tell you the truth, I thought at first that Jasper had taken me into the wrong room. I looked at the little girl on the table, and my first guess was, wrong kid, wrong room, sorry, let's get out of here. But there was Jasper, introducing me with all due ceremony, "Mrs. Biedermeyer, I'd like you to meet the doctor who's supervising me this evening . . ."

Jasper and Mrs. Biedermeyer were looking at me expectantly. I heard my own voice. "Just how premature was the baby?" I asked.

"She was born twenty-eight weeks," her mother answered in a disconcertingly deep and beautiful voice.

I looked again at the little girl on the bed, the one Jasper had heard about and looked at for an hour. She was, first of all, way too small to be a two-year-old; a scrawny one-year-old would have been more like it. She was markedly dolicocephalic, which means her head was almost square, flattened especially in the back. The slang term for this in the hospital is "toaster-headed," and you see it in kids who were born severely premature. And she was pale as death, and her skinny little chest was adorned with at least four different surgical scars, and from the door, I could hear her wheezing.

I took the rest of the history: She spent a long time on the ventilator, didn't she? I asked. (Almost two months.) She had a problem with her heart, didn't she? (Yes, she had surgery to close a hole in her heart when she was two weeks old.) She had to have a couple of central lines, didn't she? (Yes, but the last one came out almost three months ago.) I found out about the year she had spent at home using supplemental oxygen after she finally left the newborn intensive care unit, and about the various medicines she had been on at home—diuretics, antiasthma medications. I found out about the time she had the unexplained blue spell while riding in the car and had to be rushed to the hospital and resuscitated. I found out about the endless struggle to get her to grow. And all the while Jasper stood there and listened, and the poor boy was actually turning red before my eyes.

Mrs. Biedermeyer was what we call an excellent historian. Most of the mothers of these chronically ill kids are professionals at this; they can tell you date and time and symptoms and medication changes. They can tell you what mistakes the doctors made and which time the kid got sick and the doctor didn't pay attention till it was almost too late, and so on and so on. Mrs. Biedermeyer kept on stroking her daughter's little toaster head and reeled off any data I might happen to ask for. And I had to wonder: had she been deliberately putting Jasper on? Maybe she was pissed off to be seen by a medical student; she understood the hierarchy as well as any of us. Maybe she took a private vow that unless he specifically asked her, she wasn't going to volunteer any of the information that would keep him from making a fool of himself. Or again, maybe he had just been so thick and so caught up in his own list of questions, so unable to see what was in front of his nose—maybe she assumed he could see everything I could see. Who knows.

So I took the poor shmuck back out of the room. Even his ears were bright red. I couldn't exactly think how to begin, but he plunged right in. "Guess I missed a few things, huh?" he said, but he sounded ready to cry. I took him back to the doctors' desk and, without looking him in the eye, began a dry little disquisition on BPD, bronchopulmonary dysplasia, a lung disease that is seen in former premies who have spent a lot of time on the ventilator. They end up with chronic lung problems, lungs like eighty-year-old chain-smokers, they need oxygen and all kinds of medications, they don't grow well because they have increased metabolic needs. And on and on. Jasper began taking notes on what I was saying. Finally, I sent him off to send the little Biedermeyer girl for a chest x-ray, since her medical history put her at increased risk for pneumonia. I told him to have the nurse check her oxygen saturation before she went upstairs. Then I looked at his demolished face, and I said to him, "Probably you're right—it's probably just a mild cold.

She doesn't look like she's in severe distress, and Mom says she wheezes like this all the time. We're probably just going to change her wheezing meds around and and send her out. But because of her history—"

"Yes," he said. "Yes, I understand. I just didn't think about some of the things, I guess—I mean, thank you for teaching me all this." And he shuffled off, moving fast, but I saw him duck into the patient bathroom on his way to get the x-ray requisition, and I had no doubt he had made it only just in time. A perfect evening. The medical student was crying in the bathroom, and I felt guilty and irritated. What I had really wanted to say to Jasper, to tell you the truth, was something like, if your mother had spent two minutes looking at that little girl, she would have known something was wrong. She might not have known what, but she would have known she wasn't looking at a normal two-year-old. But what's the point of reminding medical students that most of their mothers know more pediatrics than they do? It just undermines all that knowledge they have so earnestly crammed in. Besides, who knows, some of them may have very dumb mothers.

This is Alexander, listening to the Greek myths, lying face down on his half of the couch, kicking rhythmically against the padded arm, while Matt reads aloud the story of King Midas. Bacchus, the deity who grants Midas his power of turning things to gold, is already a familiar character, Matt reminds Alexander, and the child agrees. "The god of wine," he says, and starts to laugh. "The fat god with the grapes in his hair."

"One day I will put grapes in your hair," Matt tells him.

Midas gets his golden touch from Bacchus and then finds he can neither eat nor drink. "What do you think happens when he tries?" Matt asks.

"It turns to gold! And nobody can eat gold because it's too hard!"

"Right. 'Then he found to his dismay that whether he touched bread, it hardened in his hand; or put a morsel to his lip, it defied his teeth.' That means just what you said, it was too hard for his teeth to bite. 'He took a glass of wine, but it flowed down his throat like melted gold.'"

"Is King Midas immortal or just a king?"

"He's just a king." Matt has been over this and over this; the thing that fascinates Alexander most about the Greek myths is this idea of the immortals, of immortality. It fits in perfectly with his recent interest in death, in who will die and when. Occasionally, he mentions to his parents, "You will die before I do, because you are older," and they always agree, and then always add, automatically trying to reassure him, "But we won't die for a long time, not till you are all grown up." But though Alexander seems mildly gratified by this information, it is not what he is really fishing for. We might as well save our breath, it has occurred to Amelia; he is just trying to put the world in order, to apply what he is trying to understand. Who is older, who will die first.

"And kings are not the same as gods, and only gods are the immortals."

"Right."

"So King Midas will die," says Alexander, with satisfaction.

While I sat at the desk, while Jasper cried in the bathroom, while Mrs. Biedermeyer waited for someone to come tell her something intelligent about her daughter, I got paged. Matt calling to say, Alexander doesn't feel too well, I think he maybe has a little fever. He had not, of course, taken Alexander's temperature—part of his total abdication from all things medical is that Matt doesn't take temperatures, doesn't look in throats, doesn't apply Band-Aids. That is all my prerogative, because I am the doctor. Or perhaps it would be fairer to say that when Matt rejected the profession for which he had been groomed, he rejected it totally, and he is still wary that it will sneak up behind him and claim him, and he will engage in no activity that might make him look even a little bit like a doctor—but that's ridiculous; if he took his son's temperature, all he would look like would be a parent.

I'm sorry. This irritates me, obviously. Also, it made me a little anxious to get the call saying Alexander didn't feel well, and to know that Matt would refuse to do more than the minimum by way of medical care. I mean, it's not so much that I worried that Alexander would suffer; I know Matt would never do anything to endanger him. But it made me feel (here comes the word) guilty as all hell to be there in the ER, taking care of other women's children (did I mean the little Biedermeyer girl or the medical students?) while at home my own was ill without me. And I suspected Matt of wanting to make me feel exactly that way, and I felt his refusal to perform as any other routine parent would during a routine minor illness was designed to make me feel even worse. And I even allowed myself an evil suspicion that the whole thing was a setup, that Alexander was just tired and cranky with a slightly warm forehead, which no one would have noticed if I had been home, but that this was some demonstration that Matt resented my working all night, even if it happened only once every couple of months, that he hadn't forgiven me for the years of working all night every third night. All of which explains why guilty is my least favorite state, why I hate to hear other people analyze their guilts, or turn over any of those stones in my own subconscious. I'm sorry. I'll stop.

I suggested to Matt that he take the temperature, told him where the thermometers and the petroleum jelly were, told him how many junior Tylenol to give Alexander if he did have fever, reminded him about lots of liquids, suggested a nice long bath and an early bedtime. Then I saw the doctor in charge of the ER heading straight for me, looking like he meant business, and I told Matt I had to go, and hung up before he could get in any licks.

All hell is about to break loose, the ER doctor tells Amelia, looking, of course, quite pleased at the prospect. His name is Dave Dwyer, and like all ER doctors, he lives for the crisis. And now he has two coming in at once, he's just had a call about a bad car accident with two badly injured children; the ambulances will be here in less than five minutes. No problem, he loves major trauma; he actually says this, running a hand through his thinning red curls; he looks lit-up and happy as a chipmunk. The only thing is, one of the residents went home sick. So he'll handle one kid himself, and his junior resident will handle another, no problem, but also, the triage nurse just let him know there's a kid out at the triage desk who might also be serious, so if Amelia would just oversee that case, he'd really appreciate it. What's wrong with the kid? Amelia asks, getting to her feet, but Dave Dwyer is off to assemble his trauma teams, and just calls over his shoulder that she can have room 16. So Amelia recruits Christine, tells her to finish up with whoever she's seeing and then come help in 16, and just as Amelia gets to the door, in comes the child, and the parents, and the triage nurse, and two other nurses. The father is clutching the child, who looks about three years old and is crying loudly. The father, however, is making even louder noises, he is almost keening, moaning from some deep agony of soul. He is a tall, well-built man, wearing a puffy blue ski parka, and the child is wrapped in a quilt. The mother, who is small and slight and not wearing any coat at all, stands pressed against the wall of the room, her hand to her mouth. The three nurses are all trying to get the child away from the father, and he will not release her.

"Hello," says Amelia, trying hard for professionalism (thinking, the child is crying so therefore the child is breathing, so what the fuck is going on here), "I'm Dr. Stern. Can you let me know what's going on?"

The triage nurse says, rapid-fire, "Twenty-eight-month-old girl fell from second-story window landed on sidewalk not sure whether hit head or not brought here in cab by parents no apparent distress but they wouldn't really let me check her vital signs."

The father suddenly interrupts his moaning to shout, at the mother, "There's the drunk bitch let her fall out! I'm gonna kill that woman if anything happens to my little girl!"

"Why don't you put her down on the table so I can take a good look at her?" says Amelia. "I can't tell from here whether she's hurt or not." Then louder, "Sir, please put your daughter down on the table!"

Whether because she's a doctor or because she's getting louder or because he wants to go kill his wife, he does put the child down. Immediately Amelia and the two nurses swarm all over her; they snap a cervical collar around her neck, they restrain her arms and legs.

"What the fuck are you doing?" screams the father, pushing in beside Amelia; one of the nurses has taken out a large pair of shears and is cutting off the child's shirt. The little girl is crying and struggling, the father's breath is strongly scented with alcohol, and as she turns to the triage nurse and says, softly, Please call security, Amelia is thinking, Oh, fuck you, Dave Dwyer.

"What is her name, please?" Amelia says to the father.

Tiffany, of course. The year that all little black girls were named Keisha, all little white girls were named Tiffany.

"Tiffany," says Amelia, "Tiffany, it's going to be okay. We just have to check you out." Then, changing tone, "Sir, I have to ask you to let us examine her. We need to keep this collar on her and keep her from moving till we're sure she doesn't have any injury to her neck. And we also need to check her heart and her blood pressure and make sure there isn't any bleeding anywhere. Please step back from the bed and let us do what we need to do." And where the fuck is security? Suppose this guy had a gun, where would I be then, waiting for them to finish their coffee?

But thank heavens the father has turned to threaten the mother: "You hear that, she might have a neck injury, she might be bleeding, you careless bitch!" And while Amelia hopes very much that he does not in fact try to kill his wife, it at least leaves her free to help the nurses get the child plugged in, make sure nothing terrible is going on. A fall from a second-story window is no joke; she could have a broken neck, a fractured skull, a lacerated liver—you name it. Right now she looks fine, probably she is fine (two-year-olds are fairly indestructible, and a good thing, too), but no point in hanging around waiting for internal bleeding to send her into shock, or for a head bleed to start showing up as mental status changes.

Two security guards have joined the party and are talking with the father, who sounds angry, but calm. Calm enough, at any rate, so that Amelia can't hear what he's actually saying over the child's cries and her own conversation with the nurses. Amelia has looked Tiffany over now, quickly. A couple of bad bruises on her thighs and a laceration on her right arm, snot all over her face from crying. Amelia wipes it off and sees a fat little face, contorted in screams. No broken bones that she can feel, no obvious distension in the abdomen. It's hard to get a good look in her eyes, since she is not interested in cooperating, but her pupils are equal-sized and both constrict when the flashlight hits them. So far so good.

Amelia wraps a tourniquet around the fat little arm; she intends to put in an IV and draw off some blood; the blood will go for tests to check for internal bleeding and also to the blood bank so they can check for type. If Tiffany needs a transfusion, everything will be ready, if she needs any medicines or fluids, the IV will be in. One of the nurses steadies the arm, Amelia swabs with alcohol and jabs the needle in. Tiffany does her best to scream louder. Amelia is going for one of the big antecubital veins, but in this little chubbette even those are hard to find, and she has to feel her way carefully. There does seem to be a good-sized vein in there, under the cushioning, but it's rolling. Finally she gets it stabilized between her fingers, slides the needle forward gently at a very shallow angle, has the satisfaction of seeing red flash back into the hub. Stops the needle, advances the plastic IV over the needle into the vein, hooks up her syringe and begins to pull back and fill it with blood, while the nurse tapes in the IV. And feels her shoulder grabbed roughly from behind, lurches back, dropping the syringe.

"What the fuck are you doing to my little girl, you bitch, you goddam bitch!" Amelia is shoved toward the wall, Tiffany's father balling up his fist, ready to punch. The security guards grab his arms, restraining him between them, but barely. Amelia, who is not hurt, leans back against the wall, wondering if he will break away and hit her, wondering whether she should run while she has the chance, wondering why she doesn't, why she says instead, shaky but still authoritarian, "Sir, your daughter needs an intravenous line in case we have to give her fluids or medications. And I was drawing her blood so she wouldn't get stuck more than once. But I can't take care of her if you go on interfering like this." She is very aware of his alcoholic breath, of the largeness and the nearness of him. He has the face of an athlete gone to seed, a big blond man turning red-eyed and jowly and piggish. Turning, but not turned; he is still big rather than fat, young rather than middle-aged.

"The IV's out," calls one of the nurses, "it got pulled out when he grabbed you."

"Now see what you've done," Amelia lectures the father. What is she, crazy? "Now I'm going to have to do it again. You're making everything much worse for Tiffany." She sees, with relief, that two more security guards have arrived, one of them downright enormous. Surely with four of them they can restrain one drunk father. The father has crumpled to his knees, his arms still clumsily up in the grasp of the guards. He is weeping noisily. "I just want my little girl to be all right."

"I know, sir, and we're just trying to make sure she is all right. We need to do our job, and you need to let us do our job."

Christine has arrived; Amelia mouths at her, "IV!" When Christine doesn't seem to understand, Amelia makes a gesture of starting one in her own antecubital and Christine nods, goes to the bed, where the nurses tell her in whispers what is going on.

"That fucking bitch over there, her mother, she didn't watch the baby careful enough. I'm outside in the street, you know, talking to someone, and that bitch opens the window and yells down at me, and then she goes away to get me something I want, and the next thing I know my little baby comes falling out the window."

"How did she land?" asks Amelia. "Did she land on her head?"

"Fuck, lady, I don't know. My little baby girl falls out a window and you expect me to be watching to see how she lands? I didn't even know what it was fell out, it was so dark, till I hear this sound and there she is on the sidewalk. Truth, lady, I thought first it was something that my wife threw out to me, being as she was all pissed at me, I thought, well, maybe it was a bag of my clothes, like, go away and don't come back, you know what I mean? Truth, just in that second before she hit and I found out what it was, I was thinking, Well, I'll just take my clothes and go somewhere else. I was thinking, I'll show her who needs her and her yelling and that fucking apartment, and I hope she put in my pajamas, being as she knows I don't sleep unless I have my pajamas—all that in just the time it took my little girl to fall."

"Did she cry right away when she hit the sidewalk?" asks Amelia.

"I think so. I grabbed her right up, and I think she was already crying."

"So she didn't lose consciousness, she wasn't blacked out?"

"If that bitch had been watching her carefully she wouldn't have fallen out at all!"

As his tone becomes less tearful and more angry, the security guards pull him to his feet and, in a phalanx of four, escort him from the room. Amelia joins Christine at the bedside; the IV is now securely taped into the other antecubital, with fluid dripping steadily in, and Tiffany has calmed down a little. Amelia beckons the mother to the bed, encourages her to stroke the little girl's forehead, talk to her, sing to her. The mother looks about fourteen, with little stick arms and legs and no bosom whatsoever, her hair an elaborate bush of curls and tendrils, brown with gold frosting at the edges, but when you look at her face, you can see she's no teenager. She looks tired and worn and a little bit soggy, like damp wrinkled cardboard. But she whispers quietly to her daughter, and Tiffany listens. The mother does not look anyone in the eye, not the doctors, not the nurses, not even the child. Is she ashamed, ashamed because of the way her husband is acting, ashamed because she feels guilty that the child fell? Is she actually drunk too? She doesn't seem to be. Or is she simply closed off from them all, protecting herself as best she can, leaving the security guards to do their job, the doctors and nurses to do theirs, coming forward when requested to do hers. Where does she live her life, this mother? What does she feel, what does she see? What would it take to make her angry? Would she in fact have thrown his clothing out the window? Would she have remembered his pajamas?

It is an axiom of the hospital that a certain number of fathers fall apart when their children are sick. Mothers, by and large, cope. Mothers have to cope. Mothers get grouchy, and touchy, and fight with the staff, but almost all mothers can stick it out by the bedside. Cancer or seizures, mysterious fevers, you find the mothers sleeping on the fold-out chairs beside the beds, sometimes in the beds with the children, eating the extra food on the hospital trays, coping with the vomit and the diarrhea and the blood. Many of them learn to refill the IV burettes. They learn the medication schedules. After all, it's just like taking care of any little baby, diapers and spit-ups and schedules, just more grotesque, more obscene, more smelly. Mothers almost always manage to cope, but fathers sometimes break down. Some of them are fine—that is to say, they act like

mothers. Others are fine, but from a distance, coming in in the evenings after work, hanging back a little, keeping away from bedpans
and emesis basins. Some fathers simply disappear. And some just
fall apart, unable to handle the hospital sights and smells, unable to
adjust to the child in the bed. Frank Blake is a father who fell apart
and wouldn't acknowledge it; everything had to be someone else's
fault. A tantrum today because the behavioral specialist who
showed up to feed Sara was someone new; how is she supposed to
learn to eat when some new unfamiliar person waltzes in here every
day? A tantrum yesterday because the child in the next bed was
coughing; how is Sara supposed to grow if she doesn't get any
sleep? Amelia would like to yell at him, to say, this is a *hospital,*
we have sick children here. To say the only reason you got a private
room as long as you did was PWS, you Newton lawyer, you. So
now we have kids who need isolation, and they get the private
rooms, and you'll just have to manage in a double.

Amelia says none of those things. Amelia knows what the real
problem is: Sara is gaining weight. Very slowly, very gingerly. One
step forward, two steps back, two steps sideways, one step forwards. But this hospitalization is going to produce the proverbial
"documented in-house weight gain." The proof that if you feed
her, she can grow. Nonorganic failure to thrive. And Sara's parents
don't like that. They have to pretend to be happy, whenever her
weight is up, but the truth is that they see every additional hundred
grams as proof positive, to them and to the world, that as parents
they are failures. They don't have a child with a mysterious disease
who can't grow; they have a child they couldn't feed, they have a
dysfunctional family. And the stress of this, added to the stress of
a child who is now living in the hospital, is making them into a
truly dysfunctional family.

UPDATE: Sara is a fourteen-month-old female with failure to
thrive, hospitalized in early December for medical workup and a
trial of nutritional supplementation. Her past medical history is
essentially unremarkable otherwise, and her family history is non-
contributory, including no history for cystic fibrosis, inflammatory
bowel disease, coeliac disease, or other malabsorptive syndromes.

On physical exam, Sara is a charming child, notably small for age, alert and engaging, in no apparent distress. Physical exam was essentially completely unremarkable. During this hospitalization, Sara underwent a medical workup to rule out organic causes for her failure to thrive. This workup included an unremarkable complete blood count and serum electrolytes and liver function tests, a negative sweat chloride test to rule out cystic fibrosis, a normal electrocardiogram, negative chest x-ray and sinus films, a negative lactose breath test, and negative stool examinations for ova and parasites. Because the mother has a history of blood transfusion, HIV testing was performed on both parents, and both were negative. Sara was also seen by the behavioral medicine team, since it was felt that she was very difficult to feed, and a behavior modification program was developed. Even with these techniques, it has continued to be a problem to get Sara to consume adequate calories, and her weight gain has been slow and irregular. However, over the past two weeks, she has shown a documented weight gain, which correlates well with her increased caloric intake. Sara's parents have had some trouble coping with the implications of a diagnosis of nonorganic failure to thrive, and also with Sara's resistance to her feeding program, and this family will continue to need extensive support.

So after Tiffany's father has been removed and restrained, thanks to the superheroes from security, and after Tiffany's mother has calmed her down, and after Christine has things under control, I suddenly realize that my beeper is making those admonitory occasional beeps it makes when it has gone off with a page and I have not pressed the button to ask who is paging me. So I do, and it was a call from outside the hospital, so I call home, and sure enough, it was Matt who had called, angry at me for not having answered my page promptly. I don't tell him the story of Tiffany, though I know he'll appreciate it tomorrow. But if I tell it now, he'll just think I'm trying to pull the old life-and-death song and dance, impress him with how important my work is; how can I answer your phone calls when I'm busy saving lives? As Matt would say, he's too old for that noise. He doesn't want excuses. But I can't help thinking resentfully that *he* isn't tied to a beeper; if I want to reach him while he's working, I take the chance that my call won't be answered.

Anyway, he's calling to say that Alexander's temperature is a hundred and two, and he has a headache and generally feels lousy. I am watching Christine while I talk, double-checking the blood pressure numbers that appear in green neon letters on the Dynamap machine; Tiffany's blood pressure is fine. I repeat my advice, Tylenol, a bath. Then give way, ask him to ask Alexander if his neck hurts (meningitis paranoia), if his belly hurts (appendicitis anxiety). No and no, says Alexander, he wants some ice cream. Okay, I say, give him ice cream, give him Tylenol, bathe him, put him to bed. I'll be home as early as I can in the morning. And I brace myself.

"You're not coming home now?" Matt's voice is full of overdone disbelief.

"You know I'm not coming home now. Don't pull this with me, you can handle a little fever."

"Are the medical students that important?" Incredulous.

"The medical students are my *job*. Not very often, but tonight they are. And anyway, it's a crazy night here, they need me to help out. There's no way I could leave, and you don't need me, anyway. Stop doing this." I can hear my voice get more intense even as it gets softer; this room is now so much calmer that I am sure everyone can hear me, and I am desperately embarrassed.

"What if he gets sicker?" Smug shithead bastard.

I raise my voice. "If he gets sicker, bring him to the emergency room," I say, and hang up the phone. And at that point, in rush Jasper Greenberg and Mark Gifford, my forgotten medical students, with a message for me from Dave Dwyer. Quote, all fucking hell is breaking loose, and if my patient is not imminently dying, will I come talk to him, please, since his is, unquote. Jasper and Mark both have that medical student look, that things-are-happening-what-do-I-do combination of eagerness and terror. They look at Tiffany on the bed, and they don't know whether she's imminently dying or not, they don't know what they would do if she were, they don't know their asses from their elbows. But they're all charged up. So I go over things quickly with Christine; we've already called for a portable x-ray of Tiffany's neck, and after that's done she'll go upstairs for more neck films, and a belly film, and the blood results will come back, and Christine will keep checking her eyes, and her neurologic status in general, and, oh, she needs a urine sample to see if there's any blood, and so on. Basically, though, I think Tiffany is going to be one of the lucky ones, an indestructible two-year-old, falling from two stories up and walking away with a bruise or two. I go with Jasper and Mark to the main trauma room, where Dave Dwyer is in his element. As we go through the hall, I am aware, first of all, that the ER is hopping, with kids bursting out of rooms and angry parents overflowing from the waiting room, and, second, that Tiffany's father is backed up against the wall in the corridor, hedged in by the security guards, and still looking angry. In the trauma room, Dave is squeezing a bag of blood to get it into his patient as quickly as possible. The two children on the two beds are connected to monitors, to a couple of IVs apiece. Nurses are recording blood pressures. A young woman I recognize as one of the senior surgeons is pressing on a child's belly.

"You're gonna need more blood," she tells Dave, who asks an intern to fill in a rec for another four units, and make sure to stamp the rec for the right kid—these are siblings, these two car-crash victims, so they have the same last name, but they may well have different blood types, and if Dave gave one the other's blood, he might actually kill the kid.

Dave looks at me. He is happy as a clam, I swear; he is the sort of doctor who complains about seeing too many sore throats and ear infections; he became an ER doctor because he likes *emergencies,* and here he is, squeezing blood back into a bleeding child's veins. It looks to me as if one or both of these kids will need to go to the operating room soon; the rule is, you give so much blood, to see if it stabilizes a child with internal injuries, and if it doesn't you have to open the kid up. Probably the surgeons are getting ready, the attending coming in from home. "Amelia, baby," Dave says, "all hell is breaking loose."

"You're telling me? I'm the one dealing with the crazy father who wants to kill me for putting an IV in his daughter."

"Yeah, I saw the security guards. Some night, huh? Well, I'm kinda tied up in here, as you can probably see, and we just got a call another ambulance is coming in, so if your little out-the-window kid is stabilized—"

"What's coming in?"

"You're not gonna believe this, Amelia."

"What?"

"SIDS baby, found dead in bed. There's not gonna be anything you can do, but someone's gotta do it." He gives the plastic bag of blood one final squeeze, then disconnects the IV tubing and hooks it back up to a bag of clear fluid. I watch the clear stream chase the red blood down through the tubing, into the child. I don't look carefully at the child; I don't want to see any more critically ill children right now. Hell night, indeed. So I march myself off down the hall to room 14, the one remaining crash room, and I corral a nurse, and with Jasper and Mark watching intently, I ask her to please help me set up for a resuscitation.

Sudden Infant Death Syndrome, more popularly known as crib death, is actually a diagnosis that can only be made on autopsy. That is to say, a baby is found dead, no one knows why. So an autopsy is done. If you find a cause of death, it wasn't SIDS. If you find poison in the stomach, or an unsuspected cardiac defect, or an overwhelming infection, then it wasn't SIDS. It was murder, or heart failure, or septic shock. But SIDS is by definition a diagnosis of exclusion; it's the cause of the death for the baby if there is no obvious cause of death, neither by history nor by autopsy.

Actually, there is one story in *Bulfinch's Mythology* that made quite an impression on Amelia when she leafed through it, looking for familiar names, for stories that *she* might read Alexander—she was happy to leave Nisus and Euryalus, say, for Matt. She came across the story of Niobe, a familiar name but not a story she could remember, so she read it, drawn no doubt by some dying-children radar, some memory she couldn't remember that told her this was the story for her. Niobe, as you may remember, was a queen who boasted of her children. She had seven boys and seven girls, and therefore dared to compare herself favorably with the goddess Latona, who had only one of each, Apollo and Diana. Said Niobe, "I have seven times as many. Fortunate indeed am I, and fortunate I shall remain!" Famous last words, as they say. Not surprisingly, Latona did not take kindly to this. Had she been one of the parents in the day care center, she would probably have said something cutting about how hard it is to give quality time to fourteen. As a Greek goddess, however, Latona had other options; she went whining to her children and sent them off to avenge her. And what they do is this: they *hunt* the children of Niobe, from the skies, shoot down the boys one by one as they play at manly sports. And Niobe comes and sees what has happened, and "knelt over the lifeless bodies and kissed, now one, now another of her dead sons." But then, thickheaded woman that she is, she cries out in anger against Latona, and therefore gets to watch as, one by one, her daughters are shot. "Six were now dead, and only one remained, whom the mother held clasped in her arms, and covered as it were with her whole body. 'Spare me one, and that the youngest! O spare me one of so many!' she cried; and while she spoke, that one fell dead."

Well, the ancient Greeks did not pull their punches. It is not, somehow, the way Amelia thinks of Apollo, shooting down children one after another to teach their mother a lesson. The golden god of music, the lord of the sun? Well, according to Bulfinch, he was also god of medicine; does that fit the story better?

In the emergency room, Amelia finds herself reflecting that virtually any mother would boast as Niobe boasted, would set her child above gods and goddesses, would consider herself richer in possession of her own children than any divinity in possession of divine offspring. If being too proud of your child makes you vulnerable to the arrows of jealous deities, then the emergency room is full of Niobes.

Niobe is sixteen and speaks only Spanish and has tied colored ribbons in the hair of her little girl, whose asthma is so severe that her lips are turning blue. Or she is a tough-talking chain-smoker from Roslindale whose son has an immune system defect and comes in yet again with a bacterial infection; one of them will kill him someday. Or she is a securities analyst whose son has cystic fibrosis, with evil bugs spawning in the thick mucus that fills his lungs. Niobe is in room 3, watching her daughter writhe in pain from a sickle cell anemia crisis, in room 7 holding her seizing baby. All of you were proud, all of you looked on a beautiful baby, and if the goddess had asked, who is richer, you or I, any of you might have given the wrong answer.

Niobe is a black woman from Dorchester who works nights as a nursing home aide, who went in to kiss her six-month-old son good-bye and found him stiff and cold in his crib.

Early the next morning, leaving the ER, sleepless and shaky, Amelia makes a very conscious effort to shut out the night. Even Tiffany, who did fine, all tests negative; she went home after the social workers had spent a long time with her mother—her father had disappeared. Tiffany, the two-year-old who fell out a window and lived to tell the tale. More especially, Amelia is trying to shut out the SIDS baby, and his family. She needs to go home to Alexander and think about Alexander. She needs her sense of proportion back.

What a night. Hell night, and with a vengeance. When the craziness finally stopped, when the futile resuscitation was called off, when the two kids from the car accident had left the trauma room, one for the OR, one for the ICU for further monitoring, when Tiffany had gone cheerfully home in her mother's arms, Amelia and Dave Dwyer and the other doctors who had been shut up in the crash rooms with these children emerged to find the ER full of all the other parents and children who had been backed up for hours. The central blackboard was crowded with lists of patients to be seen, patients awaiting lab results, patients up in x-ray. A couple of interns and a couple of junior residents had been seeing kids as fast as possible, but the rooms were all full, the waiting rooms were full, everyone was angry, children were wailing all over the place. No doctors got to go home till three A.M., though many were supposed to get off at midnight. Amelia abandoned her medical students, who were still rocky after watching the resuscitation, and processed one child after another, colds and ears and throats and wheezes, and occasionally something more, the regular ER routine. Forget about teaching, forget about everything, just get through the night. Three o'clock and four o'clock and five o'clock and six o'clock, and she scrawled hasty notes on the ER forms and filled in prescriptions, as the other doctors did the same. The waiting room cleared, slowly. The turbulence settled down. At eight o'clock the morning shift arrived, to find a calm emergency room, the interns and residents telling their replacements, You wouldn't believe it, it was Hell night. But there were no traces, the rooms were clean and ready for the daytime patients, the board was wiped clean.

And Amelia, walking to her car, her head full of snow and static, tries not to think about the SIDS baby. I am going home to my own. He needs me, I need him.

The second upstairs room in Matt's little house was the most intact. The walls were a hideous yellow, but the plaster was not coming down. The floor was blue, again, but a patch in the middle had been scraped down to the wood, Matt and Marco looking to see what they would find when everything was sanded and polished. The floor had also been swept quite clean of debris, and there were no awful secrets in the corners. The room had a beautiful set of bay windows, or what would have been a beautiful set if the frames had not been painted black, and the windows were open, so the air in the room was fresh. There was a shopping bag in the room, on the scraped patch of floor, and also a folded blanket; Matt had planned a picnic.

Amelia sat gamely on the blanket and ate pastrami and pickles and potato salad. She did not like being in this house, even in this room, which was not as bad as the others. She kept thinking about the next room, about the smell and the trash. She could not see any of this with Matt's eyes, and she wished he would let her go away and come back when things were fixed up; she feared she would always look at this house and see the mess it had been. But she was touched that he had wanted to picnic there with her, that he wanted to involve her in ceremonially taking possession. She repressed her distaste and ate more pastrami. Then as he opened the bottle of wine, she thought suddenly of a scene in a movie, *Rosemary's Baby,* where the young couple make love on the floor of their brand-new unfurnished apartment after a picnic on the floor, and she was suddenly certain that that was next on the agenda. Lord, but she did not want to take her clothes off in this house, not for any ceremony, not for any taking possession. She wanted out, she wanted to be back in her own home. She drank wine, quickly.

And then allowed herself to be seduced, allowed Matt to seduce her. Or did she allow it, was she planning all along to interrupt, to say, Look, I'd be more comfortable doing this at home? Did he just overcome her with passion and tenderness? When did she shift from thinking, I'm not going to do this, look what happened to Rosemary, after all, to thinking, Oh my goodness, hot stuff. So the plan worked; for months afterward, whenever Amelia walked past the little house, she felt for it not distaste but a sort of embarrassed affection, such as you might feel, maybe, for a sleazy motel on Route 1 if you had happened to live through some of your life's most passionate moments in one of its seedy little rooms.

UPDATE: Alexander is a four-year-old boy with an unremarkable previous medical history. Two days ago he developed fever to a hundred and two, along with general malaise, some frontal headache, and increased crankiness. There was no nausea, vomiting, or diarrhea. He continued to have fevers, reaching as high as a hundred and three point six, and then today developed vesicular lesions on his scalp and trunk. The lesions are consistent with chicken pox, with clear fluid on an erythematous base, and are intensely pruritic. New lesions have been appearing throughout the day, spreading to the lower abdomen and groin area, as well as the face. On physical exam, he is a miserable child in significant distress due to the itching of his chicken pox. He is trying hard not to scratch, as his mother and father tell him, but the itching is so bad he writhes around on his bed. Medicated baths have failed to alleviate his discomfort, and a dose of Benadryl provided only very temporary relief. He does not want to hear any Greek Smiths, or any other stories, except very simple baby stories his parents make up for him, and though he wants to be held, the itching prevents him from settling comfortably into anyone's arms. He and his father and mother and all the furniture are pink with calamine lotion.

CHAPTER VI
GUARDIANS

A melia was tired because Alexander wasn't sleeping well; the itching kept him awake, he said, and though she dosed him with Benadryl syrup and gave him Tylenol and soaked him in a medicated bath before bed, he still woke, whimpering, tossing, and above all, scratching. In the middle of the night, she had suddenly caught hold of his wrists, pulled his hands away from the pox on his thigh that he was relentlessly scratching and gouging. She pressed his hands into the pillow on either side of his head, and she growled at him, "You have to stop the scratching." And he raised his head up, moaned as he tried to pull his hands away, and then yelled at her, "Oh, you are ruining my life!"

Actually, that memory made Amelia smile as she wandered down the hall to call in another clinic patient. She had a full schedule of patients, so Matt had stayed home with Alexander for the day; Amelia had already asked the clinic secretary to call tomorrow's patients and cancel them, knowing that probably half of them would have changed phone numbers, or would have no phones, or would have deliberately given wrong numbers; the clinic population was suspicious of authority, and for whatever reason, phone numbers were among the most closely guarded secrets. Give the doctors your phone number and they'll . . . what?

And after all, Amelia reflected, going to the med room to fill yet another syringe with yet another aliquot of DPT vaccine, that's probably no more than what half the small children in this hospital would shout at their doctors and nurses if they could: Get away from me with your needles and your dressing changes and your tubes, you are ruining my life. I am just lucky, because I have a child who is basically well, so it's a joke when he says it, and also lucky because I have a child smart enough to find words for his emotions, not just "I hate you," not just screams. And then thought of her basically well, smart child, lying hot and feverish on the couch, trying not to scratch, listening to Matt read one story after another, and really, of course, she wanted to go right home and gather him up and make all the sickness go away. But she could not make the sickness go away, and Matt was home doing all anyone could do, and she marched back into her office and gave the shot, promising herself that tomorrow she would take Matt's place and make her boy feel better, cool cloths, stories, games, whatever he wanted. And noodles with butter for lunch.

"Doctor, I need to tell you something," said Bathsheba Jenkins, holding her twins securely on her lap. Her older daughter, Tayesha, was contentedly playing with Amelia's plastic alphabet blocks; Tayesha was three, and Amelia had been her doctor since birth. The twins, Jamal and Jarry, were six months old, identical butter-balls. Bathsheba herself was a stunning woman, tall and slender and commanding, who dressed in leotards and long skirts made from African textiles. Tayesha, Amelia remembered, had also been a but-terball baby but was now showing signs of growing into a long lean princess, like her mother. Presumably, if you have to carry a name like Bathsheba through life, you either retreat from it, cut it down to size, or else, if you're very lucky, you live up to it. Nobody would ever laugh at Bathsheba Jenkins.

"Doctor, the father of these little boys has informed me that he has been messing around, messing with women, and I wouldn't be surprised with drugs. He tells me he has venereal disease, and he tells me I ought to get the babies tested for it too."

"Which venereal disease? Syphilis? Gonorrhea?"

"That's the one. Gonorrhea. He has that."

"I'm sure you were tested during the pregnancy," Amelia said. "And that medicine they put in the babies' eyes when they're newborns will keep the gonorrhea from doing any damage, even if you caught it from him. That's the big danger from gonorrhea—it can attack a baby's eyes."

"So the boys don't need to be tested?"

"No, but you do."

"I'll go to the clinic," said Bathsheba. She paused, not exactly hesitating, but phrasing her next question. "Doctor, isn't it true if he has one disease like that, he could have others?"

"Yes. Actually, I was just going to bring that up. I should probably do blood tests on Jamal and Jarry, make sure they don't have syphilis."

"What about AIDS?" asked Bathsheba.

"If you think their father might have been doing IV drugs, we have to worry about AIDS," Amelia said, her voice as matter-of-fact as if she were not saying, We have to consider the possibility that you and your babies may be infected with a deadly disease. "We can't test babies yet reliably, so the best thing to do would be just to test your blood—if you're negative, then we don't have to worry about the babies. If you were to test positive, then we could go on and test them. What about Tayesha? Does she have the same father?"

"No, I haven't seen her father in more than two years."

"Well, I honestly think that since you've been healthy and the boys have been healthy and they've grown just on schedule—I really don't think there's a very big chance anyone's infected. I know AIDS is a really scary word, and you read a lot about it nowadays—" Amelia broke off. Her spiel, meant to reassure, meant to inform and defuse, was wasted. Bathsheba was obviously not listening. "I can just draw your blood right here and send it to the lab," Amelia concluded lamely and went to get a syringe.

Tayesha freaked out completely when she saw the needle, but Amelia assured her that she was the only member of her family who didn't need a shot or a blood test, and she happily stood over the twins when their shots were given and they were tucked into their double stroller, and the three of them stared at their mother's blood as Amelia slowly drew it out into her plastic syringe.

She sent it off to the lab, she promised to call with the results, and she reminded Bathsheba, and herself, once again, that the results would probably be negative. With this test, as with other medical tests for bad diseases, Amelia had developed a certain amount of self-protective denial. Probably the test would be negative. If the test came back positive, there would be time then to worry and to mourn, to think through the ramifications. It would be just so much wasted emotional effort to do it now. After all, imagine a positive test, meaning Bathsheba has the virus, meaning each twin has a 40 percent chance of having the virus. Meaning what? Meaning Bathsheba may well get sick, infections chipping away at that royal body, or meaning that one of her roly-poly boys may start to melt into skin and bones. Meaning she has to worry, will she outlive them, will they outlive her. And what about Tayesha? Well, Tayesha is old enough to be tested definitively, at least. But what sad stories, if the tests were positive, Bathsheba dying, Bathsheba fighting to keep herself out of the hospital to tend Jamal, Tayesha standing at her brother's hospital bedside, her world already shattered into pain and death and uncertainty, all promises broken (I will not die until you are all grown up).

After all, what's the point? Maybe, back when she was an intern, Amelia had the habit of writing these stories, of scaring herself with the illicit dramatic thrill—what if this comes back positive, what if something shows up on the x-ray. But she outgrew it, really; there were plenty of bad endings to go around, plenty of people to care about and keen over. Bathsheba's HIV titer was going to be negative; the worst she had was gonorrhea, a good old-fashioned venereal disease. Amelia would conserve herself, expend no anguish on anything but the real, the documented. She had enough of that. Darren was back in the hospital, and very sick.

At home he had had a cold, then he had started breathing heavily, and then over the last couple of days his breathing had gotten faster and faster, until he had no energy to do anything but lie on his back and breathe. His grandmother had stuck it out for a weekend. She had not called Amelia. But the visiting nurse had come for her regular visit on Monday, had taken one look at Darren, and had insisted on calling for an ambulance. And Roberta Wilson, as she had admitted to Amelia, had actually been relieved. She had not wanted to go on alone at home, watching Darren breathe like that. He was back on the ward, getting extra oxygen. His chest x-ray was read as suggestive of pneumocystis carinii pneumonia, but that just meant it looked the same as it had before. Darren was getting treated with antibiotics aimed at PCP, as well as other antibiotics. It looked to Amelia like the beginning of another long hospitalization, a long slow trip downhill.

After Bathsheba and her children left, Amelia called home once again, to hear from Matt that Alexander had eaten some tomato soup for lunch and then fallen asleep. Then called Darren's floor to hear from the nurse, Mary Pat, that Darren was requiring a higher flow of oxygen to keep his blood from desaturating. Amelia promised to come up and see him as soon as her clinic was over.

Oh, I tell you, I could easily give way and start in on Alexander and his chicken pox. Never mind major tragedy; all he has to do is look up at me and say, Mom, I won't be there to finish the spaceship, they'll finish it without me, and he dissolves into tears, and I swear to God, I almost do too. The colossal unfairness of it. I called Doree at the day care center this morning and asked, could she make sure there would still be something for Alexander to do when he gets back, and Doree promised she would ease off on the spaceship for a few days, most of the kids weren't as into it as Alexander, after all, and then when he gets back, they'll do the instrument panel, the controls, taking apart an old computer keyboard, making big dials and buttons. She sounded as if she thought it would all be a big treat, and I was grateful beyond words.

Oh, I tell you. I refuse to do this. Alexander has varicella virus (chicken pox), not vaccinia virus (small pox). Alexander has a mild, nonthreatening, normal childhood disease. So I am not going to moan on about his feverish little body, disfigured by the pox, his beautiful smooth limbs that I love to watch moving underwater when he takes his bath, now reddened and excoriated. His tummy—the single most basic urge of motherhood for me seems to be a yen to kiss that very slightly potbellied tummy, and now it looks as if someone had been at it with sandpaper. But for crying out loud, he has varicella, not vaccinia. Yes, it hurts, yes, it itches, yes, you get pox when you have chicken pox. But the worst that happens is a little scar or two, and for heaven's sake, you get better. Think of the parents who watched their children with smallpox, after all. Did smallpox itch, anyway?

Amelia went up to see Darren and was alarmed, immediately, by how much worse he looked. If the lung infection was PCP, the antibiotics ought to be at least slowing it down. She was worried that in fact he had some other opportunistic bug, worried also because she knew the only way to diagnose such a bug would probably be to take a sample of lung tissue, either by opening up his chest surgically, or else by passing a flexible tube down his airway. Either would be dangerous, either was possibly more aggressive than she wanted to be with Darren, than his grandmother wanted her to be. But the question was bound to come up, and also, resuscitation would have to be discussed again; the DNR status had to be reaffirmed one more time, now that it appeared it might be invoked in the near future.

Amelia sat down in the armchair by Darren's bedside, grateful that his grandmother wasn't there. Darren was in a croupette, a square plastic oxygen tent. To keep him warm inside the tent, warm in the cool oxygenated mist, the nurses had pulled the white hospital blanket up to his chin, and he had not wriggled. The IV tubing snaked in under the blanket, which looked almost flat to the bed, so that it was hard to believe there was a still little boy's body under it, however wasted, however sick. The room was full of white noise, the steady hiss of the oxygen tent making Darren's air richer, more nutritious. Something evil was growing in Darren's lungs, maybe pneumocystis, the quiet little protozoan that Amelia probably carried benignly in her own lungs, that Alexander probably carried in his—but maybe something else. Pneumocystis, at least, they were treating; that snake slithering down the IV pole and under the white blanket carried medicine for pneumocystis. But Amelia still believed that Darren had been colonized with atypical mycobacteria, even if the lab had failed to culture any out, during his last hospitalization. What if those obscure little bugs were now breaking loose, what if they were causing this lung disease? What if it was a fungus? Or the mysterious process of lymphocytic interstitial proliferation, seen in children with AIDS, when the cells of their crippled immune system leak into their lungs and they drown in their own ineffective serum.

The only way to know for sure would be to take a sample of those damaged lungs. Amelia knew she should reach into Darren's tent, push her cold stethoscope up under his yellow hospital johnny—but what would she hear? The hiss of oxygen in her ears, she would hear that his lungs were full of crackles; she knew that already. The rustling tissue paper of disease, the wetness and coarseness, would tell her only what she already knew: something was bad in Darren's lungs. The moist oxygen pumped into the tent went in down his airway, but something was blocking his air sacs, something was interfering with those delicate little bubble packs. An evil bacteria, or a weirdo fungus, or his own cells; Amelia found herself deeply reluctant to go after a tissue sample.

Another one of those awful meetings had to be held.

The initial suggestion from the intern was to hold it at five, by which time he obviously hoped he could be through with the rest of his day's business, ready to meet and then go home. Amelia sympathized, but she herself had every intention of being ready to leave before five, and she didn't intend to hang around. It might not be smallpox, but she wanted to go home to Alexander. So she pulled rank, and the group met at three.

The intern taking care of Darren was a short, muscular Californian, Clark Donahue, blond and wide-eyed, and one of the most genuinely sweet doctors Amelia had ever met. There was something so sincere and gee-whiz about him that he melted the hearts of nurses, parents, and other doctors. Also, he worked his slightly too-large ass off, as everyone knew. Mary Pat came for nursing, and the only other person present was a doctor Amelia deeply disliked. Luck of the draw; this month, the infectious diseases specialist was Andrew Carswell, Randy Andy, with his three-piece suits and his affected New England accent. Not very smart, really, certainly not nearly as smart as he thought he was, with a reputation for preying on the junior fellows and postdocs more than was proper, inserting his name ahead of theirs on their articles, then tearing them down when they tried to present seminars or lectures. Also a hospital reputation for "inappropriateness" with women; one or two of the residents had complained that he interrogated them about their sex lives, that he tended overmuch to the friendly arm around the shoulders, and everyone was familiar with his penchant for discussing suggestive research. If an obscure article in a rarely read journal publicized new data about the bacterial flora of the human vagina, Randy Andy would find a way to bring it up in a gathering that included a couple of female medical students and interns, and would discuss the data-gathering techniques until everyone was embarrassed. Amelia had heard an intern joke once that Andy sat all day at his computer doing literature searches on dirty words, like a grade-school boy looking up "intercourse" in the classroom dictionary. The wonders of the computer age.

As they sat around the Formica table, Amelia felt she could tell exactly who was in a hurry; she herself was, of course, and Clark, too, who was scribbling in a chart while he waited for the meeting to begin. Mary Pat was in no hurry; she had on her truculent I-want-to-see-justice-done expression. The other person present with all the time in the world was Randy Andy. Like any scientist with no real research, any doctor with no real patients, he dearly loved meetings. A chance to pontificate, to tell his pointless stories, his suggestive stories, a chance to make other people squirm one way or another. Amelia, anxious to get done, get out, get home, was looking at the meeting as a shoving contest; she and Clark would be pushing toward making the decision, Mary Pat and Andy would be braced against them, shoving in the other direction.

I came home from the emergency room after that hellish Hell night, I let myself into the house, and when no one called to me and I heard no sounds, I went up to Alexander's bedroom. He was asleep, twisted onto his side, uncovered, of course. He was slightly flushed, but there were no pox visible yet, that first morning; I thought he had some little bug or other.

And next to him, on his side, Matt was asleep. Alexander wore fuzzy pajamas, Matt wore army pants and a T-shirt. Matt looked to me, from the doorway, like a sentry, as if he had fallen asleep but even asleep was determined to keep Alexander safe. If I had been sleeping next to Alexander we would probably have been intertwined; I would have kept one hand on his belly, or an arm under his head. But Matt does not like to sleep with any part of his body touching anyone; even on nights when he and I make love, hug, cuddle, nestle, he eventually turns away, places himself precisely in the bed, right before falling asleep. And when Alexander was just born and I would take him in bed with us to nurse, I would fall asleep happily with the baby in my arms, or even resting on my chest, but Matt would, again, pull away right before sleep. I thought at the time this must be due to fear of crushing the baby, since I couldn't imagine any other reason for giving up the pleasure of his newborn skin, his tiny regular breathing, the sense of how near and how alive he was. But I suppose Matt likes to face sleep alone, knowing exactly where the kingdom of his own body begins and ends. But as I looked at him asleep in Alexander's bed, there was no mistaking the intimacy between them. The exhaustion that had finally beached them both was the exhaustion of love, Alexander sick but tended, Matt staying by him to see him through the night. And in spite of those intensely irritating calls to the emergency room, all I could feel looking down on them was a tenderness as powerful as ether. And not just a tenderness for Alexander; I am so used to that feeling that I take it in stride, as you might the million-dollar view in your own backyard. It was tenderness for Matt, for his little-boy-asleep-in-his-clothes vulnerability. Tenderness and also possessiveness, as I stood there looking down at the two of them and thinking, These are *mine*. And here is your profoundly tired doctor mother to take care of you.

Mary Pat's main concern was that Darren's grandmother was just too tired from taking care of him at home to make a good decision about how aggressive to be in treating him now, in the hospital. "I just think she's very stressed-out right now, and maybe we ought to let this wait till she feels better."

"The problem is," said Clark, the intern, "I don't really think we have time to wait."

"Darren's respiratory status is deteriorating," Amelia agreed. "He's not exactly crashing, but he could. And even if he doesn't crash, the decision about the ICU and the ventilator is going to have to be made in a couple of days. He's going to tire out."

"Whoa, wait a minute," said Randy Andy. "Why do you all jump to the conclusion that this kid needs to be DNR? Seems to me he could have all kinds of treatable infections."

"He was DNR last time he was hospitalized," Mary Pat began.

"That's totally irrelevant to *me*," said Andy with satisfaction.

"He's a severely debilitated child with a fatal disease who can't stay out of the hospital," Amelia said sharply. "His life has been made a medicalized hell, and his grandmother decided, very reasonably I think, that unless aggressive therapy offers him a chance for a very real improvement in quality of life, it's time to stop."

"Well, I have some sympathy for that view," said Andy, looking down at his tie. Amelia had already noted the Harvard insignias, which went so well with his college class ring and his medical school class ring. Poor Andy; would he ever adjust to the idea that he had left the Harvard hospital system? "I can certainly understand how his grandmother might feel that. I would just question whether we can support her, if we feel the child may have a treatable disease."

"He doesn't have a treatable disease. He has a possibly treatable complication of a fatal disease, and if his grandmother still wants to let him go gently, I think it's completely in line with the way we handle other kids in that situation."

"The oncology kids," Clark said, and then turned red. "I think that some of the oncology kids, if their prognosis is really terrible, don't we let them die of infections?"

The talk wound on awhile. Amelia was terribly impatient. Was she impatient because this all ought to have been irrelevant, because the issue had been discussed and settled? Or was she impatient because she wanted to go home? Because of *chicken pox*? Or was it just that she felt more and more irritated with Mary Pat, and with Andy, that she suspected them of some prurient stake in this God-playing, this judging of a sick child? Once again, as at the day care center, she thought rather grimly that she did not really like adults, not most adults. The only one in the room she liked was Clark, and to be honest, she didn't exactly think of him as an adult, short and shiny-faced, timid and insecure in the newness of his doctoring.

She won the argument, as she had known she would. When push came to shove, she said, probably less diplomatically than she would have said it on any other day, "I am Darren's attending, and I agree with the family's decision to make him DNR and to refrain from putting him on a vent. I also agree with the pulmonary people, who feel that bronchoscopy is a very high-risk procedure for him. If either of you feels uncomfortable with this decision ethically, I think you have to call in the child protection team and discuss it with the lawyers and the social workers."

They wouldn't do it, Amelia knew. For one thing, they agreed with her, more or less; they were just arguing for the sake of giving life and death due process. For another, no one wanted long meetings with the lawyers and the social workers. She wrote her DNR order in Darren's chart once again, imagining for a minute that he would get well, go home, come back, that there would always be more such meetings. But she didn't believe he would get well, go home. She believed he would die. Before she went home herself, to her little boy with chicken pox, she went back into Darren's room. Roberta Wilson was sitting in the armchair near the bed, staring down at a copy of *The Runaway Bunny*. Not reading aloud.

One of my little hospital tricks, one of the ways I ally myself with parents, is I identify the books they are reading to their children, I let them know I read the same books to mine. Sometimes I show off—I know all of *Where the Wild Things Are* by heart, for example, and most of *The Cat in the Hat*. I stand in the doorway and recite a page or two, and they look at me with surprise, and of course what I am saying is I'm a mommy, I have one too, I understand. Trust me.

When I was a resident, tired and unsure of myself, back before I had a child, I occasionally fantasized about being a hospital volunteer instead of a doctor, a cheerful do-gooder in those red-and-yellow smocks they issue. My job would be to read aloud to the sick children, and I would do it so conscientiously, so well, and never have to worry that I was falling short. The only thing was, the volunteers I met were all either sweet elderly ladies or avaricious premeds, accumulating material for their application essays.

But still, even now, I find myself wanting to do the easy things that help, to avoid the dangers and the decisions of medicine and retreat toward the gift shop, the library cart, the visiting clowns who stroll the hallway. Hello, Mrs. Wilson, I see you've been reading *The Runaway Bunny* to Darren. Isn't that nice; my little boy loved that book when he was younger. And aren't the pictures beautiful? And I've just come from another meeting where we agreed to keep Darren DNR, and decided against exploring his lungs to see if we can find an infection we might be able to treat.

Driving home, Amelia made a conscious effort to shift over. Life had to stretch, life had to accommodate both ends. There had to be a way to leave a dying child's bedside, leave behind the decision of how quickly to let him die, and go home to your own life, to your own child. And there had to be a way to take the illness of the dying child with the right degree of seriousness, and yet still have some intensity, some appreciation, for a bad case of chicken pox. And Alexander did have a bad case of chicken pox.

The whole house, it seemed to Amelia, walking in, was full of stuffy heat and the aura of illness, like a film of dust and cobwebs on top of the normal life of the people who should be living there. Especially, the little boy who should have been waiting to jump out from behind the door in the hallway, his dagger between his teeth, his cutlass slung on a sash, his pirate hat, his eyepatch askew. He was upstairs, sipping ginger ale through a straw, his face blotched and without mischief. A house with a sick child, a house full of a child's sickness. Alexander's room felt somehow squalid, crammed with discarded toys that had failed to keep his interest. His stuffed animals lay deposed on the floor; he did not usually play with his stuffed animals, except occasionally when he required pirate prisoners. Amelia had once watched Alexander and Jeremy forcing the stuffed animals to walk the plank off Alexander's bed, rabbit after bear after monkey. Still, he liked to arrange them ritually along the side of his bed, leaning against the wall, to look down benignly on him as he slept, but now he had tumbled them off, leaving room in the bed only for himself and his itching. There were some stray jigsaw pieces among the blankets, suggesting to Amelia a moment when Alexander had given up putting the puzzle together and swept it to the floor. Alexander was lying quietly enough, sipping through his straw, with Matt in the armchair in the corner, drawing on one of his graph-paper pads. But when Amelia walked in, Alexander spat the straw from his mouth and began to wail, great big feel-sorry-for-me howls, and then thrashed his legs up and down, inevitably spilling his ginger ale.

"Cut it *out!*" Matt yelled, up out of his armchair, snatching away the cup, and saying harshly to Amelia as he stomped out the door, "He's all yours."

Amelia sat down, trying to avoid the spilled soda, feeling jigsaw-puzzle pieces under her bottom. She gathered her son into her arms, envisioning, perhaps, that he would calm down and be comforted, that her presence would soothe all his various pains. Instead, he continued to thrash and howl.

"I hate this!" he screamed at her. "This is the worst worst worst day for me, and if you are a good doctor you should make me well!"

She went for a bowl of cool water, stripped off his pajamas, and sponged him off. She wondered when he had last gotten Tylenol but decided not to pursue Matt so soon. Alexander felt to her only mildly feverish, but the chicken pox lesions were ugly, and two on his thigh looked to her as if they were getting infected, with broadening red areas at their bases and pus collecting on top. Amelia sponged them off, rubbed bacitracin on them, tugged Alexander into his last pair of clean pajamas, and offered to read him any book he would like. He didn't want to hear a story. She offered to play Candyland, a game she normally avoided. He didn't want to play Candyland. Ice cream. No. His *Wizard of Oz* record. No. She got silly—Would you like me to do a hootchy-kootchy dance? No, but she sensed that he was biting back a giggle. How about if I rub you all over with strawberry jam? Or would you like chocolate-covered worms to eat? Finally, grudgingly, he giggled. She buried her nose in his belly button and blew noisily against his poor little poxy belly, and he let go and laughed.

"When you were just a baby, I used to do this all the time, and you would laugh and laugh," Amelia said, remembering the softness of infant skin against her cheeks.

"When I was how little?"

"When you were so small you couldn't talk at all. When you were so small you wore diapers all the time."

"Because I used to poop in them!"

"And pee in them."

"When I was so small, was I the same boy? When I was in your belly?"

"You were always the same boy. You were always Alexander, and I always loved you best of all."

Sounding almost like himself, Alexander told her, "That's because I am the kid *you* had. You have to love the kid you have the best."

Even with a very sick child, there are respites. Even the children dying of cancers that have already eaten big pieces out of their bones, or out of their brains, sometimes get back a few minutes to be children, even if it's a sleepy cuddle with everyone's eyes closed. Or a moment at the hospital magic show when there is no way at all to explain how the pigeon got into the hat where a minute before there was only a scarf. I have watched such moments from time to time, an uninvited and unwelcome observer (since by my presence I invoke only illness). Children who are not very sick have many such moments; that's why you read to them and bring in magicians and set up playrooms. You can actually drive away sickness and pain and fear with takeout from Burger King, if you're lucky. So I came in on Alexander, after he and Matt had worn each other out all day, and I managed a respite.

Alexander's fever came down, and he came down himself and joined us at the table for dinner; he said he felt well enough. I made him noodles swimming in butter, and frozen corn of course, and Matt turned up a bag of chocolate morsels in the closet and made tollhouse cookies, while Alexander sat like a pasha, pillowed in an armchair dragged into the kitchen, and licked the bowl and ate the chocolate chips from the bag whenever Matt's back was turned, then let out his glee when his father turned back and pretended to tear out his hair, complaining that soon there would be no chocolate chips left for his cookies. And then we all three drank big glasses of cold milk and ate the cookies as hot as we could, our fingers getting buttery, the table covered with crumbs. I dosed Alexander liberally with Benadryl, to stop his itching and help him sleep, and Matt carried him up the stairs, and blessedly, remarkably, he fell asleep almost immediately. And before we went to bed ourselves, Matt and I came tiptoeing in to look at him. In the dark of his room, we couldn't see the redness, and his breathing sounded like his nighttime breathing always does. We straightened his covers, tenderly put his splayed arms and legs back into line, and told each other that he really didn't feel warm at all.

And then we went to bed, congratulating ourselves and each other; the crisis is past.

Actually, what I felt was triumph; I had found the way. Come home and done what was needed, brought relief to Matt after a sickroom day, to Alexander. Found what the chicken pox child needed, after finding what the terminally ill child at work needed. What balance, I thought, what sanity. Oh, I was smug.

And tomorrow I would stay home, since I had canceled my clinic patients, and Alexander would recover steadily under my care (the crisis being past) and Matt would feel I had done my share. What I needed, I saw clearly, was to make love, to prove to myself that I could satisfy there too—or perhaps, to prove that that side of life could satisfy me. I was lying in Matt's embrace, he was hugging me, and I kissed him passionately and promised myself that I would not picture anyone else while we made love, most particularly that I would not picture Luke.

And I didn't, and we made love, and for all the smugness I know was there, on my side at least, I remember it tenderly. We lay in bed and touched each other for a very long time, both of us somewhat exhausted by our different days, maybe both of us a little on edge in case a noise should come from Alexander's room, in case he wasn't really asleep for the night, in case our victory was incomplete. Sometimes, starting out tired, we just touch each other and fall asleep, aroused a little, pleased with each other, unable to summon up the momentum that would pitch us forward into the more energetic rhythms of lovemaking. But that night, which I remember in great detail because of what it later brought, we managed the transition, and he moved over me and slid inside me and we made love for a very long time. And then lay in each other's arms until I was almost asleep, and only woke slightly when Matt shifted away from me to fall asleep unentwined.

Falling asleep, Amelia did not think that night about her old fantasy, Darren on the beach. Falling asleep, she did not think of Darren at all, and perhaps, she thought later, if she had, she might have warded off what happened. But she fell asleep in physical weariness and sexual satisfaction, and woke to the ringing of the phone and Matt muttering Oh, shit, and pulling his pillow over his head.

She took the phone out in the hall, still stupefied with sleep. But thinking, as her head cleared, as she felt the coolness of the floorboards on her bare feet, as she leaned against the wall, thinking, Darren must be dying, they must be calling because Darren is dying. Sure enough, it was Clark Donahue, the intern. Apologizing—you could almost feel him blushing at the other end of the phone. Never mind that it was two in the morning and he was wide awake, on call, with no prospect of sleep. Still, he was apologizing to Amelia, whom he had pulled out of a soft bed, a sound sleep.

"Is Darren worse?" she asked.

"Well, yes, he's desatting more and more, and his respiratory rate is going higher. But actually, that's not why I'm calling, exactly. I'm so sorry to be waking you up like this."

"It's okay, Clark. It's fine. Tell me what the problem is."

"Well—it's complicated. Did you think that Darren's grandmother had formal custody of him?"

This was so much not what Amelia had been expecting to hear that she took a few seconds to adjust. "No, I don't know. I don't think so. What does she say?"

"She's so upset right now, it's a little hard to make sense of what she says. But I guess she never went to court and got custody. See, apparently this afternoon, after we had our meeting, Mary Pat got called by the billing office, because it turns out Darren doesn't have insurance, because his grandmother's policy doesn't cover him, because she's not his legal guardian. I guess his grandmother never realized that, but they were just processing his bills from the last hospitalization and they found out. So someone called Mary Pat, to make sure Darren wasn't getting any extras."

"What do you mean?"

"When someone doesn't have insurance, I guess they have to check that the kid isn't in a single if he could be in a multibed room, that kind of stuff. Anyway, as soon as Mary Pat found out that his grandmother didn't have custody, she started to worry about the DNR order, and she said she was going to call in the child protection team tomorrow."

"Oh, fuck. And she didn't call me?"

"I think she might have tried." He sounded uncomfortable.

Amelia knew she had turned her beeper off on leaving the hospital, telling herself that if anything important came up, the page operators knew to have people call her at home. She also knew that ordinarily, with a patient of hers this sick and in the hospital, she would have left the beeper on, to make sure that anyone who needed her would reach her. She knew why she had wanted to be out of reach of the beeper, and she pushed aside, resolutely, the certainty that Mary Pat would have tried, exactly once, to page her and then given up.

"So, what's going on now, Clark?"

"Well, Darren's been looking kind of bad, and the nurse was nervous, because of what she heard from Mary Pat, and I was nervous too, so I asked the senior what to do, and he might have sort of overreacted, I guess, I don't know. See, he said we were wide open legally, and the thing is, they've called in a judge."

"A *judge?*"

"Well, apparently, according to Mary Pat and according to the senior, if the grandmother doesn't have legal custody, then the DNR order isn't valid, and then if he needs a tube, he has to get a tube."

"Oh, shit," said Amelia. "Listen, are we there yet? I mean, is he going to need to be intubated right now?"

"It's hard to say. Like I told you, his respiratory status is deteriorating."

"So what happens now?"

"So this judge is coming in, and they've called up the hospital lawyer—we're gonna try to get Darren's grandmother temporary custody, so we can keep him DNR for now."

"Okay," said Amelia. "I'm on my way." And then, hanging up, thought about waking Matt, about telling him that Alexander was again all his problem, for the night and probably for the next day, and felt pressure behind her eyes, as if she was ready to cry.

They assembled in the same conference room at the hospital. The doctors made a very unimpressive group, sartorially at least. Amelia had washed her face and combed her hair, and thinking vaguely that she would be appearing before a judge, she had not actually come in blue jeans. But she wore shapeless red corduroy pants and a loose gray turtleneck sweater, comfort clothes, appropriate for someone who should by rights have been in her pajamas. Clark Donahue was in his pajamas; that is, he was in green scrubs with red edging at the neck and red stitching at the seams; in the code of the hospital, this proclaimed Medium, when in fact he needed Large. The scrub pants bulged over his thighs, and the pens and file cards he carried in his breast pocket were tightly outlined against the green fabric.

The legal profession was certainly much snazzier; even after midnight they apparently held to certain professional standards of dress. The hospital lawyer, as a matter of fact, was known all through the hospital for her standard of dress; she was generally referred to as "the *Vogue* lawyer." Her name was Lana Rosen, and she was tall, and thin, of course, and impeccably coiffed, of course, with a smooth black pageboy just brushing her collar. And impeccably made up, of course; no one had even seen Lana Rosen without false eyelashes in place and full mascara, eyeliner, eye shadow, blush, and lipstick, and even in the stress of the moment, Amelia was able to appreciate that Lana was coming up to scratch at two-thirty A.M. A hospital legend in action. And beautifully dressed; haul Lana Rosen out of bed in the middle of a winter night and she dressed in a heavy black cashmere skirt, a dark red silk shirt, and a belt that was no doubt true alligator and matched her portfolio pocketbook into the bargain. Slim and tucked in and efficient, never beautiful, exactly, but terrifyingly chic and effective, at least by hospital standards, she was out of place in the shoddy little conference room, dominant and confident. In fact, she was not very well liked in the hospital; many of the doctors found her intimidating, with her alien expertise, and disliked her because they disliked being intimidated. She was angry now, because she had been bypassed; she had whispered to Amelia in the corridor that if only *she* had been called first, not the judge, she could have handled it all with much less fuss.

The judge was something else again. Amelia had never met him before; she knew, vaguely, that there was always a judge available by beeper for legal emergencies, but she had never before met with such a judge, let alone in the middle of the night. Judge Ginzberg was an enormous man, maybe three hundred pounds of judge, but also dressed to the nines. He was wearing a lush gray suit, carefully tailored to his massive body, a thick maroon-and-gold silk tie. His head was bald and shiny, with small tendrils of black hair falling in a fringe over his forehead, almost down to his eyes, which were very black, very shrewd, and sunk deep into the fat of his face. He gave a pillowy hand first to Lana, then to Amelia, then to Clark, took as his own the one cushioned chair in the room, and drew it to the head of the table. "So now we wait for the guardian," he said. "I called in an attorney to represent the grandmother, and he's conferring with her now."

"What guardian?"

"The judge has appointed a guardian ad litem for Darren," said Lana, spreading out papers on the table. "The guardian represents the best interests of the child before the court, at least until the custody issue is decided."

"But does the guardian know Darren?"

"Under somewhat more ordinary circumstances, the guardian ad litem would be expected to carry out his or her own investigation," said the judge. His voice was unexpectedly compelling, sonorous and authoritative, the trained tones of an aging actor. "Of course, given our current exigencies, the guardian will have no more to go on, for the moment, than I have myself. I have quote appointed unquote the one person available to me at this hour, a social worker named William Winter. He is on his way, but since he lives out in Needham, it may take him a little bit longer."

Roberta Wilson came in with the lawyer the judge had called in for her, who looked almost as young as Clark Donahue. His name was Marvin Bluestone, and he was tall and thin, quiet and courteous, neat in a plain black suit, white shirt, thin blue tie. He looked to Amelia like a student dressed for a job interview. Roberta Wilson would not look at him and responded to his occasional soft comments with single syllables. She was furious with them all, Amelia thought, and completely unwilling to have anything to do with the legal process. I don't need a lawyer, and I certainly don't want *you*, Amelia imagined her saying.

When William Winter arrived, Amelia disliked him on sight. He was maybe thirty years old, with profuse blow-dried blond hair and a little blond mustache. He was dressed up, wearing a blue suit and a striped tie, but formal clothes, which lent glamour to Lana and authority to the judge, made him look somehow unctuous. He was deeply apologetic but seemed somehow to relish the idea that he had been making them all wait, that he was briefly the pivot of the hearing, just by his lateness.

Amelia had to hand it to Judge Ginzberg. She was used to a variety of doctorly styles for promulgating authority, for commanding meetings, for ordering other people around. But she had never seen anything to equal the way the judge took over that little room of Formica and soothing green carpet. The judge had no particular place in the hospital, its jargon was not his, its hierarchy was presumably alien—and yet there was no doubt from the very first minute who was in charge and what was going on. At first Lana was asking the questions, but the judge leaned in to ask three for every one of hers.

Amelia found herself expertly quizzed about Darren's medical status: his long-term prognosis, his short-term prognosis. Clark Donahue was neatly turned inside out about the medical specifics of the night: would Darren definitely die by morning without intubation, what would be the indications for moving him to intensive care. The judge demanded specifics: "Yes, Dr. Donahue, I believe I understand what you are trying to explain about the methods of monitoring respiratory status. And I understand why, in your best clinical judgment, this patient is getting worse. But please tell me then, Dr. Donahue, exactly what arterial blood gas results would be an absolute indication for intubation." And Clark felt compelled to avoid the usual song and dance about every case being different and gave numbers. "I would say, Your Honor, an oxygen below 60 percent, a carbon dioxide above 60 percent—or else a steady rise in the carbon dioxide, indicating increasing respiratory failure." And then he looked nervously at Amelia, as if expecting to be corrected. But the judge nodded and moved on to his next question, absorbing all information, no matter how alien, with an air that made clear he felt his intelligence was equal to the occasion.

They were going over almost the same ground they had covered that afternoon, but with Judge Ginzberg calling the shots, the whole thing took maybe fifteen minutes. The judge did not take notes, though William Winters filled several pages of a foolscap pad with a large loose scrawl, and Lana Rosen occasionally noted down a word or two, in a burgundy leather notebook, with a tortoiseshell fountain pen.

The judge turned to Roberta Wilson. She had not seemed to be listening to anything that anyone had said about Darren; her eyes were fixed on the framed poster that hung on the wall instead of a window, that famous Kodak lineup of the babies, every ethnic variety, in colored sleepers, a rainbow of adorable infants. What on earth was she thinking about—one more obstacle thrown up by the hospital, one more insanity between her grandson and peace? Did she even bother to remember who was who in that room? Her face had an ashy tone to it, and her fingers, in her lap, were steadily rolling and unrolling a green rectangle of paper, which Amelia recognized: a parent parking voucher. Her suit, navy blue wool with brass buttons, hung on her a little, as if she had lost weight, and seemed reduced to some very amateurish homemade status next to the judge's suit, next to Lana's lush splendor, even next to Marvin Bluestone's unexceptional uniform.

Judge Ginzberg's manner changed noticeably when he began to

ask her questions. With Amelia and with Clark he had been smooth and demanding; he expected answers, and prompt answers, and correct answers. With Roberta Wilson he was much gentler. His manner was not quite paternal, nor was it in the least deferential, but he treated her as if he found her delicate, as if he knew that the truth might be hard for her to tell, and wanted to help her through. He reminded her that Mr. Bluestone was there to act as her advocate, but she said in a dull voice that she didn't know the man and she didn't need a lawyer, but she'd answer any questions they had for her.

"When your daughter was sick, Mrs. Wilson, when she knew she was dying, did she ever talk to you about who would take care of Darren?"

"It wasn't necessary for her to talk about that, Your Honor. We both knew who would be taking care of him."

"Will you explain just what you mean by that?"

"I mean, sir, that by the time my daughter was dying, there was nobody else there besides me to take care of that child. His father had disappeared, and we thought he might be dead. I don't mind telling you I hoped so."

William Winter looked up sharply from his foolscap and seemed about to speak. But the judge ignored him.

"I can understand how you might feel that way. And since the death of your daughter, you have been taking care of your grandson?"

"Yes."

"The nights he has not spent in the hospital, has he spent them all in your home?"

"It's his home too."

"Has he spent any nights with his father?"

"Your Honor," said Roberta Wilson, as if finally at the end of her patience, exhaling loudly with the *H*, then turning to Amelia. "Doctor, you know as well as I do—will you please tell the judge here that Darren's father hasn't been troubling himself to call, or come see his child; he has not seen Darren in more than two years, and he has never taken care of him. What he did was, he infected my daughter and left her to die." Her voice was full of such anger and such contempt that even the judge was silenced, for a minute.

Amelia heard her own voice, lacking the conviction of Darren's grandmother, the authority of the judge. "Darren's father has never brought him to an appointment, has never visited him when he was in the hospital." She knew those issues were important in custody decisions; several times she had been asked for letters by patients, attesting to which parent made appointments, kept appointments, tracked the child's immunizations.

Lana Rosen cut in, turning back a page in her notebook. "And yet, I'm told that the last time Darren was hospitalized here, his father did call and say he was planning to come."

"And then never showed up, couldn't be bothered," said Roberta Wilson.

Judge Ginzberg patiently took her a little further through the story of Darren and his illness: through the details of caring for him, the number of pills she gave him every day, the doctors' appointments, the schedule of the visiting nurses. Finally he said, in what could only be considered courtly tones, "I thank you very much, Mrs. Wilson, for telling us all this so clearly and well. Let me tell you that I think you have done a wonderful job with this unfortunate child, that you have amply fulfilled the trust your daughter placed in you."

Roberta Wilson stood up, shaking the table. "I don't need you to tell me that, Judge," she said. "I need for you to tell these doctors and lawyers that Darren is in my custody, and that I have the right to help him to die if he needs to. And if you do, then you know as well as I do that he may die tonight, and if this is his last night alive on earth, then I have wasted just about enough of it sitting in this room with all of you when I might have been sitting with my baby." And she marched out.

Marvin Bluestone jumped to his feet as she passed, put out his hand to touch her on the arm, and said, very mildly, "Mrs. Wilson, please don't leave yet." But she didn't slow down or stop, and the door closed behind her with an institutional metallic click.

After Roberta Wilson left the room, the judge carefully solicited opinions and conclusions from each of the people at the table. Amelia said shortly that Darren's grandmother had cared for him all his life, that she loved him and wanted what was best for him, and that she was the obvious (and only) person to have legal custody. Marvin Bluestone agreed, adding the specific suggestion that the court enter an order giving custody of Darren to his grandmother and specifying the DNR status. Clark Donahue apologized to everyone for calling them in, told them he just hadn't been comfortable without a DNR order, apologized again because of course he didn't know the family as well as Amelia did, but concluded, gratefully, that he agreed with her that Darren's grandmother should have custody, and agreed with both of them that it was reasonable for Darren to be DNR.

Lana Rosen did not apologize to anyone for anything. Tapping her fountain pen severely on the tabletop, she said that the doctors had clearly been following the wishes of a highly trustworthy and competent caretaker. "We all understand the importance of the DNR order," she said, directly to the judge. "That's why we're here tonight, we want to construct our DNR orders very carefully. And in this particular case the hospital would be very happy to see custody granted to the grandmother, since there really doesn't seem to be anyone else claiming it. There is always a very strong presumption in favor of the biological parents, of course, but if the court will grant temporary custody to the grandmother, I am very comfortable allowing her, in the context of that custody, to establish a DNR order—especially given Dr. Stern's assessment of the medical situation."

Finally the judge turned to the guardian ad litem, who had been paging through his foolscap pad, annotating his notes, getting ready for his speech. Amelia, looking at him, had the sudden impression that he was about to try to gum things up. At the same moment she was newly aware of her own fatigue, of her wish to be home in bed, asleep, next to Matt, in the warm and comfortable position she had found for herself after lovemaking. Her son safe and sleeping down the hall. It seemed far away, and her eyes felt gritty.

"Thank you, Your Honor," said William Winter. "Thank you very much for giving me a chance to respond here. There are a number of concerns I would like to raise, even though I can see that everyone in this room is coming from a real and sincere wish to do right by this child. Still, I want to share some ideas with you."

He paused, and seemed to be expecting encouragement, and the judge considerately said, "Please do."

"My first concern, speaking as the advocate for the child, centers on the relationship between the grandmother and the child's biological father. Now, I do have to go on the assumption that the child's absolute best interests, until proven otherwise, are with his biological parents. So here we have Grandmother, who clearly has a lot of hostility toward the child's biological father, for a variety of reasons, and we have to take *her* word that Father has not attempted to contact the child, or take care of the child. Now, can we be sure that Father has not, in fact, been prevented from seeing Darren? Can we be sure that Grandmother would have allowed him free access?"

Amelia leaned forward, started to speak, but William Winter sorted fussily through his pages to find his next point, and Judge Ginzberg met her gaze in a way that kept her quiet.

"Now, my second concern, as the child's advocate, are the medical facts of the matter. I'm not trying to express any doubts about the expertise of the doctors here, but it's quite clear that there are some tests they could do, and some medical operations they could perform, which might help Darren live a little longer. And I wonder, given the concerns over his custody status, whether he doesn't deserve the benefit of the doubt, whether he doesn't deserve to have everything done. I mean, as long as there are two sides to the question, I think I would have to say that he deserves to have us come down on that side. Maybe Grandmother is just very tired, very unwilling to take him home again."

Amelia did speak this time. "She's unwilling to see him suffer, she's unwilling to prolong his dying! With all due respect, if you're supposed to be acting as Darren's advocate, it seems to me that you should consider the fact that of all the people who have been in this room, Darren's grandmother is the only one who loves him. Even if there *is* some kind of legal preference for the biological father, you might remember that he hasn't seen this child in the last three years. So whatever he feels for Darren has to be pretty theoretical compared with what Mrs. Wilson feels, since she's the one who feeds him and changes his diapers and sits in his hospital room. Don't you think it's in the best interests of the child to have decisions made about him by the person who loves him?"

William Winter smiled at her, an unctuous and extremely irritating smile. "Not necessarily, Doctor. That's what our job is—to decide what is in his best interests. And the reason it's *our* job is because we can't just take it all on trust and leave it up to Grandmother."

Amelia wanted desperately to pull rank, to say, as she had that afternoon, "I am the attending, we will do it my way." She felt helpless before the real power of the judge, both legal and personal, and helpless in a different way before the sociological snake oil of the guardian ad litem. She felt angry and exhausted and very eager to be done with this day, this discussion.

Judge Ginzberg called them all to order by clearing his throat. "Thank you, Mr. Winter. I take it then that you are recommending, as guardian ad litem, that the court give temporary custody of this child to the Department of Social Services and furthermore enter an order that he be treated with full medical aggressiveness." He did not even look at William Winter to see him nod. "I think that everyone in this room has demonstrated an intelligent and sincere regard for the well-being of this unfortunate little boy. I would have to agree with Mr. Winter that the medical situation does seem to me ambiguous. That is, of the various situations in which a DNR order may be requested, this one seems to me less than clear-cut. If I understand correctly, the child could well survive on a ventilator for some considerable period of time, during which a diagnostic test could well establish the presence of an unusual organism, one which you are not currently treating but could possibly go on to treat. It is therefore not at all inconceivable that he could, in fact, survive his pulmonary deterioration, even though you feel that his general nutritional status and lack of an effective immune system make such survival especially unlikely."

Amelia, without surprise, granted Judge Ginzberg points. He understood what he had been told, he moved without floundering through the terminology.

"However, I also agree with Miss Rosen when she argues that in the absence of any other family members claiming custody of the child, we should make official what has already been the custody situation for the last several years, and grant at least temporary custody to his grandmother. And I agree furthermore with both Counsel and with Dr. Stern when they argue, from their different perspectives, that Roberta Wilson's request for a DNR order should be honored." He looked around the table, as if assessing each member of the gathering. Amelia found herself straightening in her seat. "And now, I am quite sure that everyone is as tired as I am, and it is getting on for five in the morning. I thank you all for your time, and I wish you, doctors, the best of luck with your patient. Mr. Bluestone, if you will be so good as to go and get Mrs. Wilson, I will explain to her what I have decided."

"I'll go," Amelia said. Roberta Wilson had drawn her armchair up to Darren's bed, and she was sitting forward, on the edge of the chair, her head on the bed, her arms reaching under the flap of the oxygen tent. Amelia touched her on the shoulder, and she looked up, blinking, as if coming up from under water.

"It's okay," Amelia said. "The judge is granting you custody, Darren stays DNR. You just need to go in and let him tell you so himself. I'm sorry there's been so much nonsense." The older woman got slowly to her feet, pushing back against the armchair so she could walk away from the bed. Amelia put out her hand, and Roberta Wilson pressed it, somewhat absently. She buttoned her jacket, her fingers struggling slightly with the nautical brass buttons, then walked steadily out of the room.

Amelia straightened out the plastic flaps of the oxygen tent. Tired and surfeited with melodrama, with life and death, she had a fleeting idea of dropping to her knees, of praying Victorian style by Darren's bedside. O Lord, she could almost hear herself whispering into folded hands, O Lord, grant thou eternal peace and rest to this, one of thy smallest servants. Instead, she unhooked the clipboard from the end of the bed and looked at the nursing sheets. Darren's respiratory rate had decreased slightly over the past couple of hours, while the doctors and lawyers had met. Was that because he was getting a little bit better, or was that because he was tiring out and could no longer breathe as fast as he needed to? If he was tiring, he would be unable to blow off the carbon dioxide accumulating in his blood, and he would indeed die by morning. She looked to see whether the nurse had checked his oxygen saturation, but the last check was at 2:00 A.M. Well, it didn't matter. He was safely DNR, and he would either breathe his way through the night or else he wouldn't. He didn't need to have needles stuck in his arteries. There would be no tube down his throat.

Amelia unzipped the side panel of the oxygen tent and poked her face into the misty interior. The little boy lay as quietly as he had that afternoon, in exactly the same position. His long lashes still on his cheeks, his sharp cheekbones faintly shadowed in the dim fluorescent light. Now she could hear the labored whistle of his breath, escaping regularly through his slightly pursed lips, she could see the faint rise and fall of his chest under the blanket. It seemed almost a dream, it seemed improbably familiar, this looking in on a sleeping boy. If she had been home and had happened to wake late at night and had gone wandering down her own hallway to use the bathroom, she would have wandered, bleary-eyed and automatic, into Alexander's room, straightened his covers, bent to kiss his face. She leaned farther into Darren's bubble and kissed him gently on the forehead, and like her own son, he did not stir, as if he were used to being kissed in the night, in his sleep.

"This was very badly handled," Lana Rosen said to Amelia. The two of them were alone in the little conference room. "It was a major screw-up to call in a judge without letting me know. I mean, that's really bad news, when the judge calls me, instead of me calling him. That's not the point of the emergency response number, that's not the point of having a judge available by beeper."

"Well, it worked out okay." This is not my fight, Amelia thought tiredly.

"Yes, fortunately. This particular judge is on a real ego trip—did you see how he ran the whole show? No one else could even ask a question. But he's a very smart man, all the same."

"Thanks for coming in," Amelia said, somewhat lamely, anxious to go home. "I'm sorry about how it happened."

Lana shook her elegant head. "You're lucky they didn't call in the whole child protection team, while they were at it. Some people hear the word 'custody' and they lose all sense of proportion." She shrugged and began to gather up her papers, tapping them authoritatively into a neat pile. Then she looked straight at Amelia. "And I hope that if there's another situation where custody is ambiguous and a DNR has to be negotiated, you people will talk to me sooner, not later. I have to warn you, you doctors could lay yourselves open to legal action if you aren't careful." Then, her warning delivered, she picked up her portfolio, said good night very pleasantly, and walked briskly out of the room, like a woman with places to go and people to meet, five A.M. or no five A.M., clicking confidently along in her high high heels.

The child protection team. What a concept. Surely every child needs a protection team. Does Alexander have one—me and Matt and his grandparents, and the teachers at the day care center? Parents, even good, well-meaning parents, are not enough, love is not enough, to keep a child safe. It takes a whole network of adults, representing love, and law, and medicine, and don't run into the street, and don't take candy from strangers, and no one has a right to touch you if you don't want to be touched. I like to imagine that I am Alexander's protection, that I am one of the most important people on his team. But I also include myself on Darren's team, on the teams of all the other children I take care of.

And the hospital child protection team is like so many other hospital constructs, like dialysis or heart-lung bypass machines. A clumsy, difficult invention to approximate an infinitely complex, infinitely graceful natural system. If your kidney stops working, then dialysis is better than dying. But it doesn't actually do the same constant, perfectly balanced job that your own kidney, tucked neatly into its place inside your body, would have gone on doing hour after hour, decade after decade, if disease hadn't interrupted it. And so the child protection team attempts to step in when a child's life is disordered, when parents and grandparents can't guarantee a safe home, a safe child. The natural safety net doesn't weave, and so the hospital steps in with social workers and doctors and lawyers. And what they make is not necessarily beautiful or graceful, but with any luck it will give the child a chance to grow.

Amelia spent a few minutes with Clark Donahue. The ward had stayed quiet enough for him to attend the custody hearing, which meant, Amelia knew, that under other circumstances he would have had a couple of hours of sleep. Still, he was good-natured as always, eager to apologize for having dragged her in, pleased now that he knew what to do if Darren got sicker, concerned now that in fact perhaps Darren was getting a little better, and apologetic that he might have caused all this trouble if Darren was not, in fact, about to die. Amelia reassured him, of course she had been glad to come in. Only an intern, deep into his own pattern of hospital nights, would have swallowed that. You're doing a very good job, she told him, aware that that was probably what he needed to hear above all; it was what most interns usually needed to hear. You're doing a very good job, don't hesitate to call me if you need me, I'm going to leave my beeper on now, so you can either call me at home or page me.

And as she said that, her beeper went off, shrill in the dim hallway. She dialed into the page system, sure at heart that it would be Matt, that he would be angry. In fact, while she waited for the page operator to connect her, she had already imagined the scenario, a feverish Alexander awake at five in the morning; where the hell are you? Does your own child mean anything to you at all? She reached for her own lines—I'll be home in less than half an hour, I'll take care of everything, I'm sorry—quite conscious all the while of what saintly patience she would be displaying, in her fatigued state, in her weariness after being up all night wrestling with life and death. Well, up all night sitting around a Formica table.

But Matt, though he was angry, and upset, had something else to say. "Something's wrong," he said. "Something's very wrong with Alexander. Amelia, he's very hot, and he's shaking, and he won't really talk to me. He seems very sick, I can't exactly explain, but he seems an awful lot sicker than he did last night. I'm scared looking at him."

"Do you want me to come home, right now? I'm starting—I had actually left the hospital, I came back to answer the page." (How can she be lying when her own child is sick? What is she trying to fend off? She knows perfectly well.) "If you think he's really sick, though, and you want to just bring him to the emergency room, I could meet you down there."

"You mean, just load him in the car?"

"If you think he's really sick."

"How am I supposed to tell?" Matt's voice rose, almost cracked, in outrage. "If he's really sick, do you think it's safe for me to take him out like that?"

"Night air isn't going to hurt him. Honey, I can be home in half an hour, but if something's really wrong, then we just have to drive right back to the hospital. Do you want to bring him in or not?"

"I hate you for leaving me with this!" Matt said, exploding, letting it all out. "I hate you for being gone right now, with Alexander so sick. I'll never never forget this." He made his voice cold and calm. "I'll bring him in to your emergency room. Why don't you go there and get things ready for us. We'll be there in half an hour or less." And he hung up.

Amelia, riding down in the elevator to the emergency room, was shaking a little. Not surprising really, when she'd been up all night and her son was sick and her husband was bringing him in and her husband hated her. She felt helpless before Matt's coldness; it was a million years ago that they had been warm and in bed together, a million years since they had all three sat at the kitchen table and eaten too many chocolate chip cookies.

If you look at Amelia, alone in that bright elevator, in that faintly humming nighttime hospital in that still-dark winter morning, you will see someone who looks defeated, beaten, bereft. Around her, on the floors where the elevator does not stop, the hospital day is beginning; miserable surgical interns drag themselves through pre-rounds, checking on their patients so they can speed through rounds with the senior people at six, so everyone can be in the operating room before eight. The custodians move through the corridors, emptying pails of the night's garbage, their hands protected by thick gloves, since who knows what might be in hospital garbage. On the second floor, the cafeteria is gearing up for breakfast, with tubs of scrambled powdered eggs and trays of perfectly square cakes of hash brown potatoes. And Amelia leans back against the corrugated metal of the elevator wall, and what she is thinking is something like this: Suppose those were the last moments, suppose that time around the kitchen table was the last time we ever laugh together like that, the last dessert we gobble as an intact family, the last time I can kid myself that my world is safe. Suppose that turns out to be the last time Matt and I make love, ever.

And here you see the effects of fatigue; she knows perfectly well why Matt is angry, and she knows this is the kind of anger she has faced before, and will again, and she knows how much of it is fear, pure and simple, because he is alone with Alexander and feels that if she were there she would know what to do. And knows also, probably, that when she asks herself in fear if something bad is about to happen to her family, she is focusing on the unlikely possibility that Matt is so angry that he will leave, specifically in order to avoid wondering what is wrong with Alexander. She could analyze all this, if she had to, but she is tired, and you can look at her and see that she looks hunched, defeated, crumpled.

But actually, it is a very short elevator ride, and when the doors rumble open at the emergency room level, she straightens up and marches herself off down the hall, like any tired doctor at five o'clock in the morning.

When Matt brought Alexander in, Alexander in pajamas and his blue hooded parka, Amelia had everything ready. She was trying to propitiate, to smooth the way, so Alexander would get cared for right away, so Matt would be grateful she was there. She had said apologetically to the ER charge nurse and the late-night resident that she didn't mean to get all excited over nothing, and probably it was just chicken pox and fever, but still, her husband was bringing her son in, and she was a little bit worried. She tried to sound calm and reasonable, like a doctor, not like an off-the-handle mother, but the resident was worried enough to wake up the ER supervisor. Reasonable enough; no resident really wants to take care of a senior doctor's kid.

So Matt was whisked through registration in the almost empty waiting room, and in record time, Alexander was on an examining table in a little cubicle of a room, and Amelia was unzipping first the parka, then the pajamas, while Matt refused to meet her eyes, and a nurse took vital signs. Amelia stripped him to his underwear. He didn't really wake up, which was after all not so unusual; once asleep, Alexander was always hard to rouse. But he was hot to the touch, and she wondered if he was limper under her hands than mere sleep would suggest, if he was somehow without the resilience of his normal vigorous sleeping self. When he was on the table wearing his little-boy underpants, Amelia could see that there was a really ugly area of infected pox on his right thigh, stretching up into his groin. The whole upper part of his leg was hot and red and swollen, with two big pus-filled swellings surrounded by an even darker red.

The ER supervisor pushed in beside Amelia, looked down at Alexander's thigh, and shook his head. "Lousy-looking cellulitis he has there," he said.

"What's that?" Matt's voice was angry, anxious.

"I think your son has a bad infection of his skin coming from those pox." He started to ask the routine questions, how many days of fever, what other symptoms, when did the pox appear. Amelia answered, but then broke into her own series of calm answers. "Listen, Joe, my husband couldn't really get him awake at home, and he won't wake up here—what if he's septic? The way he looks is making me nervous."

Joe shook Alexander somewhat roughly by the shoulder, then tried sitting him up, then pressed down on the hot red skin of his thigh. When Alexander did not respond to any of these maneuvers, he asked the nurse to recheck the blood pressure.

"What is it," Matt hissed in Amelia's ear. "What's going on?"

It was Joe who answered, looking past Amelia and speaking in a reassuring tone, a tone designed for anxious parents, who had every reason to be anxious but would be less in the way if they were calm. "Your son isn't really waking up, and his blood pressure is just a little low. Probably he's just sleeping soundly, and maybe a little bit dehydrated from all the fever, and from not drinking enough. But we sort of have to worry about what else could be making him look so out of it, and since he obviously has a bacterial infection of his skin, I need to be sure he doesn't have bacteria in his blood too, because that could be more dangerous. So I think we'll just move him down the hall to room 14, and get some blood to test, and I'm going to put in an IV and give him a little fluid."

Even as he was talking, the nurse had the door propped open and kicked off the brakes on the bed, and she and the doctor rolled the bed down the hall. Amelia followed them, and Matt followed her, and as they went into room 14, he grabbed for her hand. They stood together on the side, watching the bustle with IV poles and bags of fluid, and though Matt might have wanted to whisper *This is all your fault for going off and leaving him*, what he actually did whisper was *What the hell is going on?*

The truly nightmare glow this scene assumes for Amelia, as she whispers somewhat reassuring explanations to Matt, is from the memory of her most recent sojourn in this room, that last night in the ER, the little SIDS baby. This is a room set up for serious illness, for resuscitation. How can Alexander be in it? Amelia can remember that night so well, the feel of the shockingly cold baby chest under her fingers when she took her turn at CPR, watching the cardiac monitor to see if she could bring back a pulse. The baby never regained a pulse; the only cardiac activity was what the chest compressions produced.

She stands now in the room, watching Joe search Alexander's limbs for an IV site, and remembers the lines they put in that SIDS baby, one in the antecubital, one in the groin. "Listen, Joe, he has a great intern's vein on the left," she says, in the voice of one bringing glad tidings, and Joe immediately checks for it and finds it. The intern's vein, so called because it saves many an intern who needs a fast IV, snakes around the inside of the wrist, from the back of the hand to the front of the arm. Joe slides an IV in, and Amelia shrugs and apologizes to Matt, *It may be kind of morbid, but I know where all his good veins are*. Matt doesn't really understand, of course, that finding a vein on a little kid can be life and death, he doesn't know why she would need to look her son over every now and then, in the middle of a cuddle on the couch, and reassure herself that he has access possibilities. For that matter, Amelia thinks to herself, almost amused, Matt doesn't dream that I know that he has a great big straight vein in the back of his right hand, and a couple of pipes in the left antecubital.

Alexander does cry out when the IV goes in; an excellent sign. Matt doesn't quite know to see it that way, of course, but Amelia is remembering that cold baby on the table who neither flinched nor cried as two doctors dug around in him with one needle after another. Amelia, pressed against the wall to stay out of the way, is remembering how she looked up, once the tube was in, and the lines, the cardiac monitor hooked up, the first round of meds running in, and she looked up and saw that baby's parents standing there, waiting for the miracle. Surely, Alexander is only feverish and tired—but words appropriate to a crash room keep coming into her head: He's in shock, in septic shock. He's comatose, his brain is swelling. Some catastrophe has happened inside him, a hemorrhage, sepsis, shock, necrosis.

"I'm gonna go ahead and push some bug juice," Joe calls over to her.

"Okay," calls Amelia back, and then explains to Matt, Alexander is getting IV antibiotics in case his bloodstream is full of bacteria. Also fluid, since he may be dehydrated. And she remembers her own voice calling out the orders for the resuscitation medications, the ritual doses of epinephrine and atropine to stimulate the heart that wouldn't start up beating, bicarb and calcium, again and again, always with that commanding politeness that residents learn to use in cardiac arrest situations. Let's give another round, please. And she delegated an extra nurse, who had come in to help, to take the parents into the little interview room across the hall, bring them coffee, wait with them if necessary, just keep them out of room 14.

She sees Alexander's eyes opening and hurries forward to take her place beside him, to take his hand and put her head down next to his and whisper to him over and over, Mama's here, darling, Mama's here with you—almost as if she too believes that he got sick because she left him. Alexander looks unfocused, but when he tries to move his left arm and finds it taped to a board to protect the IV, he begins to cry with anger and hurt and fear, to Amelia's great joy. He is awake, he is reacting, his brain is working. She puts her arms around him and allows herself to cry a few tears into his sweaty hair.

Thank you for waiting in here. I'm sorry we didn't have a doctor free sooner to come talk to you. I'm Dr. Stern, and I'm the one who was in charge in there, I know it was a little confusing to watch. Let me just sit down and I'll tell you what I can. I'm afraid that there wasn't really anything we could do, as you probably guessed from the beginning. I'm afraid your son had already been dead some time when you found him, and when someone is already dead, you can't bring him back. You did exactly the right thing when you found him, giving mouth-to-mouth and calling the ambulance. And we did everything we could, because with a baby you always do, you never want to give up. But I'm afraid we just couldn't get his heart started again. We were giving him oxygen through that tube you saw in his mouth, we were giving him drugs to make his heart go, and also pressing on his chest to make it pump blood, but he was beyond us.

Well, you've probably heard of SIDS, sudden infant death syndrome. It's another name for crib death. No one knows what causes it, and this looks very much like that syndrome. If that's what it was, no one can predict it, no one can prevent it. You did everything you could.

Are there other family members you would like to call?

Would you like us to call in a priest or a minister?

The nurses will have him all cleaned up in a minute, so you can spend some time alone with him.

I'm terribly, terribly sorry.

Here is one thing I didn't say: This was definitely not your fault. I didn't say it because, after all, this could perfectly well have been a murdered baby. And for the same reason, I eventually said what I had to say: This case will have to go to the medical examiner, there will have to be an autopsy. SIDS is a diagnosis of exclusion.

I'm sorry, but you have no choice. The cause of death has to be established if it's possible to do so.

Matt came and stood on the other side of the stretcher, stroking Alexander's shoulder. The flurry of medical business had calmed, with the blood sent off, the IV taped in, the fluid running in, the antibiotics given. Alexander had calmed down and was beginning to ask some grumpy, cranky questions. Amelia looked up and met Matt's eyes, and to her surprise, he smiled at her. And she smiled back; she could not guess what his visions had been, but perhaps after all they had not been so far from her own: sickness, death, despair. And here was their boy demanding in his own voice why he was in bed in only his underpants. Matt mouthed some words at Amelia, so the nurse wouldn't hear: I'm sorry. I love you. And into Amelia's mind, tired and relieved and still very worried, really, flashed bad-movie dialogue. Oh, darling, it took this for us to find each other again!

She ushered the stunned parents back into room 14. The baby was wrapped in a blanket, tube and IVs and needles and monitor leads all removed. Just a little body, wrapped in a blanket, lying on the stretcher. But in spite of all efforts to make him look natural, no one had bothered to put up the side rails of the bed. He lay on the flat hospital surface, three and a half feet above the floor, with nothing to stop him from squirming or crawling or rolling off.

CHAPTER VII
ORCHARD HOUSE

I know what you're thinking. I know what you think is going to happen. You think it's all a setup. You think that Alexander is going to die, that I have set this all up for the ultimate pathos, that Matt and I will stand locked together in our helpless grief at the deathbed of our darling boy. It's obvious, isn't it? All my mouthing off about the death of children, Beth and little Eva and Nell and all the rest of the fictional angels, Darren and the other pediatric patients—what does it come to if not to this. I am a mother, and my child is also vulnerable; I do not buy him off just by trying to prevent the death of other children. What else could teach me my lesson, hit me and my story hard enough to elevate it into art? What else could happen to me that would leave me a worthy narrator for the stories I have chosen to tell you?

Well, to be perfectly honest, I thought about it. Death, or at least very near death, I thought about it. I wasn't sure I could actually bring myself to kill him off (you know, superstition, evil eye, that kind of thing), but I was going to let him come very close to death. And, who knows, the temptation might have been just too strong; when I got close, I might have let him slip away over the edge. What authority it would give me, after all, what an explanation for everything else that goes wrong in my life, above all, what a tragedy. My story would have its very own solid onyx teardrop at the center, not just the scraps and shards from other people's funeral monuments.

I had a disease in mind too. There's a syndrome that sometimes follows on chicken pox, very uncommon, but something that we always worry about. Reye's syndrome, it's called, and what happens is that the liver fails and the brain swells, for mysterious reasons. And when the brain swells, it starts to press against the inside of its box, and those precious cells of the cortex, the outer layer, are squashed against the protective bones of the nonexpanding skull. With those cells, the body snuffs out its own memory, intelligence, personality. And if the brain keeps swelling, you get brain death, and then death. Reye's syndrome used to be more common, but some fancy epidemiological detective work turned up evidence that 80 percent of cases were connected with giving children aspirin when they had chicken pox, or certain other viral illnesses. So we don't give children aspirin, and the Tylenol people got rich, and now there are only very, very rare cases of Reye's, those 20 percent or so that never did have anything to do with aspirin.

Anyway, that was what I thought might happen to Alexander. It has the advantage of being rare and deadly and unpredictable. And Alexander has already actually had chicken pox, as you know, so he won't ever get it again. So if I had written those deadly scenes, if I had written in Reye's syndrome, and even death, I wouldn't have had to worry about him really getting chicken pox, and then Reye's syndrome, sometime in the future. He's immune now, for life. So I thought about bringing him into the emergency room, lethargic and woozy and vomiting, and how they would do a spinal tap to make sure he didn't have meningitis or encephalitis (other complications of chicken pox, usually less serious). I thought that I would insist on standing by the bed, and as I watched them stick a long needle in between two of the vertebrae of his down-covered spinal cord, I would think about all the spinal taps I had done myself, all the other women's children whose secret inner spaces I had pierced. And then they would get back the blood test, showing that his liver function tests were elevated, and they would start to worry about Reye's syndrome, and of course I would know exactly what they were thinking of, and of course Matt would have no idea, never having heard of the disease, and I would be placed in a situation of terrible anguished delicacy—when to tell him, what to tell him.

And our boy, our lovely boy, would grow blurry before our eyes, less and less himself. And finally Matt would turn to me and say, Just what the hell do you people think this is, and as if pushed into professionalism by that phrase "you people," I would tell him about Reye's syndrome, in words out of some textbook, offering him no comfort (since I would have none left for him).

And so on and so on. Into the intensive care unit. Alexander on what we call ICP precautions, to decrease his increased intracranial pressure, limited fluids, the head of the bed elevated. As I say, I thought I might spare his life, but the possibility of killing off a child, especially a loved and beautiful child, a child who is the heart of his parents, is very tempting from a literary point of view. If I have made you believe at all that my own child is alive and graceful and gallant, then surely you must have been expecting his death, at least a little bit, at least in some dark corner of your imagining.

Alexander spent three days in the hospital with his superinfected chicken pox. He could probably have gone home the second day, since his blood cultures were negative, showing that he hadn't had any bacteria in his bloodstream. His doctors would have sent him home on oral antibiotics, but they extended a kind of professional courtesy to Amelia, understanding that she and Matt were worn out, and let Alexander stay one more day. After all, in the hospital, the nurses took care of putting lotions and dressings on the worst patches of skin, the medications and fluids went silently in through the IV, and even the meals appeared promptly through the door. True, the food was disgusting, but Alexander loved it and took tremendous pleasure in ordering his next day's menu each afternoon when the dietician came around. French toast *and* sausages, macaroni and cheese *and* a hamburger *and* french fries, fried chicken leg *and* grilled cheese *and* multicolored Jell-O *and* canned peaches. And he at least tasted every single item; he was eating, Amelia figured, much more than he would have eaten at home, even not sick.

After the first twenty-four hours on IV antibiotics, Alexander stopped having fevers. No new chicken pox were appearing, and the old ones were starting to crust over. The areas of superinfection and cellulitis improved steadily. His spirits were excellent by the second hospital day, and he was demanding entertainment; he wanted to leave his room; he knew from his mother that every ward had a playroom. Unfortunately, chicken pox is highly infectious, so for the protection of the other patients, Alexander was confined to his single room with strict precautions to be observed, dictated by signs on the door, the door that must never be left open even a crack.

To get from Cambridge, Massachusetts, to the famous old town of Concord, now a classy upscale suburb, you take Route 2. Immediately outside Cambridge it's a very big road, four lanes each way, and yet very quickly it feels rural. By reputation, it's a bad road for commuting; Amelia is used to hearing on the traffic report that Route 2 is backed up, moving slow, not moving. But Amelia is driving out to Concord just after noon on a Saturday, and the road is almost empty. There are no houses to see, just snowy slopes on either side, though the exit signs name familiar towns, hidden from view. She is passing signs for Lexington now, another big-deal American Revolution town. Looking at the signs, she thinks automatically that probably Alexander is now at an age to enjoy an excursion to revolutionary battlegrounds; she and Matt could take him, could buy him some helpful book first, maybe. Surely, if you raise your child in this area, you should expose him to his colonial heritage. She herself has never been to Lexington, or Concord, not till today. But there should be sites ... and then of course she remembers that everything is falling apart, that she and Matt may not take Alexander on any such excursions, ever again, and she has a vision of herself, alone with Alexander, taking him to the Old North Bridge, or whatever it is, on her weekend with him—the cliché of the separated parent trying to fill up assigned time, make it exciting, make it educational.

By the side of the road now are big new buildings, red brick and dark glass against the snow, signs advertising space for rent, eight thousand square feet. And at some point the road narrows, two lanes only. Amelia makes herself think calmly about the boring and completely irrelevant topic of commuting; lots of people must turn off onto 128, the ring road around Boston, so Route 2 gets smaller after it feeds its cars into 128. Of course. She is not going to fantasize ghoulishly about separation, divorce, custody. It is possible for two people to fight, even badly, even over days and days, and still find their way back to each other. Just as it is possible for a little boy to be groggy and out of it and feverish in the emergency room and still turn out to have nothing too serious wrong with him at all. Instead, she will think about how glad she is that she doesn't live out here in the western suburbs of Boston, doesn't have to commute twice a day along this road.

Really, Alexander's time in the hospital has resolved itself, in Amelia's mind at least, into anecdotes that are mostly mild, some even humorous, stories she might tell on herself. It was just that first day, the end of that long night with the custody hearing about Darren, the way Matt spoke to her over the phone and then looked at her at first, that was the only really hard part. The low point. But then things started to get better. It was confusing and disorienting for her to be twenty-four hours a day in the hospital, but as a parent, not a doctor. It was a place she knew so well, but she seemed to be in a different dimension of that place. Because Alexander had a private room, because of the infection precautions, she and Matt were both able to sleep there with him; the nurses brought in an extra cot. The cot felt remarkably familiar to Amelia—all those residency nights on these same standard-issue hospital cots. She felt the familiar jut of the central bar, insufficiently cushioned by the thin mattress pad, hitting her at the top of her hip, just where it always had, and she bunched up the blanket and tucked it under her there, just as she always had.

Actually, Alexander fell asleep almost immediately after they had been taken up to their room from the emergency room, and Amelia lay down next to him and fell asleep as well. Matt, glad to have a mission, had gone off home to collect clothes and pajamas and favorite toys and books. He didn't wake Amelia, or Alexander, when he returned, and when she did wake up, almost three hours later, and saw Matt sitting in the armchair, reading, she imagined that he had been looking over every now and then, smiling to himself at the picture of his exhausted wife and child, zonked out together. She remembered how she had stood, herself, looking down on Matt asleep next to Alexander that morning, four days ago. And in fact he smiled at her and asked, "Feel better?"

"Yes," said Amelia, softly, struggling to sit up, climb off the bed, without waking Alexander. "And he's going to be all right, that's the most important thing."

Matt's face cracked into remembered terror. "God, I was so scared this morning, I didn't know what to do. I'd never seen him look like that."

"You did exactly the right thing. You brought him here, and he's going to be fine. You knew what to do, really, you were just scared because he was sick. And I was too, but he's going to be fine, thanks to you."

He stood up from his armchair and Amelia went to him and hugged him, and as he folded his arms around her, she thought back blearily to the way he had held her in bed the night before, to how they had made love. Between that and this had been so much, but they were safe again, their child was safe, and this hug, she thought blearily, would bring the bad part to an end; she could shower now, and change her clothes, and face the day.

Later that afternoon, after Alexander had woken, and condescended to eat some hospital chicken noodle soup and watch some of Walt Disney's *Sleeping Beauty* on the hospital channel, and gone back to sleep, Amelia walked down one floor to see what had happened to Darren. She supposed they would have paged her, actually, if he had died, but perhaps not; hospital news travels quickly, and the people taking care of Darren probably all knew that her own son had been admitted in the morning. She was therefore prepared to arrive and find that Darren had died.

To be honest, it was more than that. I had been prepared to trade Darren for Alexander. Shutting Alexander's door conscientiously, I had thought of that earlier hospitalization of Darren's, when he was on respiratory precautions for possible TB. It's the same sign, since the precautions to be observed are almost identical; the only difference is that with chicken pox, people who have already had the disease don't have to bother with masks, and people who haven't ever had the disease are nuts to enter the room, so, effectively, the masks go by the board. But I looked at the sign and thought of all the confused ways that Darren and Alexander sometimes have crossed in my mind. The guilt because of what Alexander has and Darren doesn't, what Darren has and Alexander doesn't. The knowledge from watching Alexander grow up that tells me what Darren *should* be doing, should want to do, should be able to do. The moments of Alexander's joy that I have wanted to transfer over, so I could see on Darren's face one of those smiles, hear one of those laughs. The contrast in birthrights, in births. And so on. So here they were, actually under the same roof. And I was ready to trade, right then and there: let Darren die, be dead, have died already this morning, if that's what it took to make Alexander better in the ER; just keep Alexander safe, and well, and himself. *My* boy is coming home from this hospital, back to his life, with nothing but a few chicken pox scars at worst, and if the price is that the other's time is up, that's okay with me. You will see, I think, that I was still much disturbed and frightened, and that fatigue and fear and relief and upheaval had left me at my most superstitious.

The door to Darren's room was closed, and there was a sign posted there, too, not the official printed PRECAUTION sign but a handmade construction-paper plea: Please check with desk before entering room, please no unnecessary visitors. It would be too crazy and unbearable and heartless for the hospital actually to print up CHILD DYING signs, I thought, looking at the crayoned letters, imagining the nurses who each and every time, as though it's a new problem with each death, letter the signs for a dying child's door, to keep away occasional medical students, volunteers with Nintendos, visiting clowns, and costumed Sesame Street characters.

So I knew Darren was still alive in there; I had thought perhaps to find family and friends weeping at the bedside, the enforced quiet of dying replaced by the bustle of mourning. Did Darren's grandmother have anyone to call, anyone to come in and mourn with her? She must, I had told myself so many times, she must have friends from her block, ladies from her church. I liked to think she was a heroine to her friends. Or perhaps I would arrive too late for all that and find the maintenance people already cleaning out the room.

Instead, I pushed the door open on exactly the same scene I had left behind the night before: Darren in his hissing tent, his grandmother in the armchair, also asleep. Her mouth hung open and she snored very softly, a rhythmic rasp against the endless level noise of the oxygen. I knew she would not have wanted me to watch her sleeping, and it did seem a pointless intimacy, when she had been forced into so many unwanted intimacies already, so I cleared my throat loudly, said her name, and then advanced at once to pick up Darren's clipboard so I could be studying that as she opened her eyes and pulled herself together.

This is the reality; the reality is that children do better than you think they will, that you plan for a death and prepare for a death, and then they hover and linger and hold on. Is it because they want to live, because their bodies are still straining, improbably, to heal and even to grow, not having read in the journals that there is no recovery, no further growth, no developmental trajectory to travel? Or is it just that we tend, wisely, to pessimism, so that we prepare ourselves, and then the families, for the possibility of these deaths, which are, after all, by definition the deaths we are none of us prepared for. Soppy literature notwithstanding, the death of a child is a terrible thing. An unbearable thing. An impossible thing. I have a child, and I cannot imagine it. So therefore, when the unimaginable looms on the horizon, the unimaginable that is also the most hideously familiar of all nightmares, the parents need to be prepared.

I am getting carried away, obviously. I was carried away. Looking at Darren's nursing sheets, which reflected only a stability of extremis, a child who remained as close to death, as far from death, as he had been the night before, I felt guilty, as if I had promised his death. To whom? I wanted to call the judge and explain, the lawyer, the grandmother.

Roberta Wilson got slowly to her feet. She did not look at the boy on the bed but came to stand beside me, looking down at the clipboard in my hand. The numbers neatly registered in the tiny boxes meant little to her, I suppose, intake and output hour by hour, respiratory rate, oxygen saturation. She was not the kind of person to take tutorial in hospital routine, to check the charts herself.

"Doctor, I have something I wanted you to have." From her pocketbook, big and black and discolored slightly at the seams, she took an envelope and then put down delicately, on top of the clipboard, a studio portrait of Darren. He was dressed up for it, in a white shirt and a red tie and a pale blue suit jacket, and posed against a backdrop painted with a rainbow. It was, amazingly enough, a happy picture; you couldn't see the thinness of his arms or legs because of the clothing, and his face, turned to the camera, was rounded into a smile. He looked like a child who would get up soon and muss his shirt and leave the tie far behind. "I wanted you to have this," his grandmother said again. "I had it made while he was home, so I would have one really good one, and I made a copy for you. And you know as well as I do, he won't look that good again."

"Thank you. Really, thank you very much."

"I had a blowup done for me, ten by twelve. You know, I have so many pictures of Darren's mother, but the only ones I like to look at are the ones when she's just a baby. I can't bear looking at her when she looks more like she did when she died."

"Maybe when more time has passed—"

"When I look at her all grown up, I just want to start scolding her, telling her that I know the way for her to save herself. Isn't it sad to think that with just a few changes she would never have been sick, she could have had children and had them be healthy, too. It wouldn't take such big adjustments, not like she'd have to begin her life all over and live it differently."

I said, "It's very sad, how we want to protect our children and we can't."

"I look at her picture and I'm not sad, I'm angry. I want to know, where does she get her nerve, looking past me and walking right on into danger? Who does she think she is, leaving me behind, leaving her child to die with me? Whoever heard of such a thing, a woman outliving her child and then her grandchild?"

The grandmother's voice was still soft and very calm. There was simply nothing left between herself and her tragedy. The little details of her life, which presumably have kept her going and will continue to keep her going, had receded from her, and she was left only with the truth, stranded alone on her desolate planet.

"It's a beautiful picture of Darren," I said. I could not join her there, and I would not try.

Amelia takes the exit to Concord and drives slowly down the suburban road, following the directions given over the phone. Orchard House is marked by a sign and a small parking area, where she leaves her car, then climbs carefully up a snowy hill, toward a brown wooden building. It looked small from the road but turns out to have a rather rambling backside. Amelia turns in to the entrance, which leads into a souvenir shop, noticing that farther up the hill is another wooden structure, ramshackle and weathered, with a triangular tower. A small sign labels it: CONCORD SCHOOL OF PHILOSOPHY.

The souvenir shop is crowded. The woman who spoke to Amelia when she called that morning told her that in the winter Orchard House is open to visitors only by appointment, but added that a book club from Tennessee was taking a tour at two and that Amelia could join up with them. The members of the book club are all female and mostly in their fifties and sixties. Well-dressed and also warmly dressed, several of them even in furs. A couple of the younger women have children with them, and as Amelia gets in line to buy her ticket, she listens to a mother, in front of her, arguing with two pristinely beautiful blond daughters. Each girl is choosing a clothespin doll off a display, and the younger girl wants to be sure she chooses the youngest sister from Little Women. The mother says, That would be Beth, but the older sister knows it's Amy. The rather frail lady at the cash desk confirms eagerly that it's Amy, and then goes off and fetches the dolls, Amy for the little sister, Meg for the older, Marmee for the mother. The older girl takes a good look at the doll display and decides that on the whole, she likes the Jo doll better than the Meg doll.

Amelia expects the tour to be led by another elderly lady like the one at the cash desk, thin and wispy, slow at addition. Instead, the group is called to order and led through a door by a pretty, buxom adolescent girl with curly brown hair down over her shoulders, wearing an extravagant long sweater, magenta and cobalt blue, over black lace tights. She beckons the tour group like a Christmas tree, and they follow her obediently into the kitchen, where she delivers her opening spiel. "Seventy-five percent of the furniture in the house did belong to the Alcotts. They lived here for twenty years, but by the time they moved in, they had already lived in twenty-two houses, and that was because of *Mr.* Alcott and the kind of person he was. When they moved here, Louisa was twenty-six."

Amelia focuses on the heavily ornamented iron stove; the kitchen is warm on a cold day, though of course that is not actually by virtue of the stove. The room also features bits of dried flowers, token pieces of china, a breadboard decorated by wood-burning with a reproduction of a Raphael painting by May Alcott ("the artistic sister, who Louisa called Amy in *Little Women,* she just reversed the first two letters of her name"). Amelia closes her eyes briefly, shutting out the book club, the guide, trying hard to imagine herself into this house, which she has imagined, without trying, so many times. She does not know exactly why she is here, why today, why now, but clearly she has come looking for help. "The doorways are kind of low, and lots of people think that's because people used to be shorter, but in fact, the Alcotts were tall, the girls were five eight and five nine. But watch your heads when you go through."

Amelia, naturally, was the kind of adult who read her child's chart. She tried not to be. She tried, in general, to be well-behaved and grateful, so the nurses would like her, so they would not think she was too much of a pain in the ass. She did not reach for doctorly authority, she did not remind them that she knew the proper terms. She did not ostentatiously pick up the clipboard whenever a nurse made a note on it, as if checking to be sure the blood pressure was correctly recorded. But late at night, with Matt and Alexander asleep in the hospital room, she found herself drifting down the hall to the nurses' station, trading hellos, gossiping with nurses she knew . . . and inevitably pulling Alexander's chart out of the rack with the same casual interest she might have shown in some other child's chart.

There was nothing particularly interesting in Alexander's chart; there was nothing particularly interesting about Alexander's case. Yes, it was a little strange to read the intern's description of his physical exam, but except for the skin lesions it was such a normal physical exam that it was basically boring. The short write-up had nothing in it besides what she remembered saying, the assessment and plan was as simple as: (1) IV antibiotics, (2) skin care, (3) IV fluids as needed. What Amelia read, guilty and compulsive, were the nursing notes, easily distinguished from the doctor scrawls by the careful round looping writing. Neatness counts in nursing school. The nursing notes were where the observations of her family were recorded. Parents coping well with hospitalization. Father *very* involved. (What was that supposed to mean?) Father spending night. (What about *me* spending the night—don't I rate a mention?)

They were all watching her, Amelia felt. They were watching with trained and concerned eyes to see how her family functioned. Matt didn't understand; he thought the nurses were there to provide services for Alexander. He didn't know he was being judged. Amelia would head back down the hall to put on her nightgown; it was very disorienting to be in the hospital at night wearing a nightgown, to be sleeping on that cot in proper nightclothes, her teeth brushed, with no expectation of awakening before morning.

Unbelievably, Mrs. Brandon called while Alexander was in the hospital, Saturday morning. Brandon, it turned out, had already had the chicken pox, so she thought maybe she would drop him off at the hospital so he could play with Alexander and cheer Alexander up, and she would come by for him late in the afternoon. No, Amelia told her, please don't, I'm just not up to watching two little boys instead of one. Oh, but two is so much easier than one, said Mrs. Brandon. Maybe so, said Amelia, but Alexander isn't up to it and I'm not up to it. Well, why don't I just ask Alexander, said Mrs. Brandon, proceeding like the human battering ram she was. Because I already said no, and I'm the mommy, said Amelia, and hung up.

Randy Andy felt the need to come around and visit, offering his services as ID man of the hour to my stricken family. That is, he had the fucking nerve to invite himself in on Alexander's case, to examine my son with his sticky little hands, and then treat me to a little disquisition on chicken pox and its complications. And then segue into related infections, most particularly his favorite, you guessed it, herpes simplex virus type two. Cases he had seen. Rashes, superinfections, meningitis—all leading up to the question of sexual abuse. Good thing, heh heh, he told me, that Alexander's groin rash is so obviously varicella. I thought of hitting him over the head with Alexander's bedpan, and perhaps if it had been full, I wouldn't have been able to resist. He could see, I'm sure, that I wasn't in the least amused, which fed his nasty fire. He likes to see people uncomfortable, especially women.

He free-associated rapidly from herpes to syphilis and began to tell, at length and in disgusting detail, the story of a nine-year-old girl who had come into the emergency room complaining of an itch and ended up being diagnosed wtih gonorrhea, a vaginal yeast infection, and syphilis as well, all of which were traced to her father. I had heard the story before; it had happened a year ago, and it was one of those cases that everyone in the hospital discusses. I did not particularly want Alexander to hear it, though, and it seemed to me exactly in character for Randy Andy to rattle on without even thinking of that. Or maybe to get off a little on embarrassing me in front of my son. I had already noticed, those days with Alexander in the hospital, that I was rather prone to violent angry impulses, all of which I restrained. I thought at the time that it was stress, and perhaps especially the stress of trying to behave like a patient rather than a doctor, of losing all my accus-tomed power. Now, looking back, I think it's more likely that I knew deep down that something was very wrong, something in my family, something worse than Alexander's illness; and the bursts of anger were the lava and the poisonous gases that reached the surface, evidence of the disturbances below.

Anyway, I was totally furious at Randy Andy, this relatively harmless asshole doctor, who was just being his stupid self. I would have cheerfully pushed a button to eject him from the sixth-story window. Instead I smiled at him, a big idiot grin, and cut him off in midsentence, asked him to walk down the hall with me so we could discuss Darren.

He's hanging in there, I see, Andy said. Yes, do you think the antibiotics are kicking in? Oh, I doubt it. I think he's just coasting along on what's left of his lungs, and it's a question of waiting till he tires out. And he babbled on till I got him to the elevator and smiled him in and sent him away.

The fact is, of course, that it's nonsense to think of the Alcotts as in any way proper, standard, normal people. They were weirdos from start to finish. The father most of all, dragging them from one utopian community to another, from one failed school to another, making up his maxims for the education of children while his wife kept the family together and his girls went out to work as soon as they could. But there was his youngest daughter, May, drawing on the walls, getting ready to head for Paris and artists' studios. And Louisa scribbling away at her tales of wholesome girlhood and her sensational gothics. But somehow, when I think of this family, or really the family in the book, I guess, one of the qualities I envy is a sense of place, of propriety. I let myself believe that a hundred years ago, Louisa and her sisters were at least secure in who they should be, how they should act. And probably there were lots of nineteenth-century New England women who were secure like that, doing what they were brought up to do—but I'm not sure it has anything to do with the Alcotts.

The last night that Alexander was in the hospital, the night he probably didn't need to be there at all, Amelia wandered down to the nurses' station. Matt and Alexander were asleep. Alexander's forehead was cool to her hand, his breathing deep and sound. There was nothing fussy, nothing marginal, about his sleep. All through the hospital, Amelia imagined, were sick children sleeping sick sleep, medicated sleep. Darren sleeping hypoxic air-hungry sleep while the tubes piped in extra oxygen to help him stay on the right side of the edge. Asthmatics wheezing in their sleep attached to monitors to track their breathing and alarm if it faltered. Whole wards of children with cancers, sleeping while the poison drugs fought out the battle in their bone marrows. Children with heart defects, sleeping blue while the blood mixed inside their hearts, shunting away from their lungs and coursing, unoxygenated, back through their bodies. A ward of newborns, too tiny to be alive, sleeping the heavily monitored medically assisted sleep that cannot approximate the wet nighttime of the womb. And Alexander, his little belly full of a hospital dinner, a brand-new plastic pirate ship in full sail on his night table, sleeping a normal childhood sleep.

Amelia was wearing a flannel nightgown and Matt's navy blue terry-cloth bathrobe. Again this feeling, as she walked down the corridor, of having switched dimensions. This nighttime hospital was so familiar—the nurses on their errands in and out of patient rooms following routines which she knew so well. Vital signs, ins and outs, oxygen-saturation checks. Medications into IV burettes, penicillin every four hours, gentamicin every eight, morphine every one to two hours as needed for pain, aminophylline running constantly on an IV drip. Interns writing in charts, taking the moments when things were quiet to fill in their paperwork, hoping for a quiet night, a not too badly broken sleep. But although the hospital ward was so familiar, even reassuring to her, she felt herself an alien observer, in pajamas and bathrobe and bedroom slippers. She was seeing a place she knew, and through her own eyes, and yet she felt almost as if she were peering from inside a flying saucer, surprised to recognize the landscape.

Sheepishly, she pulled out Alexander's chart, ignored by the nurses, who knew, disapproved, and understood in varying proportions. The day-shift nurse's note commented on Alexander's much improved spirits, then on how well his lesions were healing. *Parents very concerned, staying on for additional teaching. Family continues to need extensive support.* Amelia put the chart back, looked up to find Frank Blake, Sara's father, staring at her from across the desk. He wore a suit and tie, not even loosened. He looked disoriented.

"Hi, Mr. Blake."

"Doctor?"

"My son is in the hospital, in a room down the hall," Amelia said, almost apologetically.

"I'm sorry to hear that."

"No, it's okay, he's going home tomorrow."

"I suppose you get pretty special treatment here. Are you in a private room?"

"My son was potentially contagious, so we are in a private room. That's what they save the private rooms for. I'm sorry that Sara has to share a room. I know it's been hard on you all."

"*You* try living your life in a room with some strange little kid coughing and spitting up all night, and parents who don't seem to be on any schedule at all, and the TV on at all hours."

"Mr. Blake, I know it's hard. If I were designing a hospital, everyone would be in a private room."

"And you and your kid just happen to get one. My son comes to visit his baby sister in the evening and the goddam TV is on— you understand, the patient is a baby in a crib, but her parents are sitting there in armchairs, practically drooling down their chins, that's the level of mental activity, and my boy just hangs around them and watches whatever crap they happen to have on. Is that your idea of helping out my family?"

It is hard to be firm and doctorly wrapped in a bathrobe. It is hard to talk down an angry and crazy father when you keep wishing you had a gun so you could just put a bullet through his head. Amelia did not even try to be a good person, did not even repeat over to herself, This is a man under tremendous stress whose family life has been badly disrupted, who has been faced with what he sees as parental failure, who is used to being in control. The hell with all that.

"Mr. Blake, I'm going back to my son. I'll come around and see Sara tomorrow, and that would be the appropriate time to discuss this." With what dignity she could, she bedroom-slippered down

the hall, closed the door behind her, bent to kiss her son on his cool
forehead. And Frank Blake had the fucking nerve to follow her and
knock, too loudly, on the door of Alexander's private room. Amelia hurried back out into the corridor, before the noise woke up
Matt, or woke up Alexander.

"Do you know what that goddam bitch of a nurse said to me?"
demanded Mr. Blake.

"What happened?"

"Up on our floor tonight, when I needed to make a long-distance
call. Sara is asleep, of course, or at least sleeping as well as she can,
considering that there's some strange woman snoring in the room,
and this other baby, who probably has nine different contagious
diseases that you people haven't even gotten around to thinking of,
is waking up and crying every now and then, and her mother
doesn't even notice, that's the kind of people you have us in with.
Anyway, I went out to the nurses' desk to use the phone to make
a business call, and believe it or not, along comes a nurse to tell me
patients and their families can't use this phone. So I try to explain
to her, using very simple words, that I don't want to make a long
call late at night from a phone right next to the bed where my one-
year-old daughter is sleeping, and of course she doesn't listen to a
word I'm saying, just stands guard over the phone and tells me
again how I can't use it. So what do you think of that, Dr. Stern?
What do you think of your precious hospital?"

"I think," said Amelia slowly, "that you are very tired, and
under a lot of stress, with your child in the hospital, so that you
are behaving in a way you would probably not behave under other
circumstances. But I am pretty tired and stressed-out myself right
now, and I am not in any mood to hear about your problems making a long-distance phone call. I am going back in to see my son,
and if you bang on my door again, I will call the security guards
and have you thrown out of the hospital."

Those three days in the hospital Matt held up very well, I must
say. Matt truly does hate hospitals, both viscerally and on principle.
Every time a nurse bathed Alexander's sore spots and he cried out,
Matt would wince in agonized sympathy and look ready to punch

the nurse. He also seemed to feel that if he cozied up to the nurses, they wouldn't hurt his son. He couldn't even look at the IV, at the point where it traveled into Alexander's hand, even though it was covered with tape and plastic shielding. Instead, he focused on helping Alexander choose meals or TV shows, or going out to buy new books to read aloud. He alternated Bulfinch with a string of new picture books, so it was Dido and Aeneas, Frog and Toad, Cupid and Psyche, Babar and Celeste, Jason and the Golden Fleece, Bartholemew and the Oobleck. Looking back on it I would have to say, however, that Matt and I didn't really talk very much those three days. Of course, we were tired and confused, camping out away from our home. I thought obsessively about home, about domesticity and protection. We would get our boy home, safe in his room, in his bed, we would wall him round with his very own house, and there we would be. I did not know exactly what to say to Matt when I found myself face to face with him, Alexander asleep in the hospital bed; I felt there was still some kind of unfinished tension between us, as if he somehow blamed me for our being in the hospital in the first place, or maybe blamed me for being at home in the hospital.

I thought, in my silly and misguided way, that I was offering comfort when I introduced him to Gabriel D'Alessio. I ran into Gabriel and his father in the little patients' kitchen, where I was making two cups of tea in the microwave and stocking up on graham crackers for Alexander. Gabriel's father was carefully spreading peanut butter on saltines, one-handed, Gabriel in the crook of the other arm. He recognized me before I recognized him; five months earlier he and Gabriel had come to the second-opinion clinic, referred in by a pediatrician who was unable to find a reason for Gabriel's very slight but persistent limp. One thing led to another, and very soon after meeting Gabriel, I sent him to get a CT scan of his head and discovered a medium-sized tumor in his brain. After that I sent him to an oncologist, and I lost track of him. I knew, after talking to the oncologist about him, that Gabriel's story was unlikely to have a happy ending, and since I had hooked him up with one of the best doctors I knew, I was content to bow out. I would probably have recognized Gabriel, since my memory for children is better than my memory for adults, but Gabriel had changed since his visit to my clinic. Gabriel was about two, and he had been a good-looking boy with sleek black hair and a red-cheeked cherub's face. Now he was bald, of course, from chemotherapy, and he had obviously had extensive surgery as well—a zipper-track scar curved across the side of his head, and the left side of his face was caved in slightly, making him look mangled and lopsided. Bare, his head also seemed inappropriately large, and he looked for a minute like some science fiction baby, alien and clumsily put together, but menacing.

I asked Mr. D'Alessio how it was going, making the question general enough for him to answer me vaguely. Instead, he told me in detail about the surgery, the radiation, and the chemotherapy. Gabriel was actually hospitalized because he'd had a fever, and they were treating him with antibiotics, but his father was such an old hand already at serious illness that he went straight to the ongoing story, the serious story. One little fever, one little hospital stay, hardly mattered. I did not, of course, ask anything like So, do they think he has a chance? I was sure he didn't. But I let Mr. D'Alessio tell me his details, and then in return I told him briefly why my own son was hospitalized, and I was careful not to sound apologetic. Yes, I was lucky, he was not, but you can't keep that imbalance away from a father whose two-year-old has a fatal brain tumor. Everyone else is lucky, he is not, and that's the way it is.

I had been talking in the kitchen for a while, and Alexander got impatient for his graham crackers and sent Matt along to find me. And so I made a big point of introducing Matt and Mr. D'Alessio, and then I kept the conversation going, about Gabriel, I mean, so Matt had to stay and hear it. Looking at Gabriel made me feel very sorry but also very lucky; with all the horrible interruptions illness can make in a child's life, my own son had been struck by something small and treatable, and he would be all better. I wanted Matt to feel that too, that this little stay in the hospital had been no disaster. I wanted us to be happy and grateful together.

"How has he tolerated the chemotherapy?" I asked. If it had been just Mr. D'Alessio and me, I would have called it chemo, but I didn't want Matt to miss anything.

"Not bad, not so bad as some kids. He had a lot of vomiting at first, and of course he's lost some weight, but the doctors thought he did well. My wife—well, you know . . ." He looked expressively at Matt and shrugged, as if to say, you know, women. "She never got calmed down about his hair, about it falling out."

"He did have beautiful black hair," I said.

"Sure he did. Same color as me, only soft, like little feathers, or you know what the hair on the front of a dog's neck is like? But still, I told her, they would have shaved it all to do the brain surgery anyway; who worries about hair at a time like this?"

"For a lot of people it's the hardest thing," I said. "Gabriel is lucky that at his age it won't bother him at all to be bald; for the older kids, it's very hard."

"You think he's too young to know that people stare at him? He's a very smart boy, and he knows. My wife, she went out and got him a wig, even, but he won't keep it on for even one minute. But I take him to McDonald's for a treat, and people stare and stare, and Gabriel, he turns his face in against my shoulder and he won't look at them."

Gabriel was, however, looking straight at Matt, who put his thumbs in his ears and waggled his fingers. Gabriel smiled condescendingly and remarked, "Peanut butter cracker."

"Yes," said his father, who had by now made a plateful of them. "Well, nice to see you, Doctor, and I hope you get out of here soon and don't have any more problems. Gabriel and I have to get back to our room in time for *Sesame Street*, and we have to have enough peanut butter crackers to get us through the whole program." He left, with Gabriel still held against his shoulder and the paper plate of crackers held carefully out in front. I handed Matt the graham crackers, took the two Styrofoam cups out of the microwave, and as we headed back to Alexander, Matt asked me what was wrong with Gabriel.

"Brain tumor," I said. "He started limping a little, and he turned out to have a brain tumor."

"Is he going to be okay?"

"No," I said. "No, he's not. He's going to die."

Finally, Louisa's bedroom, where she wrote *Little Women* at that
desk right there, in the year 1868, in six weeks. Louisa's bedroom
is actually a big, comfortable, airy room; it is perfectly pleasant to
think of her there. Even if she was tall and saw herself as somewhat
ungainly, surely in this uncrowded room she had enough space.
Surely in here she could move with confidence, from bed to desk,
enjoying the flowered panel on the wall that her sister May had
painted for her, looking with satisfaction at her books in the
glassed-in shelves. An adult's room, a writer's room. And a desk by
the window to write on.

"It's ironic," the guide is saying, lacing her fingers into her mass
of hair, beginning to sound a little tired, "but in fact Louisa might
not have written nearly as much if she had been healthy. She went
to be a nurse in the Civil War, you know, and she caught typhoid
fever, and in those days they treated that with mercury, so she got
mercury poisoning, and she was never really well again. She had to
stay in bed a lot and take it very easy after that."

Over and over, in the hospital, I had a fantasy of Alexander well,
Alexander back in day care. But it wasn't actually a happy fantasy;
I would start out by imagining him racing into the room, then I
would see him looking at the place where the spaceship should have
been, and the spaceship would be gone, and he would run back out
of the room.

In fact, by the morning he was discharged, all his chicken pox
that I could see had crusted over, and the next morning I ruled that
he could go to day care for a couple of hours, if he really wanted
to. Matt reported to me over the phone that Alexander went running into the room, grabbed the back of Doree's skirt, and began
tugging on it, demanding, was the spaceship all finished, what
could he do, was there more stuff he could do. Matt said Alexander
suddenly looked to him pale and drawn next to the other children,
and he was seized with apprehension: the spaceship was a thing of
the past, the other children had moved on, Alexander had stumbled
and been left behind, and nothing would ever be the same again.

Instead, of course, Doree told him she had a computer keyboard
for him to make into a spaceship dashboard, and the other children

had all been told that he had been in the hospital and were at least marginally interested, and he was as completely absorbed into their whirlpool as he always was. But Matt told me that for a minute or two he had worried, worried that somehow Alexander's illness had thrown him out of step, left him alone to watch the happy room of children his age. Is it as easy as that, could it be? Matt asked, then immediately started in about the schools, the applications. Where will Alexander go? Will they be nice to him? Will he learn, too early, that there are children who don't make it, who don't fit in? Will anyone, ever, dare to be mean to him? And how can we protect him?

I should not, obviously, have lost my temper with Mr. Blake. I don't know exactly what the approved and professional response would be to that kind of behavior, for the doctor, standing outside her own child's hospital room, wearing her husband's bathrobe. Presumably, I should have managed to keep in mind that his child was sicker than mine. Again we see how if my own son had been sick with a mysterious, life-threatening, even fatal illness, my behavior would have been justified.

But Frank Blake's daughter has an illness that may not be cured. That may rip his family to shreds. That had already had them in the hospital for weeks—many days of the kind of upset and confusion that Matt and Alexander and I endured for three days only. I should have remembered all that, I suppose, and spent the extra minutes with her father, but I didn't. And the next day, when Alexander was ready to leave, I told Matt I wanted to run up and see a patient for just a few minutes, knowing he didn't really like that much, and when I got up to see Sara, I found that her parents had already arranged for a transfer to another hospital; they were firing me, firing my hospital, taking themselves and their daughter off somewhere where they would be treated right.

I found the entire Blake family standing in the hall, arranged as if for a Christmas card picture. Both parents formally dressed, Frank in a charcoal gray lawyer suit, Geraldine in a close-fitting white wool dress and a heavy gold necklace. A princess in a painting, or maybe a Madonna: against her dress she cradled Sara, who was chewing on the necklace and looked to me rather pleased with herself. Frank held the older child's hand, and the little boy stood straight as an arrow, enjoying the spectacle of his parents telling off the hospital. Frank was letting the head nurse have it. His tone was not very loud, but his projection was excellent; I wondered if this was a courtroom technique. He was telling over his wrongs once again: the sick baby in the next bed, the phone call, and on and on.

"Mr. Blake," said Mary Pat, who looked as flustered as Amelia had ever seen her look. Interested parents were peeking out of doors all up and down the corridor, and other nurses were hovering. "Mr. Blake, why don't you come into my office and sit down and we'll discuss all this calmly."

"I attempt to make my important phone call from one of the many unused phones at the nurses' desk. Now, I realize that all of you have calls you need to make; on many nights, I have listened to nurses talking to their boyfriends, nurses calling home to check on their children, nurses calling up their friends on other wards to talk about their sex lives. But I want you to understand that all the phones at the desk were free at that particular moment, that, remarkable as it may seem, all the nurses were either in the back room eating and gossiping, or maybe even emptying bedpans. So I pick up the receiver to make my call, and what happens? Do you know?"

"Mr. Blake, why don't we continue this conversation in my office?"

"Dr. Stern knows what happened, because I endeavored, last night, to explain to her why I was so fed up with the treatment we have all received here. Oh, I know I'm not supposed to criticize the experts who are taking care of my little girl, but you have to admit, they've had her under their supposedly expert care for weeks now, and all they've done is turn a little girl with a nutrition problem into a little girl with a nutrition problem *and* a behavior problem." His voice had risen, and he looked around demandingly at his audience. Some of the parents didn't meet his gaze, some shook their heads, some just watched, without reacting, as if this were just one more show put on for their amusement by the patient-entertainment people. At any moment, perhaps, Frank Blake would saw Geraldine in half, or turn Sara into a pigeon, or pull a long chain of knotted scarves out of her ear.

I decided to speak. I didn't particularly see how I could make things worse. I looked directly at Mrs. Blake, remembering that day we had coffee together in Harvard Square. "Hi, Mrs. Blake," I said, trying to keep my voice casual. "It looks like Sara likes that necklace." Surprised, she looked down, then took the links out of Sara's mouth, and Sara immediately started howling. And, God bless her, she howled good and loud; the corridor was immediately filled with a much more familiar sound, a screaming baby. When I was an intern and that kind of noise suddenly filled the air, we used to look at each other, shrug, and say in unison, "Another satisfied customer."

Frank Blake did not look particularly pleased at having to compete with his daughter for airtime. In fact, he looked angrily at me, then at his wife.

"Let's go into Mary Pat's office," I suggested, speaking again to Geraldine, who was joggling her daughter up and down. "Let's talk in there and see if we can get all this straightened out."

"There is nothing to straighten out," Mr. Blake informed me, now almost yelling. "I was merely trying to explain to the head nurse on this so-called hospital ward why my family has decided to seek medical aid in another place. Doctor, I would be grateful if you would complete whatever paperwork is necessary; we are transferring today to Boston Central." He pivoted sharply and marched his small son back into Sara's room.

Sara herself was still yelling, eyes squeezed shut and tiny pink hands gripping folds of her mother's dress. Her mother stood still in the hallway, holding the baby who wouldn't grow. Was there something I could have said to her? Your husband is an asshole; therefore your daughter won't eat? I had no right to see into her family like this; they were flayed open before me and I felt deeply reluctant to take advantage of this exposure and diagnose pathology.

I did not know, right at that moment, that my own family was within forty-eight hours of dissolving. That Matt could have, if he had chosen, treated the hospital staff to his own anger, to the soap-opera treat of watching us fight, watching me cry, watching our son try to hold us together. Matt hadn't done that, and therefore I had no idea, as I watched the Blakes in action, how vulnerable I really was.

I said to Geraldine Blake, "I'm sorry it's been so upsetting."

I swear to God, I think I could see the struggle in her face. She knew that her husband was out of control, and something in her wanted to apologize for him, to align herself, at least behind his back, with me and with Mary Pat. She knew that we had not made Sara sick, that we had not dreamed up the double room to torture her daughter, or prevented her husband from using the phone on purpose to ruin his career. She knew, unless I was kidding myself, that the hospital was not a place of evil. We were all trying to help. (And yet, hadn't we done exactly what Mr. Blake said? Didn't Sara now have a much bigger behavior problem than before? Hadn't we stuck her with needles and pushed tubes into her orifices and exposed her to x-rays and still failed to find a reason for her failure to thrive? Hadn't we shut her family into a room with a succession of total strangers? And in exchange, what? A complicated mealtime routine, a few hundred grams. The unsatisfying explanation that the child didn't take in quite enough calories, the amorphous suggestion of something dysfunctional in the family. You didn't feed her enough, so she didn't grow.) More important, Sara's mother knew that she needed our help, that her little girl wasn't ever going to grow without the blundering awkward interventions of nurses and therapists and pediatricians like me.

But Geraldine Blake was not going to acknowledge me. I could see it in her face; she was going to stay loyal to her husband. Perhaps if you are married to someone who behaves (or misbehaves) like that, you have to decide early on: are you with him or against him? The world was against him, clearly, the doctor and Mary Pat and the nurses, and she was not going to betray him. She hefted her screaming child a little bit higher and followed her husband into the hospital room.

And then, unfortunately, it turned out there actually was quite a bit of paperwork involved in transferring Sara Blake to Boston

Central Hospital; I was reluctant to let her go without a detailed letter from me explaining the medical ins and outs of her case, and also the social mess. *The family continues to be extremely stressed by the child's unresolved illness, but they have declined social service intervention, as well as other supports; for example, it was suggested that both parents speak with a psychiatrist, but they were unwilling, at this time.* I figured I would just call over and speak to their new doctor, tell the story of the phone call (and the double room, and the HIV test, and the blood test done in bed, and my own threat to call in security) with the kind of frankness you can use when you aren't writing things down. But I needed to put something on paper to explain the transfer. *Although Sara has made some progress during this hospitalization, and has recently shown some evidence of beginning weight gain, her parents have been dissatisfied with certain aspects of her care. They are alarmed that her mealtime behavior is at times more difficult than it was prior to the hospitalization, and they have also experienced some conflicts with nursing staff and medical personnel centered mostly on issues of ward policy and hospital rules. They have therefore arranged transfer to another facility.*

Unfortunately, though, I had to spend almost two hours getting Sara ready to leave. So I had to call down and tell Matt to take Alexander home without me, which I hated to do. I wanted to be there to help carry plastic bags of clothing and new toys and books, and I wanted to see Alexander installed in his own bed. Matt was not pleased, of course; I had not expected him to be. But he was calm about it and didn't nag me. I thought that must be because, after three days in the hospital, he understood that there were serious hospital exigencies to which I had to respond. What a dope I was. And how self-righteous—was Frank Blake's temper really one of those life-and-death exigencies?

This is how it happened: Alexander was admitted to the hospital Monday morning and discharged Thursday morning. Sara Blake transferred out to her new hospital Thursday afternoon. Alexander went to day care for a couple of hours on Friday, and Matt and Amelia had a friendly phone conversation about him, about how well he was doing, about how hard it was to protect him. Then, Friday night, Matt and Amelia had a fight, and he told her he didn't want to go on like this. Saturday she went to Concord and took a tour of Orchard House, and when she came home to her own house, Matt and Alexander were gone. Sunday she sat home alone all day and finally called her mother. And Monday morning she walked into the hospital to find that Darren was in the intensive care unit, intubated and on a ventilator. Which was exactly what was not supposed to happen.

In the gift shop of Orchard House, I bought a copy of *Hospital Sketches*, Louisa May Alcott's account of her experiences as a Civil War nurse. And in the car, driving home, I realized I might have found myself a guidebook, a formula. Domesticity and gore.

Louisa May had been a nurse. It seemed to me, I think, that if I read *Hospital Sketches*, I would find out how she had managed domesticity and gore within her not-very-long life, her life as a New England spinster. All the cozy domesticity of my fantasies, the *Little Women* mix of loving family, hard work, and moral uplift, was written by someone who had gone off into Civil War hospitals, which surely must have been charnel houses. No antisepsis, little or no analgesia, no antibiotics. Blood and death and excrement had not been swept under the rug in Louisa's life, to keep the parlor neat. She must have seen suffering and pain and death, and then she went home to Orchard House and wrote her stories for girls.

I drove back to my own house, which was empty. Full of Legos, of course, and books, and disordered, in a rather pleasant sort of way, like a house that held a little family. But it didn't hold a little family anymore. There was no one in it but me.

The day after Alexander went home from the hospital, the day after Sara Blake transferred to another hospital, that Friday night, Amelia got home a little late. She knew Alexander had been to day care for a couple of hours, and she knew from talking to Matt on the phone that it had been a success, that Doree and the spaceship had been waiting for him. She came home full of that Friday evening feeling, it's been a hard week but it's over. And my boy is home, and healed, and waiting for me.

She stopped at the Star Market on her way home and bought ingredients for spaghetti and meatballs; Alexander really preferred plain butter on his noodles, but he liked making meatballs, and his pride in the meatballs he made was so intense that he condescended to eat them, and also the tomato sauce, instead of insisting on his spaghetti plain.

Together, she and Alexander made the supper. Matt drifted into the kitchen while Amelia was chopping an onion for the sauce, but he didn't seem to have much to say. He hovered over Alexander, while Amelia, by way of conversation, chattered on a little nervously about the Blakes, about the phone conversation she had had with their new doctor, over at Boston Central, about her fear that they would now go from doctor to doctor, hospital to hospital. About her sense that she had failed this family, that she would have done better by them if they had been poor and disadvantaged, that she had never really been on their side the way she should have been, just because they were a pair of lawyers from Newton.

"You know what I mean? I expected them to behave, and to understand, even if what they had to understand was that they had a screwed-up family and a screwed-up daughter; I thought they should be enlightened and agreeable—oh, yes, Doctor, it must be a psychological problem, bring on the shrinks and the social workers, help us figure out what is wrong. And of course they took it all much worse than a poor family would have; it put their backs up right away. They didn't see why I had any right to evaluate them from that point of view; they just saw me as a failure because I couldn't find the organic disease. Well, I guess it will serve me right if someone at Central does find an organic disease."

Amelia had her onion and garlic cooking in the pan, and she opened a can of tomato puree. Alexander was filling a big dinner plate with meatballs, working inward in concentric circles, starting at the rim. Every so often he made a meatball he wasn't sure of, and called his father over to judge, is it too big, is it not round enough? Matt told him, each time, that's fine, it'll taste delicious.

When the plate was almost full, Amelia drew a chair up to the stove. Alexander climbed up, and was allowed to tip in his plate of meatballs, edging them into the pan with a long wooden spoon, grimacing and pulling back if anything spattered. When the meatballs were browning, he climbed back down and went off obediently to wash his hands, while Amelia tended the sauce. Matt said to her, very quietly, "Amelia."

"Yes, sweetie?" For days she went over that conversation, wished she hadn't called him sweetie, thought she must have done it out of nervousness, feeling that something was wrong.

"Amelia, I'm angry. I'm really angry. All the time."

"Angry at me?"

"Yes, I guess so. And I don't think I want things to go on like this."

At that moment Alexander reappeared, anxious to inspect his meatballs, and the conversation stopped. Amelia started water boiling and made spaghetti, and they all ate dinner, conscientiously making conversation about day care and the spaceship, and the important work Alexander had done, that very day, taking apart a computer keyboard with a screwdriver and a hammer, and reassembling the pieces into spaceship controls, with the help of construction paper and Elmer's glue.

Plastic and paper, disposable wrappings and needles, all these things make hospitals much less awful than they would otherwise be. The gauze you use to absorb pus from a wound you throw in the garbage; no one expects you to launder dressings and reuse them. Needles go into the needle boxes, IV tubing goes into the garbage. Scalpel blades are disposable. The toilets, naturally, flush. It doesn't take away the smells or the sights, but it helps. When Louisa May Alcott encountered the Civil War wounded, she had none of this to lean on. "The first thing I met was a regiment of the vilest odors that ever assaulted the human nose, and took it by storm."

I may as well say that I didn't quite find what I was looking for in *Hospital Sketches*, if I was in fact looking for some magic template. She does not go into the kind of detail I really crave; I want to know how she coped with hospital reality, and she evidently does not consider that her audience is ready to face that reality, however ready she herself might have been. "I witnessed several operations; for the height of my ambition was to go to the front after a battle, and feeling that the sooner I inured myself to trying sights, the more useful I should be. Several of my mates shrunk from such things; for though the spirit was wholly willing, the flesh was inconveniently weak."

I admire her, I like her more than ever. She valued domestic security above other, ostensibly higher, states; her sainted father, for example, spent his life pursuing improvements in the human condition, schlepped his family into frequent discomfort—but Louisa, like her mother, knew that a family needed a home. But she also understood that the strength you draw from home and family is the strength that lets you turn outward.

I went to the right place that day. And when I came back from Concord to find my house empty, I got through the evening on the strength of Louisa May Alcott. I straightened up the house, I vacuumed the living-room rug, I dusted the books. I scrubbed the kitchen table, sorted through piles of old mail and day care notices and out-of-date birthday party invitations piled up next to the phone. I would tend my house, I would keep it neat and ready to hold my family. They would be back soon; we would be together. And I would also be ready for the hospital, for vile odors and trying sights.

Amelia was babbling. The spaghetti was eaten, the meatballs extravagantly complimented, and here she was, sitting in the living room, trying to engage Matt, trying to distract him from his anger, from whatever was making him angry. Trying to remind him that it had been a hard week for her, too, a hard week for them all. Thinking maybe it would interest him, the legal problems of Darren's custody, interest him the way Agatha Christie novels interested him. Problem-solving, legalities, courtroom drama. She had never really told him the story, since they had ended up in the emergency room with Alexander, et cetera, et cetera; now she rambled on, Lana Rosen, the judge, the custody, the DNR.

"And he's still alive?" Matt asked.

"He could hang on awhile longer, or he could go tonight. We don't really know what's going on in his lungs, so we don't really know how to predict. I know it sounds a little like we don't know what we're doing, but the fact is you never know when someone's going to die, especially a child, until it's really imminent, like in an hour. And even then you're sometimes wrong."

"So if you know so little about what's going to happen to him, where do you get off deciding to let him die? Maybe he might live for months if you gave him a chance."

"He might. It's true. It's a really tough decision."

"Don't get all melodramatic about it or anything. For you it's a really tough decision, quote unquote; for him it's whether he dies or not."

"He's going to die, though. He has a disease we can't cure; he's just wasted away."

"You couldn't give him food somehow or other, if you really wanted to?"

"We could try—like by IV. But all those things have risks."

"Well, if it were my kid I would want you to take all those risks, if there was any reasonable chance I could have him for a couple more months."

"Why are you so angry at me, Matt?"

"I guess because I'm tired of this."

"Tired of what?"

"Of how we live—of what our lives together are like. I'm tired of hearing about every sick kid in the world, who means more to you than your own kid does, because your own kid isn't sick."

"How can you say that? That's a horrible thing to say. It isn't true at all." She will be ashamed of having called him sweetie, and even more ashamed of starting to cry, helplessly and messily, in her own living room.

"You take everything for granted—you have to be at a life-and-death emergency whenever, no matter what, so I can just cope with everything. And for Christ's sake, when your own kid is in the hospital, all you can do is make lists of all the terrible things that *aren't* wrong with him, that make him less important than the sicker children."

"What are you talking about?"

"You think I'm stupid or something? You think I don't know why I had to hear about the kid with the brain tumor, and the kid who can't grow, and the kid who has to be DNR? You think I don't pick up the message, that Alexander isn't really so sick, that he doesn't really matter?"

Amelia wiped her nose with her one wet tissue, tried to answer. "It's true, one of the things I do is make bargains all the time, so the bad things I see won't happen to Alexander. So when he was sick enough to be in the hospital, I couldn't help it, I had to think about all the worse things that could have been wrong. And it *is* worse to have a child who limps a little and then turns out to have a brain tumor. Those people came into the hospital one day thinking their kid was going to grow up and be fine, and then nothing was ever okay again. That's worse than what happened to Alexander, and I see those things every day. I know what can happen to people."

"Well, I don't appreciate your little lessons, the way you keep trying to show *me* what can happen to people. Alexander matters, all by himself, and what happens to him matters, even if it's not the worst thing that could ever happen to a kid, it still matters more than all the other kids put together. I don't need to know about them, and if you need to, and you need to worry more about the ones who are more sick, then I don't want to have to hear about it."

"Okay," she said, crying again. "I'm sorry. I won't talk about it anymore. I didn't mean it."

"Amelia, I'm just angry at you all the time. I mean, really angry. Look, I don't even know why, exactly. I'm going to try stepping back, I want to see if that helps."

"What do you mean?"

"I mean I don't exactly want to go on living like this—I think I'll stay away for a while and see how things go."

He slept downstairs that night, and then, in the morning, when she tried to talk to him, to touch him, he pulled away from her. Please leave me alone, he said. Please go away. Please let me spend the day with Alexander, please go away and leave us. So she drove to Concord, and when she came back, he had taken Alexander and gone, and she was not surprised.

Sunday she sat around the house, imagining every now and then that she heard footsteps on the porch, that Alexander would come rushing in to hug her and tell her his adventures, with Matt hanging back behind him, a little ashamed but glad to see her, glad to be home. It didn't happen. Monday she went to the hospital and Darren was intubated in the ICU. While Amelia had been playing the abandoned wife, Darren's father had marched onto the hospital ward. Confronted Roberta Wilson, demanded details of his son's medical condition. Quizzed the nurse, quizzed the intern. Found out about the DNR status. Declared he wanted everything done that could be done for his son.

The intern called the senior resident. The nurse called the head nurse. The senior resident called the lawyer. The head nurse called the child protection team social worker. The lawyer called the judge. No one called Amelia in the confusion, and no one really needed to, because the judge and the lawyer agreed that there was no question. Darren's father had to be presumed to have custody. If he wanted the child intubated, then the child should be intubated. You couldn't make a child DNR against his parent's wishes, especially when the DNR decision was an iffy one to begin with.

Darren's code status was officially changed back to full code. And then, of course, that very night, he obliged by trending downward, just a little, in his respiratory status. The intern, unnerved by the day's confusion, called the senior again, who called the ICU team, who evaluated Darren and decided he needed the unit. And after four or five hours of careful monitoring in the unit, they decided he needed a tube, and a ventilator. So Amelia found him, Monday morning, the clear plastic tube passed in through his nostril, fogging with every breath. And the breaths themslevs, deeper and longer than any he had taken himself for days and days, generated by the ventilator next to his bed, a magic box decorated with dials and indicators, passing through a hose into Darren a measured amount of oxygen, with a certain prescribed force, so many times a minute. And in and out and in and out. The monitors over Darren's bed recorded the result: heartbeat, respiratory rate, oxygenation. Stable on the ventilator. And in and out and in and out.

CHAPTER VIII
A BETTER NURSE THAN I

Saturday morning she marches herself over to Matt's house. It's a warm Cambridge December day, dark and menacing, the streets full of melting slush. An appropriate day for slogging, everything that was clean and white with the last snow now gray and dirty. She thinks, of course, of that morning in November when the blizzard hit and she took Alexander into bed with her, thinks about it as if she is trying to make herself cry; lost, lost, all lost.

And yet, why all lost? Surely she can have mornings (and afternoons and evenings and nights) with Alexander, have them often and undisturbed. Alexander is not going to disappear from her life. Over the week, Amelia has tried to make herself fantasize about life after Matt. Twice he has brought Alexander over to spend the evening with her, both times he rang the doorbell, waited to see her opening the door, then turned away and started down the steps. She watched him hurrying away: life without Matt. She has a feeling that she used to have such fantasies—doesn't every married person? Didn't she ever used to think about how simple and lovely everything would be if only Matt would go away and she could live according to her own rhythms, and Alexander's? All the little changes, the little trivial things, all the household chores that Matt takes for granted are necessary to a pleasant life. In other words, Amelia has often noted, with mild resentment, he likes at least to approximate the standards established by his mother. Laundry, for example—laundry must be sorted and folded and put away immediately or the world will come to an end. Amelia wonders why not just dump all the family laundry in a heap somewhere, warm from the dryer, maybe on the old armchair in the upstairs hallway, outside the bathroom, where no one ever sits, the chair exiled from more useful places because springs are starting to poke through the bottom. So if you dumped all the laundry there, then everyone could just grab a clean pair of underpants, a shirt, socks, passing by in the morning on the way out of the bathroom. Why sort the clothes into three piles, fold the T-shirts, tuck everything carefully into the correct drawer, only to have three people go from drawer to drawer each and every morning?

What nonsense. Unsorted laundry is hardly the stuff of which emancipation is made, especially since Matt did most of the sorting himself. And who really minds a drawer full of clean underwear?

Amelia turns the corner onto the block where Matt's house is waiting for her. Suppose they aren't there? Suppose Matt has taken Alexander and gone away somewhere? Suppose the house is empty, or even worse, suppose Marco is there, grinning at her? She has never really truly liked Marco, she admits freely to herself now; and probably this is because Marco is too much what Matt might like to be. Marco really did grow up to be a carpenter, trained carefully by his father, a cabinetmaker in Chicago. Marco is loose and easy and proud of his work, efficient and responsible without being at all self-conscious. Marco has one girlfriend after another, enjoys their company, treats them well, probably remembers them fondly. Marco likes Alexander, and Alexander adores Marco, and they wrestle nonstop whenever they meet, Marco always a little bit rougher than Matt would dare to be. And Alexander of course always tougher than he would be wrestling with his father, never allowing a stray bump or knock to send him into tears. Marco is good-looking and graceful, and Marco, Amelia supposes, would think nothing of having sex with a bored lady client; he would see it as a joke. The rich housewife and the handyman, a dirty joke. And why not?

She presses the doorbell but cannot hear it ring, and perhaps it is not in working order, so she pounds on the door with her fists, trying to compose her face so that if Marco answers the door, she will look amused, unsurprised, in control. But it is Matt who opens the door, and he does not look any of those things. He looks angry, guilty, and maybe just a little bit pleased to see her. Does he look that way becasue she is still, in spite of everything, the love of his life, and he is angry at her but happy to behold her? Or is she an adversary now, and is his pleasure in victory: she has had to come to him, not he to her?

She steps inside the hallway and is overcome. It is all spotless white and polished woodwork, clean and welcoming and even bright. She can see into the right-hand room, where Matt and Alexander have evidently been camping, see the two cots, the familiar suitcases, a pile of Alexander's coloring books. Then Alexander himself comes out of the left-hand room, and she waits hopefully for him to run to her. He doesn't, though. He stands in the doorway, looking at his parents and thinking whatever he is thinking. His face is a little bit thinned down after his sickness, and there are two healing pox visible on his forehead, no longer red, but still blemishes; his forehead is like silk, Amelia knows, and she wants to smooth his hair back over the top of his head, and check the pox with her fingertips in passing. Standing there, doubt in his eyes (or does she imagine that), he looks to Amelia like a waif, an orphan of the storm. Thinner, and can it be that he has grown taller, too? His cheeks shadowed, almost smudged (reminding her disturbingly of Darren), his forehead marked and perhaps soon to be scarred, he stands there warily. Children cannot be protected. You cannot keep them safe. Alexander has had to learn this twice over now, bang, bang.

Amelia holds out her arms to him and then he does, finally, run to her and hug her. Over his head she says to Matt, astonishingly calmly, I came to get him, I'd like to spend the day with him today. And Matt, who is perhaps relieved, perhaps disappointed, that Amelia has not come to harangue or plead or weep or accuse, nods, and says, Actually, he's supposed to spend the afternoon at Jeremy's, we set it up yesterday. Okay, says Amelia, I'll take him there.

And he can sleep at the house tonight. Yes, says Alexander, I want to sleep in my own room. Amelia feels powerfully triumphant; Matt will not dare say no and disappoint his son, any more than Amelia would have dared cancel the promised visit to Jeremy. Amelia has an inkling of the power that a child gathers, by default, when parents no longer present a united front, when parents fragment into competitors.

She takes Alexander out for a pizza lunch, not wanting to bring him back to the house. When she set out to get him, she had thought that all she wanted to do was get him home, where he belonged, and hug him and hold him until it began to seem ordinary again that he should be there, until he went for his toys and left her to sit on the couch, like any mother on a Saturday. But now she is content to defer that pleasure until the evening; instead she orders his favorite, extra cheese and pepperoni, and, unable to eat more than half a slice herself, stares at him dreamily as he, also dreamily, immerses himself in pizza. By the time she drives him over to Jeremy's house, a cold and nasty rain is falling.

Luke answers the door, and he and Amelia stand back, smiling, as Alexander and Jeremy coalesce like two raindrops. Deprived of each other's company since yesterday, but now of course entitled to the special weekend intimacy of best friends, not just two boys in the day care group. "Come on," says Jeremy, urgently, "I have to show you my new knights."

They head for the stairs immediately, Alexander asking with absorbed interest, "Are they horseback knights or standing up?"

Amelia turns back toward the door, wondering what she will do while Alexander is here. Maybe go to a bookstore, maybe take herself out for tea and cake?

Luke pushes the front door shut. It's lousy out, he says. Come sit down and have a drink or something.

They sit together on the big beige couch, modern, unadorned, and quite comfortable. Diana, Luke explains, is at her gallery, presiding over a show she is sponsoring for two local potters; Amelia hopes politely that the bad weather won't put people off. She tells Luke that Matt is at work restoring his little house. The windows are gray and wet, as if this perfectly warm dry room is only an illusion. Amelia chooses wine, and Luke brings it to her in an enormous goblet, and as he settles down beside her with his own, Amelia almost wonders for a second if there is something charged between them, if there is any possibility that he has thought of her in the way she has thought of him.

Such things do not, of course, actually transpire between two parents whose four-year-olds are happily at play upstairs. Already Amelia is thinking that soon Luke will learn that she and Matt are not together, and then perhaps he will think back to sitting on the couch and drinking wine with her during the rainstorm, and then what? Wonder whether she was trying to seduce him? Wonder if he should perhaps have made a pass at her, sex-starved as she must be in her single state?

To ward off all this ugliness, all the nice things that will never happen and the bad things that have and will, she looks down at the *Boston Globe* lying on the floor and makes conversation about the page-one new-AIDS-drug-offers-promise story. Complains about how long it takes before a drug gets approved for children. Idle obvious things she's said a hundred times before.

"Do you see a lot of children die?" Luke asks. It is the kind of question she often resents, often finds prurient, but not this time.

"Not so very many. Most children get well. That's why I like pediatrics. But now that I'm taking care of so many kids with AIDS—"

"I can't imagine what that's like, seeing a child die. Isn't it awfully hard on you?"

"Actually, I've been reading all these nineteenth-century novels, books with dying children in them. I mean, children really did die, regularly, a hundred years ago. Everyone lost a child or two along the way. So you might think you could go to nineteenth-century literature and find some kind of wisdom, some way of accepting a life in which children die. But instead it's all nonsense about ascending to heaven, and the Lord calling his angels home."

"Some would say that if great literature can't equip you at all to handle those deaths, then what good is great literature, and we might as well burn the books to keep the children warm," Luke says. "But others might say that great literature exists on its own behalf and doesn't need to justify itself by any kind of function."

"All the deaths are so terrible, and so ridiculous and soppy. I can't even talk about the worst parts of my work, because it would just seem like bad soap opera. And when children die in books, that's exactly what it is. I mean, the death scenes in books make me cry, and then I feel like I've been had."

She has never exactly said this before, not to anyone. But Luke is her crush object, and he works all day with books into the bargain, and perhaps they will never leave this room, this warm pocket in the cold wet day.

"I'm trying to think of examples for you," Luke says. "Great books where children die."

"Do you read the books you work with?" She can picture him, humming absently to himself, big and sloppy, but handling the crumbling pages with most extreme delicacy.

"Bits and pieces sometimes. I went into this line of work because I'm happiest in libraries, really. Couldn't think where else I would rather spend my life." Amelia has the distinct sense of coming up against a catch phrase, something he has said again and again. Tit for tat; fair exchange for her own well-worn outrage about AIDS drugs and children, for that line about how she likes pediatrics because most children don't die. You'd think that if a person really felt that way, she'd find some job that let her work with healthy children, with children who are all going to grow up. Not choose medicine, choose pediatrics, choose AIDS. "I don't feel that way about hospitals," she says, somewhat ruefully.

"No, I don't really imagine one could. But I look back on my life as a succession of libraries; I spent adolescence in one, college in another, and they were always my refuges, my holy places. I knew where everything was, and the librarians always liked me, of course, because I was so well-behaved, and because I came every single day. Even my first daydreams about girls were in the library, the only place I guess I felt secure enough to let go and fantasize."

"No, I definitely don't feel that way about hospitals."

"Then, later on, I got into the technical aspects of it, I got interested in rare books and preservation as a skill, as a science. But I wouldn't ever have come across it if I hadn't been searching for a way to spend the rest of my life in a library."

"I like used-book stores," says Amelia, and tells him about the copy of *Uncle Tom's Cabin*, the copy of *The Old Curiosity Shop*. That sets him off again, trying to think of other works of literature with dead children in them.

"What about Shakespeare?"

"I haven't really gone back before the nineteenth century. But I guess there are the little princes in the tower, right?"

"Well, they get killed. And there's a child in *Macbeth* who I believe gets massacred as well. So Shakespeare would seem to be into killing children for effect."

"Why not? Everyone else is. Must be because it's so effective."

"And there's *King John*. All I know from *King John* is a famous speech about a murdered child."

"What's that?"

"I'll find it for you later, you'll recognize it. It's very famous."

"Dying children on the stage," says Amelia. "Talk about melodrama."

"Must be a bit of a problem, though—I mean you couldn't kill a very young child on stage because you wouldn't be able to rely on a very young actor. And it would lose some of its impact if you used a large doll."

"That's all they are, though, these children. In the books, I mean. They're just dolls. Wind them up and they die, beautifully."

A crash from overhead reminds them of their own two children, strong and warlike. Wind them up and they duel for hours, wind them up and they turn into pirates, wind them up and they fight wars in outer space.

Luke and Amelia settle back and sip their wine. Yes, something is most definitely charged between them; they are not two strangers making conversation. She is not kidding herself. What she doesn't know is what will happen, what could possibly happen. What happens is this: his hand comes suddenly to rest on the back of her neck, begins to rub it gently. It is one of the most highly sexual moments she has ever known, this moment of acknowledgment, of breaking all the boundaries that hold them both. He is married and the father of Alexander's friend, she is married and the mother of Alexander, and yet here is his hand on her neck, his fingers rubbing gently under the back curls of her hair.

So she turns slightly and looks at him, and still they do not lean toward each other, do not kiss. The connection, his hand and her neck, is too strong to need that. Amelia finds she is breathing hard, and she closes her eyes for a minute to think of nothing but the warmth and weight of his fingers, rubbing back and forth, exploring up and down, edging out with the curve of her skull, down very slightly into the neck of her shirt.

Her eyes closed, she hears especially clearly the intensity in his voice when he suggests, whispering, "We could go take a nap. Upstairs. I could give Jeremy one of the videotapes he likes, that would keep them for an hour at least."

And so she finds herself in Luke and Diana's bedroom, waiting while Luke goes to check on the boys, to make sure Alexander knows that his mother has left, to hand over the videotape of Walt Disney's *Robin Hood* and establish the two boys in front of the VCR. The bedroom is all decorated in white and gray and silver. The big bed is covered with a heavy quilted white spread, the bed headboard outlined with silver chrome, a stark half-circle like a moon against the white wall. A large skylight in the ceiling is streaming with water, and the noise of the rain is of course much louder in this room. Now the noise reassures Amelia, makes her sure that whatever goes on in this room, amidst this wash of water, will not count. She slips her shoes off, and goes across the pale gray carpet into the lavishly outfitted bathroom. Matt is not interested in this kind of project, so their home will never have a sunken tub, or an illuminated makeup mirror, or heated towel racks. But in the bathroom Amelia takes off her clothes, imagining a scene in which Alexander bangs on the bedroom door and she retreats into the bathroom, leaving Luke to cope. Then she is too embarrassed to lie naked on the bed, but also too nice-minded to strip back the spread and contaminate Diana's sheets, so she takes a black bathsheet, warm from the heated bar, and wraps herself up, sits gingerly on the edge of the bed. Doesn't think once even, What am I doing, is this really happening, won't we be sorry? She is at the bottom of the ocean, she is far away from her life.

Luke comes into the room, carefully locking the door behind him. "I told them I was going to lie down for a while. Jeremy told me they were going to watch *Robin Hood* nineteen times."

Amelia watches him unbutton his shirt. Not surprisingly, he is bolder than she, in his own room, and unhesitatingly strips back the bedcover. With the light off, the room is very dark, since the skylight is dimmed by the water flowing over it, by the dark day outside. Still, Amelia can see that she has imagined his body quite accurately, love handles only beginning, but a good-sized potbelly. Still, a sort of confidence in the way he moves, as if none of that mattered, as if he would have been perfectly happy in a society in which he could have run around naked all day, potbellied and furry.

Perhaps it shouldn't surprise her, given all the fantasies she has had about this man, but the level of arousal, of passion, of sexual magnitude, truly astonishes Amelia. Why isn't she more self-conscious? Why isn't he? Instead, as he pulls her onto him, as she plants her knees on either side of his hips and leans down, pressing on his chest, she can sense only his delight, and her own. He reaches up with his own hands, clasps them over her breasts, and they rock against each other, and then he moves his hands to her hips, and it doesn't even occur to her to think that he will feel the soft embarrassing folds around her waist. He just holds her at the hips and pushes her, firmly, up and down, until she begins to come, and then cannot stop coming, writhing around on him, calling out very softly, until he has come himself, and is lying very still, watching her.

And after all that, they actually do take a nap, curled up together under the bedspread, with the rain hard on the roof. A short nap, in each other's arms; then Amelia goes into the bathroom and dresses and brushes her hair with what she hopes is Luke's brush, not Diana's, and she and Luke slip downstairs, and he reaches out his own front door and rings the doorbell, in case the boys are listening, then goes back upstairs to tell Alexander his mother is here, and he can have another fifteen minutes to play.

Darren's father was not quite what anyone would have imagined. The bad guy, the drug addict, the villain of the piece. If he had come in dirty and obstreperous, a street person yelling in the hospital corridors, no one would have been suprised. But he came in neat and well dressed, well spoken, intelligent, and aggressive on his son's behalf, and no one knew what to make of him.

Amelia heard about it from several people, from the apologetic intern, Clark Donahue, from Lana Rosen, even from Roberta Wilson. Darren's father had interrogated Clark for almost an hour. He had demanded that Clark go through the medical chart with him, page by page, and explain what was wrong with Darren, what drugs he was getting. Another intern might have refused, might have said he had no time, but Clark was having a relatively quiet afternoon, and Clark was much too conscientious to say no to the father of a dying child, even if that father did begin the interview by scrutinizing his scrubs and demanding to know why he didn't dress like a professional. So he went through the chart patiently, honestly. Even braced himself and explained the custody issue, the judge's ruling. And then found himself told by that father that the hospital had obviously given up on Darren, and why was that? He's going to die, Clark said helplessly.

We are all going to die in God's good time, said Darren's father. But there is no rule that we have to give up and kill one another. You have no right to decide that my son should die here and now. To everything there is a season, but it is not you who make the seasons.

At which point Clark called in the senior resident, who made the mistake of trying a little medical authoritarianism. We are doctors, and we have discussed this at length, and we know what is best.

So Darren's father said, Might this possibly have anything to do with the fact that my son is black? Would you have written Do Not Resuscitate upon his forehead if he were white?

When he had first walked into Darren's hospital room, Roberta Wilson had almost not recognized him. But he had introduced himself, had told her he was sorry he had been away so long. He had been in prison, he said, and ashamed to have his son know it. But he was out, he was clean, he was through detox, and he was saved, into the bargain. Darren's grandmother, whose own religion was quiet and close to her heart, and who had no particular use for those who wore their salvation on their sleeve, told him perhaps more abruptly than she should have that Darren was near death, that he would not wake up again, that his short life had been lived out completely while his father was away. I'm sorry you won't see him walking, talking, she said, and realized as she was saying it that it was true, she *was* sorry. I mean, she told Amelia, I suddenly thought that here was one of the only people who might ever have looked at that child walking and been specially proud of him. You know what I mean, one of the people for whom Darren would have been one special little boy. The steps that your own child takes mean something to you. And I felt all mixed up, because I hated him so much, even then, even looking at him looking down at Darren, but I also thought that if my boy was dying, here was someone else who would notice his going. And then he started in on me, he demanded to know, wasn't there anything anyone could do? Couldn't the doctors try anything they hadn't tried yet?

Alexander is edgy. How could he not be, passing back and forth between his two parents all week long, between his bedroom and the room in Matt's little house. He does not ask Amelia anything point-blank, and, cowardly, she does not open the subject. Occasionally she makes up little sentences (Daddy and I were having too many fights so we decided to take a little vacation from each other), but she keeps them to herself.

The most alarming thing Alexander does is refuse to let her praise him. She looks up one evening from the medical journal she has been reading to admire a picture he has just colored in, a knight on horseback, meticulously crayoned inside the lines. He must have every coloring book ever made that touches on pirates, knights, castles.

"It's very nice, such lovely colors," she tells him, with the false enthusiasm parents manufacture for coloring books, paint-by-numbers pictures, tracings, all the art forms children prefer to their own attempts at representation. "You certainly are good at coloring," she says.

"No, I'm not. Don't say I am, because I'm not." He closes the coloring book and puts it away, and though she protests, he will not discuss it any further; he finds his copy of *Happy Birthday to You* and demands to hear it read aloud.

And again and again. "I love you," she tells him, another night. "You're such a nice kid."

"Don't ever say that, don't say I'm nice." His voice is severe, absolute. Is it possible that he blames himself, that he feels guilty because his family has dissolved? Or is it less specific; perhaps, now that his parents are no longer together, his rock is gone, his most basic store of self-confidence emptied. Perhaps he sees himself as some new boy, Alexander who passes back and forth from one house to the other, and perhaps he doesn't like that boy.

Her voice is teasing, joking, maybe pleading just a little. "Why not, why can't I tell you how nice you are?"

"Because I'm not, I'm not nice at all. You just can't ever say that."

Amelia is not embarrassed, thinking of Luke. She believes several things at once, without thinking them over seriously. One, he was telling the truth when he said he had never done such a thing before. Two, it will never happen again. Three, no harm done. She is no longer fantasizing about Luke, she is not going over and over their lovemaking in her mind. What she thinks about, when she thinks about it at all, is how cozy it was, being with him in that comfortable bedroom on a rainy afternoon while the children played safely nearby. It was an alternate domesticity rather than a seedy adventure.

Or she smiles, thinking of a joke she made to him as they were falling asleep, a joke he perhaps thought was in bad taste. He had said, You know, this is not the kind of thing I usually do, in fact I never have, and she had said, Me neither, then added, I guess that makes this safe sex for the heterosexual white upper middle class. When he looked blank, she explained—when monogamous married heterosexuals commit adultery together, that's safe sex.

Once, one day that week, standing in the doorway of Matt's house, waiting for Alexander to get his coat and boots on, she is almost tempted to come right out and ask Matt, does he in fact ever go to bed with his customers? He is standing so near, he looks so familiar. She is so impressed by the beauty and order he has made in this house, and it is so easy to imagine how another woman, watching him at work, might be attracted. But she doesn't ask, and probably won't ever ask. Even at her lowest, she doesn't believe he has left her because he is in love with someone else. Maybe he is in love with the idea of being on his own, being without her, being free to be with anyone he likes, but that's a different thing. And really, see what he has created here in this little house, a camping place for himself and Alexander. A determined approximation of home comfort in the sunny little room that he has spent so many months making beautiful. Alexander's T-shirts and underpants are neatly stacked in an open suitcase. *Bulfinch's Mythology* lies on the folding chair. Every night, in that room, Matt reads aloud at bedtime.

Actually, the really important things Amelia believes, without daring to examine them, are: one, Matt will come home soon; two, this is not a real separation; three, soon we will all be together again.

The intern called the senior resident. The senior resident called the lawyer. Lana Rosen marched into the hospital, spent thirty minutes with Darren's father, and then called the judge. Lana said to Amelia on Monday, Look, he's the kid's biological father, and I told you all along that the courts give custody to the biological parents unless there's a compelling reason not to. I mean, if the guy had been obviously drugged out, or if he was off the wall in some blatant way, then I might have tried to block it. But here's this perfectly sane guy, unless you happen to think that Bible-quoting makes you nuts, and he was obviously entitled to claim custody. The judge agreed with me totally. I mean, you can't do anything about that. I just had to hope that since you guys said the kid was dying more than a week ago, and he still hadn't died, maybe he would just keep going and the whole DNR issue wouldn't come up. But there's no way your DNR order could be valid when the biological father didn't want it. And I know it was a controversial order to begin with.

Amelia did not want to go see Darren in the ICU. She didn't want to see him intubated. She found his father sitting at his bed-side and wondered, of course, where his grandmother was. Darren's father was a small, good-looking man, just a little bit too thin. He looked, in fact, like Darren, or at least the way she remembered Darren looking back before he got so emaciated. A square face, a boxy little jaw, and very black eyes with a slightly green glint when the light hit them. Darren's father wore a gray suit, wrinkled now, after twenty-four hours at his son's bedside. He gripped Amelia's hand firmly, shook it only once, ceremonially. Doctor, I hear you've been involved with my son now for a long time, and I want to thank you. I'm sorry I wasn't here any sooner to tell you how I felt, but we serve where we are called.

The intensive care unit did not offer separate rooms. It was a large, oddly shaped open space, designed with bays so that each bed would occupy a slot next to a wall bank of monitors, oxygen outlets, suction, electricity. But the unit was overcrowded, and extra beds had been squeezed in. Between Darren's bed and the next one over, there was barely room for the nurse to stand as she checked the tubes, adjusted the monitors.

The intensive care unit had to offer maximum visibility, maximum accessibility, since all the patients were maximally sick. They were assumed to be beyond privacy, or at least to need close observation more than they needed privacy. Darren was connected to so many monitors now; his heart and his respirations were monitored, of course, and there were additional gauges to read that tracked the ventilator itself, reassuring the nurse that he was getting the proper number of breaths at the proper pressure. Besides the arterial line, he had two IVs in. His stuffed animal, Mouse, had been propped up at the foot of the bed, out of the way of all the tubes and wires, one small forlorn relic, in this ultimate efficient room, of an abbreviated childhood. Darren was covered with a sheet, but he still looked exposed and vulnerable to Amelia, out of the shelter of the oxygen tent that had covered him back in his room on the ward, his body now out in the open, maximally wired to reveal its functions, its numbers, its performance.

He was very far away from me. He was far from his grandmother. He was far from any gentle death scene I might have imagined for him, far from Beth and far from little Eva, far from every child who ever slipped quietly into the kind arms of death, its little arms too weak to hold the painful life any longer. From every little angel who ever left behind the darkness of its earthbound life to find peace, joy, and light with the heaven-borne multitudes.

There was this one very strange moment, when Alexander was in the hospital. His first night there, after a long and cranky day, he finally found some relief from his itching with an increased dose of IV Benadryl, which I had nagged and nagged them into giving. Matt and I had sponged him off a little and tempted him with a cup of chocolate pudding decorated with pink-icing flowers, which I had saved off his dinner tray. We encouraged him to eat it, we clapped and cheered and told him how good he was as he took one bite after another. And when he handed back the dish, he reached out suddenly and hugged me around the neck with his one free arm. He was smiling, almost laughing, and he wrapped his thin little arm around me and said, Oh, I am just so entirely proud of myself, and then shifted around to hug his father. He was actually laughing out loud, he had won some kind of victory, though I didn't know whether it was eating the pudding, or feeling the itching stop, or just making it through the day.

As I straightened up from his hug, I felt an impulse surely out of a Victorian novel, to look Matt in the eye and exclaim, "O!" Or even, perhaps, "O Husband!" And then, "If we should lose him!" I was overwhelmed with the thought What if he was this sweet, this beloved, and he was dying. What if there was something terrible within his body, something that would take him from us. And then, oppressed by the hospital, I could not help thinking of all those parents who would lose their children, of those moments when they succeeded in making the children laugh, and of what they would feel, hearing the laughter.

"Dodie, I've realized something."

"You've realized that marital troubles offer a rare opportunity for personal growth."

"No, really, I have realized something."

"Hit me."

"I've been thinking about how Matt lived through my residency—you know, the hours he's put up with, back then and all these years. And I realized I would never have done it for him. Isn't it bizarre that I never thought of that before?"

"Why should you have done it for him?"

"No, I mean that if he had gone on and become a doctor, or if he had any other job that called him out at random bad hours, and I was just supposed to adjust to it, I would have refused. I would have told him we shouldn't have a child if he couldn't get things under control."

"No, you wouldn't have. I can just imagine the two of you, with a little doctors' office together somewhere. I can see the story now: M.D. Marriage, Mr. and Mrs. M.D. 'Amelia and Matt admit shyly that their shared profession has brought them closer together. Their handsome young son, Alexander, who has had a toy doctor kit since the age of one and a half, is determined to join his parents' practice as soon as he can. He is well accustomed to spending his afternoons quietly playing in one corner of their homey office.'"

"I wouldn't, you know. I would never have made it through Matt's internship. I would have been too angry at the idea that I was shaping my whole life to the convenience of someone else's idiotic training program."

"So what is it you've realized, then—that you are a selfish and ambitious monster, or that Matt is an angel of marital tolerance?"

"He wasn't an angel about it, by any means. But he did put up with it."

"He put up with it because he wanted to stay together with you. Don't make a big thing out of it, Amelia. People don't get that much credit for holding on to the lives they want for themselves."

"You think I'm just talking nonsense?"

"No, I think you're being pathologically calm and collected about this whole thing. Your husband takes your kid and moves out of the house, and you sit around deciding whether you would have been willing to see him through medical school. Look, even when you just break up with your boyfriend, I happen to know, there are at least five emotional steps you have to go through."

"Don't tell me."

"First there's *shock*. You can't believe he would do this. You can't believe it's over. Then comes *self-reproach*. How could you have driven him away? I guess you might be up to that, though you're doing a pretty half-assed job, I must say."

"Dodie, that's enough. I don't need to know the other steps. I'll figure out my own, thank you very much."

"Third is *grief*. You have to mourn the relationship, almost as if it were a person you loved who died. And then *anger*. How could he do this to you? The bum, you want to kill him. Don't worry, it's perfectly healthy."

"I'll look forward to it."

"And last, of course, is *acceptance*. You understand that it's over. You start looking around and noticing that the world is full of attractive men."

"It is?"

"You get a new haircut, you join an aerobics class. You're starting to feel alive again, excited about the possibility of flirting, dating, new adventures."

"I invest in liposuction."

"You give in to temptation and buy those Hawaiian colored condoms."

In the hospital, in her clinic, Amelia feels busy. Lab slips pile up on her desk, and when a patient doesn't show up for an appointment, she spends her free half hour sorting them. Bathsheba Jenkins's HIV test is negative. Amelia calls her up, but the woman who answers the phone says Bathsheba has moved out, no, she doesn't know where. Amelia calls directory assistance, and there is indeed a Bathsheba Jenkins listed in Jamaica Plain, a new number, but it's unlisted. So Amelia pulls the old routine, I'm a doctor, I need to reach this mother. The operator puts her through to a supervisor, and the supervisor calls her back at the hospital to check that she really is who she says she is, and then condescends to dial Bathsheba's number, which she still cannot give out. Finally Amelia reaches Bathsheba and tells her to come in to the clinic, and when she does, tells her the good news. You're negative, Tayesha is safe, Jamal and Jarry are safe—all your children. But you need to protect yourself, because the twins' father could be positive, or could turn positive.

Amelia doesn't actually say, As the potential pediatrician of your potential future children, I need to try to protect you from infection, protect them from infection. But she cannot help, of course, thinking of Darren, of his life and death. Cannot help imagining herself weighing and measuring a newborn, doling out shots and polio drinks, protecting the baby from all the now obscure diseases (diphtheria, for example), when all the time the baby will have a virus in its blood because, somehow, she failed to convince its mother that the world is a dangerous place.

Because she is upset, because her own life is off course, there is almost nothing that Amelia recognizes as outside her jurisdiction, beyond her responsibility. One morning the newspaper announces in big black gravestone letters another crash, another two hundred plus dead, holiday travel, no survivors, question of pilot error. And the little follow-up stories on the inside pages list the fifteen worst air disasters in history, the ten biggest domestic crashes. A little chart gives safety records for major airlines, and Amelia has to tear it out and save it. It would be a crime not to use all available information, next time she has to book Alexander onto a flight. Should she book the airlines with the best safety records, or are those the ones that are due for calamities? You can choose as carefully as you like, but there are bombs in luggage compartments, there are sudden unexpected winds, there are cargo doors that open. Or you can be sitting on a runway, and another airplane can crash into you, over five hundred dead. Amelia is not a nervous person; she does not worry about the brakes or the tires on her car, driving to work on icy Boston roads. She does not mind sleeping alone in her house—not from the safety point of view. Flying alone never bothers her at all, and neither does walking alone to her car in the hospital parking lot, though there are women who insist on being escorted by security every evening, now that it gets dark by five.

What she cannot do is accept any responsibility for Alexander, for the life of her child. Sitting in her office, looking at Bathsheba Jenkins's lab slip, she is amazed that she was ever brave enough to have a child. She will never drive again with Alexander in the car, never make an airline reservation for him. For a moment, she is almost ready to relinquish him to Matt altogether. Just let him be safe. Let Matt take the responsibility.

What a histrionic piece of nonsense she is becoming. Amelia sorts through hematology slips, thinking of all the mothers who bring their children in to see her, from lousy underheated apartments, from homes where there is no space for one more child and the baby sleeps in a cardboard box on the kitchen table. Standing on buses, holding the pole with one hand, the baby with the other, begging a ride in a neighbor's car. Bringing the children in for their checkups, their shots, their protection. Amelia dutifully asks them, Do you have a car seat? Do you have smoke detectors? Accidents kill more children than diseases do; poverty is linked to accidents: kerosene heaters to keep out the cold, fires in buildings with bad wiring where the landlord can't be bothered to keep the smoke detectors functional. Lead paint. Windows without screens, gratings, bars. And yet they come in, week after week, month after month, carrying the children, accepting the responsibility. If Marcelle can do it, sixteen years old, Amelia can do it. And without making such a fuss, too.

Darren's father watches her closely as she leafs through the sheets on Darren's clipboard. ICU nursing data sheets are far more complex than the ones the nurses use on the regular wards. The sheet spreads out to a width of four pages, with columns to chart every parameter of the ventilator, every blood gas value, every breath he takes for himself. Any change in the boy, or his ventilator, or his monitors is documented in the rows of cramped numbers, marching down the sheet as the hours go by. And even if he is stable, the numbers chronicle that precarious engineered stability.

Darren's father is watching; Amelia can feel his anger. She recognizes it, the anger of the parent who is cut off from understanding. What do those numbers tell her? Are any of them important? Do they threaten, or promise, or predict? She stands there, silently reading them over, and he watches her and resents her secrets.

Amelia wonders how long Darren will last on the ventilator. There seems to her no reason why he shouldn't go on and on. Except, presumably, Darren's father will now want to go on and do the diagnostic procedure, the open lung biopsy, and that might be too much for the child. On the other hand, of course, they might find something treatable, and start treatment—Amelia is half resolved not to interfere. Darren seems to her now already in limbo. She hopes, of course, that he is feeling nothing, that they have him properly anesthetized. Let him float then in this medical twilight world, let the machine breathe for him and the intravenous lines nourish him, until there is nothing more anyone can do.

"Doctor, I am not ready to give up hope for this boy. I know how very, very sick he is, believe me, and I think his illness has worn your faith away."

"Doctor, tell me, have you never seen a miracle?"

"Doctor, do you go to church? Are you a religious woman?"

Amelia seeks out Roberta Wilson, who is keeping vigil in the parents' room attached to the ICU. It is a long L-shaped room, decorated in standard hospital blue with accents of hideous orange. Tattered magazines, a TV that seems always to be tuned to a talk show. And also the residue of too many parents, too many vigils. The mortality rate in the pediatric ICU is about 50 percent, since only the sickest children ever get there.

Roberta Wilson sits in an orange armchair, her hands in her lap. She seems smaller, as if losing formal rights to Darren has diminished her. Her eyes are closed, and perhaps Amelia imagines the defeated look on her face; she could not protect her grandson, as she could not protect her daughter. She is wearing, incongruously, a bright yellow suit, made of a rather stiff woolen fabric, and like Darren's father, she has a wrinkled, hospital-weary look about her.

Amelia sits beside her and says, I'm sorry this had to happen. Amelia remembers, months ago, Roberta asking her to run interference if Darren's father ever showed up. She didn't want anything to do with him, and here she is now, trapped with him in this vigil, with Darren far away inside his devastated body. This poor woman, Amelia thinks, has been deprived of Darren's life, and now his death has also been taken from her; he belongs to his father, to the ICU doctors, to everyone else, but not to her.

I'm so sorry this had to happen. Amelia is ready to sit down with her and weep.

Darren's grandmother reaches out, takes hold of her hand, squeezes. Don't bother yourself about it, Doctor. Darren's had a long hard time, and it just doesn't seem like we were meant to end it the way we wanted to.

"Do you want me to talk to his father? Or I could call the judge, we could see what your legal options are."

"No, Doctor, I don't think so. It's a very hard thing to ask a man to meet his little boy and agree, all at once, to let him die. You give him a little time to watch that baby and think about it all, and ask God what's the right thing to do. That man does so much praying, he must be getting answers back pretty quick."

"You want me to just leave things the way they are?"

"Well, what's done is done. I never wanted him to have that tube. But it seems like taking it out is a whole different thing."

And suddenly Amelia thinks, They've made an alliance. Darren's grandmother has accepted his father; family is family, and I am not family. She wants another mourner at the bedside, she wants someone else to feel the pain of losing this particular child. In the cold bare place where she waits for Darren to die, this is the only company she can accept, and the more pain she sees that man feel, the more welcome he is. And, Amelia thinks, I am not welcome there, I do not belong.

"I want you to be able to spend time with Darren, I don't want his father to keep you away."

"Doctor, you know as well as I do, I have spent hours and hours sitting and watching my boy try to breathe. Now I know he's going to go on breathing, since the machine is doing it for him, so I can take a little break." She reaches down to her feet and picks up a brown shopping bag.

"I brought this in for Darren. I saw how the other children, they get cards from their schoolmates, or their relatives. I wanted to hang something up on Darren's wall, since there aren't really very many people to write to him. Don't you think that's sad, Doctor, that a child should live three years and more, and almost no one knows about him, and then no one ever gets the chance, because that's all the life he has?" From the bag she takes an oval of wood, wreathed round its perimeter with children's faces cut from photographs. In the center, carefully lettered in red paint, following pencil marks that can be clearly seen where the paint strays, are

the words FOR MRS. WILSON FROM ROOM 3C WITH LOVE YOUR
CHILDREN.

The last thing she wants to do is call her mother. Mother, give
me advice on being left. Mother, give me advice on being alone.

The details of her own parents' separation are somewhat vague
for Amelia; they didn't actually split up until she was in college,
and they had planned it out so thoroughly between them that she
was left with the impression that Daddy had a new job in California, so he was moving there, while Mommy wanted to stay in New
York and finish her degree. Then, a year later, Daddy remarried.
Amelia's mother talks about him with patronizing amusement, as
though he had become very rich out in California. Hot tubs, she
says, waving her hands, Jacuzzis, sports cars, horseback riding, wine
cellars. In fact, Amelia knows, he is living some kind of regulation
California good life. He is a moderately successful designer of mar-
keting surveys, not, as you might think to listen to Amelia's
mother, a meganational tycoon. He is also, unfortunately, obsessively interested in his own health, and when he calls Amelia, he
usually reports his latest cholesterol level. Again and again she has
told him that she knows nothing about adult diseases, but he keeps
coming back for more advice. HDLs and LDLs, oat bran, should he
try fitness walking if his knee is too weak for serious running,
should he take vitamin B supplements, should he see a doctor if he
sometimes feels a pain in the side of his neck after long drives?

Her mother lives her messier, more crowded life in New York.
Never finishing the master's in social work, or any other degree.
Turning up her nose at her ex-husband's lush life-style, she in fact
lives largely on money left her by her parents, who made a modest
fortune in costume jewelry in the 1920s. And she lives in an enormous rent-controlled apartment, more precious than gold. It was
more than big enough for the family, and now it holds Amelia's
mother and whoever else happens to be living there. Often there is
a boyfriend in residence, usually recently divorced and marginally
academic. And there is often also a stray or two: an unmarried
mother who had been a clown in a small Southern circus, a seventy-
year-old woman who was going to own an enormous townhouse

on the East Side if only she could win her lawsuit, the runaway twin teenage daughters of a minor rock star, a young man who was about to go on a mission to interpose his body between whalers and whale.

Amelia feels fond of her mother, but she cannot imagine calling her with this news—Matt and I are separating. She has told only Dodie. If she tells even one more person, she decides, she will be making it real. The thing to do is to keep it a secret, to go on marching day to day, believing that the whole thing is strictly temporary.

"How are you doing, Mom?"

"We're having a very cold winter here."

"They aren't heating the apartment?"

"No, I mean the whole city. We've had eight subzero nights already this month. So you can imagine how full the shelters are."

Actually, Amelia can. She has written two letters already this winter on behalf of patients whose apartments are not being properly heated. She writes letters for gas, oil, electricity, even phone, all the services that get turned off for nonpayment. So what if the electricity also goes to run the television set, so what if the phone bill is for long-distance calls to relatives in Alabama. Without electricity the apartments are dark; without a phone, you can't call the doctor when the baby is sick. Amelia is mildly suspicious of herself whenever she finds herself doing anything that echoes her mother's somewhat simpleminded us-against-them do-gooding; she has wondered from time to time whether she became a doctor to be irreproachably beneficent. And now, of course, she cannot bear the thought of what her mother will say when she learns that Amelia's family has disintegrated. Her mother will be disappointed, but maybe a little too eager to welcome Amelia into some kind of aggrieved fellowship. They have failed us; we have failed. Amelia likes being a success, she likes having a reputable job and a happy family, she likes telling her mother casually that she has just flown out somewhere to give a talk.

"It's cold here too, Mom."

"How is my grandson?"

"He's beautiful, Mom. But I have to tell you, he thinks about nothing but weapons and war."

"He needs to feel powerful. He needs to feel safe."

"Lately, whenever I tell him anything nice about himself, he tells me it isn't true. Like if I tell him he drew a beautiful picture, he'll say, No, it isn't really beautiful at all."

"You were exactly that way," Amelia's mother tells her. "No matter what you did, you always insisted on applying ridiculous standards. Even when you grew up. When your father read a paper you wrote in high school and told you it was good, you said, Well, for a high school paper. And that's all you would allow. I think the first time you let me compliment you without making any excuses was after Alexander was born, when I told you what a lovely baby you had."

"He's a lovely boy."

"Yes, but you were a lovely girl, too."

I am going to have to write a death scene, I warn you. What happened was that after three days in the ICU, Darren's father decided to have Darren removed from the ventilator, and I was there when he died in his father's arms, with his grandmother holding his hands. I am going to have to write this.

In *Hospital Sketches*, Louisa May Alcott deals out her deaths like blessings, for the most part, and I suppose they may have been, in an army hospital without much to offer to ease pain. "I touched his forehead; it was cold: and then I knew that, while he waited, a better nurse than I had given him a cooler draught and healed him with a touch."

And Darren's death was a blessing, certainly, or so I had persuaded myself, and so his grandmother had persuaded herself, and finally his father. Or at least, so his father was eventually told by God, who is certainly a useful consultant to have on hand when you are in a pediatric ICU.

Everything I hate most about my job, and about the death scenes of children, in life and in literature, rises up to help me write about Darren's death, to stop me from writing about Darren's death. Did I love Darren in any real way? When I say I love my son, I know exactly what I mean; I can taste it in my mouth when I watch him sleeping. When he wrapped that arm around my neck, reaching up from his hospital bed, I would have let him pull me forward off a precipice. And Darren? If I think back, I can conjure up a child who could laugh, if I tempted him and tempted him. I can remember drawing his blood, and dreading drawing his blood, back months ago when he was awake and responsive to pain. I would like to say I loved him, I would like to give myself that much right to his story, to the intimacy I was allowed at his death. But if I had loved him, could I actually do the job I do? If I had to lose children I loved, if "love" is a word with any power at all, then surely this job would stop with the first death. With the first death scene.

I have not offered any medical heroics on his behalf. I have predicted his death again and again, and the predictions have not come true. I have deprived him of what little three-year-old character he might have had to begin with, by letting his illness drag on. That is how he died. That is how many of them die. Would you feel better about it all if I let him wake up in his death scene, recognize his grandmother, whisper her name, and smile?

Darren's father and grandmother sit side by side next to Darren's bed. The ICU bleeping on around them, heartbeat tracings travel across screens and then endlessly back from the beginning. The trained ear can pick out the whoosh of the ventilator breaths, the high bleats of the IV pumps calling for more fluid, the metallic buzzing of the cardiac monitors, and then of course the alarms, the distinct whistles and beeps of the various machines: heartbeat too slow, oxygen dropping, probe disconnected.

What do they talk about, the father and the grandmother? Do they talk at all? Is this the final heroic nobility of Roberta Wilson, yielding and allowing Darren's father a little time at his son's bedside, without putting up a fight? Giving him a few days as the father of a sick but living child. Or is it, whether she knows it or not, the punishment she feels this man deserves: feel like a father, recognize your child.

Darren is stable, on the ventilator. The open lung biopsy is tentatively scheduled for the end of the week; the surgeons said they wanted to give him a little more time, see if his lungs improved, so the procedure wouldn't be so dangerous. His lungs aren't really improving, and Amelia knows the ICU doctors are a little wary. They like boom-crash medicine, they like kids who come in sick as shit, as the expression goes, and then get better fast, by means of ICU magic, and out they go. Or else they don't get better, and they die. The kids who do neither are the bane of the ICU: the kids who can be kept alive forever, without getting better. Already Darren has that air about him, and the ICU staff is pushing for action. Do the biopsy. Treat what can be treated. Fish or cut bait.

"Doctor," Darren's father asks her once again, "have you never seen a miracle?"

"But should we keep every child on a ventilator, hoping for a miracle?"

"He has to hope for a miracle," says Roberta Wilson. "I hoped for months. It's only normal to do some hoping first."

"You've given up, you've stopped asking for it," Darren's father says to her, not angrily, just sadly.

"I have a choice," she says to him, with great dignity. "Either I can pray to God for another child, another life, a boy who might get well, or else I can pray for this exact little boy, and the only thing anyone could ask for him is peace. And I think you're even farther away from peace than he is, so I'm willing to give you a little time. But don't you start telling me what to ask for." And she turns back to the boy on the bed, strokes his arm, and starts whispering to him, whispering whatever private comfort she wants to repeat over and over, filling up his ears.

Darren's father says to Amelia, and this time there is real anger in his voice, "How do I know you people did everything you could? Maybe you just decided, Here's this boy got a disease from a jailbird father, this little black boy—who wants to waste our good time and money? I wasn't here, I never saw what you did."

"But you have to know that for this disease there isn't anything we can do, in the end. You can find that out in the newspapers— black or white, people don't get better. I think we did everything there was to do for Darren, but I also think you have to be really careful with kids. I mean, if *you* were sick"—she almost stops, since she suspects that he *is* sick—"you might want to fight as hard as you could for every last day. Even if you were in pain, you might have good reasons to want to go on living. You might have things you wanted to do, or people you wanted to talk to. But for children, the whole business of their lives is to be happy and to grow. I mean, if you're three years old, and you're in pain, and you can't grow, is life worth so much to you?"

"I've been reading about new drugs they're making, some things they're testing out in California. If I had enough money, I'd take my son to wherever they have the newest things."

"Look at him, look at his body. The disease has already eaten him up. Look at his arms and legs. You have to understand, the virus is everywhere. It's even in his brain, I'm afraid."

Roberta Wilson looks up from the head of the bed, and gives a tiny soft cry, as if this is something new, some new arrow shot into her.

It's true, though. The HIV virus likes the brain, the tissues of the central nervous system. There's no way to say how much Darren's deterioration has been due to that, how much to his respiratory problems, how much to other illnesses and general weakness. It isn't always easy to say exactly why a sick child dies; no one really understands how cancer kills, for example. But Amelia doesn't believe there is any way for Darren to fight his way back to a reasonable facsimile of the child his grandmother knew, even a couple of months ago.

Amelia writes a courtesy note in Darren's chart. She is no longer even nominally in charge of his care; he belongs to the ICU doctors. *Darren remains stable with a moderate-to-high level of ventilator support. Current plans, following family wishes, include maximal medical supportive therapy and diagnostic workup, with open lung biopsy planned for the near future. In this setting, Darren's nutritional needs will also have to be addressed, since he constitutes a nutritional emergency after this prolonged hospitalization. Would suggest a dietary consultation, and also consider physical therapy, since he is at risk for contractures. I will continue to discuss with the family members what the most appropriate level of medical inter-*

vention would be for this very unfortunate child. Appreciate excellent care Darren is receiving.

"Can I sleep in your bed with you?" Alexander asks.

"How come?"

"If I sleep by myself, I might have a nightmare." He sounds just a little bit proud of the possibility.

"Sure, you can sleep in my bed." She feels sure this is not recommended, not sound child-raising policy, but what the hell. She's a pediatrician, isn't she? And Alexander sleeps beside her like the proverbial rock, untroubled, determined, warm, and a great comfort. In the morning, when her alarm goes off, she gets up and turns it off and comes back to the bed to hug him, but he is already sleepily on his feet, heading for the bathroom, the plastic feet of his pajamas slapping softly on the floor.

"I love you, my beautiful boy," she calls after him.

He turns and faces her, with what looks like real distress on his face. "Don't say that! Don't say I am a beautiful boy, because I'm not, I'm not. I'm not beautiful at all."

And then he disappears down the hall, before she can run to him and pick him up and tell him over and over, Of course you are, you're the most beautiful thing I've ever seen.

I am going to have to write a death scene. I am going to have to show you how Darren died. And more than anything, I would like to make it beautiful, sad, and faintly full of hope, a scene a hundred years ago, and very far away.

How would this be?

Darren lay cradled in his father's arms, arms that would have happily encircled him against any danger. Oh, those helpless arms, those useless hands which would have beaten off any enemy! A tear, and only a single tear, found its way slowly down that father's face and dripped down onto the silent visage of the boy below.

The child's eyelids flickered. Perhaps in his leave-taking, in leaving behind the loving arms that held him, he remembered for an instant the human love he had known in his short sojourn on earth.

At any rate, his eyes opened, and he looked, one last time, into the loving face of his grandmother, the grieving eyes of his father.

"Oh, Darren," cried the woman, weeping unashamedly, "is the pain better?"

"Grandma," whispered the child, and then pursed his lips as if to kiss her, and the last breath to pass from his poor sickly body left it with a little puff, as if to convey the kiss to its destination.

That isn't how he died.

Darren is still stable, in ICU terms, but he had a rough day. The arterial line stopped working, and they had to put a new one in, this time in the artery on the inside of his left ankle. And he had a high temperature too, and so blood was drawn and another chest x-ray was done, and some doctor or other raised the question of a spinal tap, in case he had an infection hiding there. A hard day for the patient, a hard day for those who sit at his bedside.

Darren's father asks Amelia a new question: Doctor, what will happen?

I don't know, she says. Either the lung biopsy will kill him, or else it will find something treatable, or else he will go on like this.

Until?

Until you change your mind and decide he can come off the vent. Or else until something kills him, probably an infection.

He shakes his head. He wears brown suit pants and a white button-down shirt, the tie loosened and the sleeves rolled up. He looks ill, there is something feverish and burned-away about his face. He says, but halfheartedly, if he was a white boy, if he was a rich child ...

If he was the son of Prince Charles and Princess Diana, it wouldn't matter, Amelia says, sounding tired. He has AIDS. He's been sick for a long, long time.

I prayed, Darren's father says. I asked God.

Did God answer?

You only can do what you only can do. I'm here too late, I'm asking too much for this little boy. Doctor, I'm thinking my son has had enough.

His father agreed to let him die. I have to let him die too.

It seemed to those who watched and mourned that in these last moments, all the strains of illness and pain had been erased from the child's brow, and they were vouchsafed one last look at the child he might have been, at the serenely sleeping face they might have looked down on, night after night, if only he had escaped so harsh a fate. It seemed also to his grandmother that the limp, cool hand she held gave back, for just a moment, a small loving pressure, as if to say, Fear not! I go before to show the way, but we shall have our happiness together by-and-by.

That isn't how he died. This is how he died.

The nurses pulled a curtain around the bed. The curtain, a rather grubby white-and-yellow print, hung from a little track in the ceiling and was designed to shelter the bed in a little tent. There wasn't quite enough material to reach all the way around, though, and a little gap remained open to the ICU. The chaplain had come by and prayed with Darren's grandmother; his father had prayed alone, striding back and forth across the parents' room and then finally collapsing on his knees, his face buried in the couch. The ICU doctor hovered nearby, but Amelia had volunteered to preside. The nurse gently peeled back the tape that held the tube in place, the tape that covered Darren's nose and upper lip. Then Amelia pulled the tube out, and the nurse turned off the ventilator. The tube slid from Darren's nose in one easy graceful move, as if it had been eager to come out. The nurse had already disconnected the probes and monitors, and now, together, she and Amelia lifted the light little body and put it in his father's lap. The tattered stuffed animal, Mouse, was left at the foot of the bed. Darren's father sat in an armchair, holding the child. The grandmother had a chair too, but she leaned forward out of it, and fell to her knees. Her arms went out around her grandson, and for the first time in weeks she hugged him as fully as she could, not worrying about oxygen tents or ventilators, tubes or lines or monitors. Darren's grand-mother's sobbing was so convulsive, her shoulders moving so harshly, that at first Amelia could not tell whether Darren was breathing at all. Then she rocked back slightly and seemed unsteady, kneeling there, so Amelia went to her and took her arm and helped her back into her chair, moving it so that she sat knee to knee with Darren's father, the child lying between them. Yes, he was breathing, though his respiratory rate was irregular, and the individual respirations long and drawn out. Agonal breathing, the breathing before death, when rhythm is gone and respiratory drive is going.

Amelia looked away; the faces of the two adults held too much pain. She had no business there, but then, she could hardly leave them with their dying baby, could she? She crossed her arms over her chest and felt tears in the back of her own eyes, but she blinked them back. If she looked at Darren, she would count his breaths; otherwise she would keep her eyes to herself and allow this family, what was left of it, some semblance of privacy.

It took him less than half an hour to stop breathing. He breathed more and more slowly, and his lips grew darker and darker, deprived of oxygen. His grandmother looked up once and asked Amelia, What's happening?, and Amelia said, He is going to breathe less and less, until he stops. Had Darren's grandmother been hoping for a miracle? Had his father been expecting one? Per-haps not, but just because you give up hoping for a miracle doesn't mean you're really prepared to hold a three-year-old while he breathes less and less, until he stops. Actually, what Amelia was fearing was that, once again, Darren might do better than pre-dicted. He might linger on, in respiratory distress, for hours, maybe even, nightmarishly, for days. So she, at least, is grateful that he dies so promptly, that he cannot survive at all off the ventilator.

His eyes never open. He doesn't squeeze anyone's hand. He doesn't blow a kiss, or speak at the last to promise a better world, a golden door opening. He just breathes less and less. Carbon diox-ide is building up in his blood, suppressing his respiratory drive. The tissues of his body are getting very little oxygen, and they are dying, brain and liver and kidneys. And finally he is breathing almost not at all, and then both father and grandmother look up in unison, as if something has changed in the little body they hold. And Amelia steps forward, feels for a pulse, and finds none.

Oh, Alexander, I love you. You are beautiful. You are smart. You are so good at coloring pictures. You are, without question, my favorite kid.

CHAPTER IX
MY SORROWS' CURE

New Year's Eve, and Amelia is alone, in her house. There is a party she could be at, given by a nephrologist who did his residency with her, and briefly, once or twice, she thought of going, and talking eagerly all night to hospital people, and telling patient stories. And eating and drinking, and who knows what else—do people her age still pair off at parties and go home together? But actually, Amelia is something of a traditionalist about New Year's Eve, and though she does not make formal resolutions, she does believe that you have to begin your year as you want it to continue. She will not begin the year with people she doesn't care about, with noise and nonsense. She will not make an exhibition of her solitary state in front of hospital colleagues.

She thinks, instead, that she will buy an expensive bottle of champagne and get expensively drunk, all alone, in her own house. And maybe buy some fancy food as well. Greet the new year stuffed with champagne and goose liver. That's close enough to the way she and Matt and Alexander usually spend their New Year's Eve, sometimes with friends, sometimes just the three of them. In fact, last year they drank champagne and ate tacos and chocolate cake with Jeremy and Diana and Luke, for heaven's sake. Amelia and Matt made the tacos, and Diana made the chocolate cake, which had too much instant coffee in it; it came out black as mud and a little bitter. And Alexander and Jeremy made it up till midnight, very thrilled to be staying up so late, very disappointed that nothing happened at midnight except a half-assed chorus of "Auld Lang Syne" and some kisses.

Amelia buys supplies: a container of butter pecan ice cream, a quarter pound of goose liver pâté, a small jar of red caviar, a box of water crackers, a quarter pound of smoked salmon. Little packages and overpriced jars fill her shopping basket: olives from Nice and prosciutto and a half dozen dark chocolate hazelnut truffles. Too much for one person, really. And Matt is the one who really likes caviar, anyway. She pays at the cash register, caviar and all. Goes into the liquor store and drops thirty dollars on a bottle of champagne. Gets into her car and drives home slowly, imagining herself, tomorrow, with the food neatly laid out on her dining-room table, with the champagne filling her glass. Stops the car in front of Matt's little house and writes a note on a piece of brown bag, sitting in the car. Writes, without even thinking about it, *Please come home for New Year's Eve.* Doesn't sign it, pushes it through the letter slot, then rushes down the steps and drives off, afraid someone will come after her, Marco to smile at her, Matt to refuse.

Darren was buried in the last week of the year. Christmas was over and Boston was dark and wet and dirty, but not very cold. Amelia paid a formal visit to the funeral home, and when she signed her name in the visitors' book, Roberta Wilson whispered to her to add *M.D.*

Darren's casket was open, and they had dressed him in a miniature black suit, white shirt, navy blue tie. Surely they had stuffed something into his cheeks to make his face look fuller. His face, on a white satin pillow, was full and round. Amelia looked down at him, paying respects. She was not deeply moved by his dead body; perhaps she had pictured him too often like this, finally still and quiet. It did not clutch her heart to see Mouse resting on his chest, tucked beneath his folded hands. The only thoughts Amelia could come up with were clichés—finally at rest, so lifelike, so peaceful. Or, more savagely, what a waste, why so much pain.

Darren in the funeral home seemed to have escaped not just the pain of his life and the rigors of the intensive care unit but also the dominion of medicine. Medicine had failed him, and he did not belong to the hospital. So let him be dressed up, and let his cheeks be stuffed with cotton or whatever, and hope that at least this way he looked right to his grandmother, to her friends, and even to his father.

In the new year, Alexander will have his fifth birthday. Five seems much more than four, as four does than three. What will happen about Alexander's birthday if she and Matt remain apart? She refuses to believe that they will remain apart. If Matt had had no little house to run to, no easy dramatic gesture, this would never have happened. They would have fought and yelled at each other, maybe even in the hospital, and at most he might have slept in some other room for a night or two. But they would have gone on rubbing up against one another in the setting of all their books, all their furniture, and finally they would have talked calmly and apologized. He would have come into the bathroom one night when she was brushing her teeth, and said into the mirror, Let's stop fighting. She would have tiptoed down the stairs in the middle of the night and found him sleeping on the couch and crowded on beside him, and he would have awakened to find his arms going round her. Instead he was angry and he wanted to punish her and he happened to have a little house nearby. How convenient.

Alexander spent several nights with her that week. Anxious to make him welcome, to treasure up her hours of his company, she spent Tuesday evening making mosaics with him, with a box of little tiles bought in the toy store and two round metal plates to glue them on. At the beginning of the evening, he was in an unexpectedly prissy mood. Each time he poured out some glue, he would ask, Wasn't it good of me not to spill it? When she dropped a tile, he slipped off his chair to retrieve it: Wasn't that very nice of me? Yes, she told him patiently, very good of you, very nice. Was he advertising himself, she wondered, was he demonstrating what a good boy he was? Don't you want me, Mommy, when I'm so good? But there was nothing pleading about his tone; he sounded very satisfied with himself indeed. Mama, if you like, I will share some of my tiles with you, he announced, in the tone of a boy who knew all too well that "sharing" was a magic day care center buzz-word. Isn't that very generous, sharing my tiles? Because really, I could use them all if I wanted to.

He was making a rainbow in the center section of his metal plate, carefully arching blue over green over red. Amelia arranged various designs on hers but glued nothing, saving the plate in case he wanted to make another.

She would not have expected this, Amelia thinks, opening the envelope. Who would have thought Luke capable of a romantic gesture, a little gift and a note. The note in fact is tender and quite remarkably unembarrassing, no protestations of love, no assump-tion that anything big is beginning. How lovely to have spent a rainy Saturday afternoon with you. Here is the most famous exam-ple from Shakespeare, and I have marked the speech.

The paperback is a copy of *King John,* a play she has never read or seen, a play she knows nothing about. A bookmark touting a Harvard Square bookstore protrudes from Act III, Scene iv, and she opens to the page and finds herself in the middle of a scene between Constance and King Philip. Constance's son is a prisoner, and she is afraid she will never see him again. She says of her boy:

> For since the birth of Cain, the first male child,
> To him that did but yesterday suspire,
> There was not such a gracious creature born.

And then someone called Pandulph tells her, "You hold too hei-nous a respect of grief," and she responds, "He talks to me that never had a son."

Ah, here is the cue, this must be the speech that Luke is pointing out to her. Reading it, she feels at once that she has heard it, read it, seen it, somewhere else. The king tells Constance, "You are as fond of grief as of your child."

And then Constance's response, stripped and terrible in all its pain, especially next to the furbelows of the nineteenth century:

Grief fills the room up of my absent child,
Lies in his bed, walks up and down with me,
Puts on his pretty looks, repeats his words,
Remembers me of all his gracious parts,
Stuffs out his vacant garments with his form.
Then have I reason to be fond of grief.
Fare you well. Had you such a loss as I,
I could give better comfort than you do.
I will not keep this form upon my head,
When there is such disorder in my wit.
O Lord! My boy, my Arthur, my fair son!
My life, my joy, my food, my all the world!
My widow-comfort, and my sorrows' cure!

I knew I would not, ever, see Roberta Wilson again. I wanted, of course, to say something wise to her at the funeral home, something that would let know how much Darren had meant to me—but what had Darren meant to me, compared with what he meant to her? I felt, in that moment, that I had failed them both. She ought to be my friend by now, after all this time. I ought to understand her. I get this feeling only occasionally: the lives I cross, the access I am allowed into other people's tragedy—why doesn't it make me greater, why doesn't it give me wisdom and understanding? Or at least the ability to find good words to say to a grandmother standing in a funeral home, where her grandson's vacant garments are stuffed out, not with grief, but with an undertaker's artifice.

"Thank you so much for coming, Doctor," she said to me, loud enough for other people to hear the title. Was she showing me off, or was she explaining me, the only white face in the room.

"He was a lovely, lovely boy," I said.

"He never got a chance to be more than a baby. It's unfair that he never even got a chance to be a little boy, really, but you know that as well as I do."

"It's all unfair. But the luckiest thing that ever happened to Darren was he had you to take care of him."

She drew herself up, short and firm and steady on her high heels. For the first time since I had known her, I saw her in what was obviously a store-bought dress, black with black lace at collar and cuffs, with jet buttons down the front.

"That isn't what I call luck, Doctor. It isn't luck that makes a woman take care of her baby, or her grandbaby." Then she relented. "Never mind," she told me. "You took care of him too. And you took trouble." She also wore a small round black hat, with a little edge of black netting.

She lowered her voice and told me, "Go over now and say something to his daddy. Most of these people aren't going to say a word to him."

Darren's father stood alone among the bouquets, which the funeral home had exhibited on tripod stands. There were only four or five floral offerings, but they did offer some small amount of camouflage. Darren's father stood straight and tall among the tripods. I was struck again by how thin he was, how painfully well-groomed and formal. Had I ever cried with this man in a hospital room in the middle of the night? Who would cry for him when he died—Roberta Wilson? They had kept vigil together in the hospital and Darren had died in their arms. She might never forgive this man, but she would hold on to him as long as she could, the only other person who would go through each day aware that the world was short one little boy. It occurred to me that I was in at the end of a family; the daughter had died, the daughter's child lay in his coffin, and the mother, who had buried her daughter and her grandson, would live long enough to preside at the death of her son-in-law, and then eventually die herself.

"The Lord giveth and the Lord taketh away," Darren's father said to me, sounding bitter.

"Sometimes the Lord takes too much," I said without thinking.

"Thank you for coming, Doctor. Thank you for all you've done."

Even more than Darren's grandmother, Darren's father reminded me that this was their tragedy, not mine. A medical horror came into a family's life and destroyed it.

Eight o'clock on New Year's Eve. Amelia is wearing her very favorite dress, the only dress-up garment she owns in which she feels both comfortable and beautiful, almost invulnerable. It's a full, soft graceful dress, and the pattern is a tiny paisley, blue and brown and gold on a very dark red background. Whenever she wears it, people remark on the beauty of the print, but lately she has worn it very rarely, convinced that something will happen to it, it will get stained or torn, leaving her with no fully satisfying dress for that future occasion, that most important day when she will want to feel most protected, most assured. The living room is as clean as she can make it, every book in place, every windowsill dusted. She will make New Year's resolutions, and one resolution will be neatness and order in the parts of her life she can control. If she spends this evening alone, she will be in a room that comforts her, a room that has not been neglected, and she will be wearing her most beautiful dress.

Her food is spread out on the coffee table, everything neatly laid out on pretty little plates. She could go get the TV and see what's on. She could read *Little Women*—anything but the chapters about Meg's marriage and children. She could call Dodie, whose new year will begin three hours later. She could even try her mother, who might well be home.

She gets up and gets the phone, carries it over to the couch and sets it ready. If I need to, I can dial up a friendly voice. Perhaps she will shut her eyes for a while, perhaps when she opens them, Matt will be sitting across from her on the loveseat he has never gotten around to reupholstering, smiling at her sheepishly. With no effort at all, she falls asleep, her head drooping back against the couch cushions. She wakes up with a start after an hour's nap, to discover, to her intense disappointment, that she is still alone.

Most children flourish. Most children live and grow up. Even the children in the hospital, most get well and go home and live happily ever after. Pediatrics is a comparatively happy field, a field full of happy endings.

Most of Amelia's patients do not have AIDS, she acknowledges, do not have any serious diseases. Most of the children she sees in her clinic have tiny problems, the sort that get dealt out to healthy people, so many apiece. Her own child is healthy. True, he is not safe, but no one is safe. Yes, obviously then, Matt is right. The well children have to matter, even if you are a pediatrician, even if you sometimes see the other kind. You can't focus on the dying children; if you use dying children to draw up a scale of relative importance, then all the healthy children end up bunched together at one insignificant end. That won't keep them healthy. You can't protect them, you can't make deals—you may focus on the sick, but that doesn't guarantee continued health to the ones you are ignoring.

But that still doesn't show you how to stretch your life so that both kinds of importance can be successfully accommodated.

Suppose I had no child. Suppose the hospital children were the only ones I knew, the well babies coming for their shots, little Sara Blake, who is not in immediate danger but who may not easily get well, Darren and his complicated death, medical and ethical and legal. If they were all I knew, I suppose my scale would be accurate, my perspective would be consistent. I would spend most time on the sickest, the most complicated.

Does that mean Amelia would need an empty hospital before she could focus properly on her own healthy child? Imagine an empty hospital. She can't. The hospital is full, and she is sitting alone.

I have to leave their sickbeds, and even their deathbeds, when I've done what I can, and come home to the importance of everyday life, the transcendence of a healthy child. Doctors are bad at this; doctors like the drama of what we do. Think of all those surgeons who stride through life with the swinging arms of men who know they are more important than their fellow mortals.

Sneak it in among the New Year's resolutions: one, lose weight; two, balance the checkbook; three, strike some reasonable balance between life-and-death and daily life. Not just in what I do, but in how I feel, in what I allow myself to feel. And in what I spend my time thinking about.

But will anything ever stop me from looking at my son and seeing not only all his possible deaths but also the deaths of other children, the deaths I cannot prevent? I can let Darren go, I can recover from his death, because I was only his doctor, in the end; his death doesn't shadow my life from now on. But what happens when the next AIDS baby starts to spiral down? What will protect me, what images of Alexander will rise up and counteract the death scenes?

Amelia knows who the next child will be, probably, the next AIDS baby in her group of patients who will get sicker, who will require the attentions and the decisions commanded by the dying. Amelia has avoided thinking too much about her, or rather, has only allowed herself to think about her medically. Can you handle one more sick child, maybe the saddest of them all? A one-year-old girl named Marie Duchaune, alone in the hospital this New Year's Eve. Her mother has been dying for days, in a hospital far away in New Bedford. Her father no one knows about. No grandparents have been located; the mother's parents may still be in Haiti. When the mother went into the hospital, she gave the child to a friend, and then, when Marie got a high fever, the friend brought her to the hospital, and she hasn't been back since. Marie is going to need foster placement, which may not be easy to come by.

Marie turned out to have a bacterial infection in her blood and responded beautifully to antibiotics. Not only that, but nutritional supplements did wonders for her; she was a thin, wasted little girl but has gained a couple of pounds during her two-week hospitalization. At the beginning, she wouldn't respond to anyone at all, she would sit strapped in a high chair out in the hall on the infants' ward, staring ahead as if she saw the end of the world. The nurses tend her and care about her as well as they can; they cheer her on as with the improved nutrition, the antibiotics, she begins to show more interest in what goes on around her, begins to act a little more like a one-year-old child. The nurses have given her a plastic activity board with dials to turn and buttons to push and bells to ring, and at first it lay neglected on her high-chair tray. Now she hesitantly touches the bright buttons, slips a finger into the dial. She is not firm enough to produce a noise, but she is interested. Her arms, often, are wrapped around herself, her hands hold tight to her thin little sides.

Maybe somewhere in her mind are images of love and comfort, of the first months of her life, when her mother held her and admired her and expected her to grow up. Maybe she remembers lying in bed, cuddled close to her mother's body, the center of the universe. Now she has hospital comfort, endless clean sheets, attentive sponge baths from plastic tubs. She knows hospital routine, she loosens one arm when a nurse approaches with a blood pressure cuff. The nurses do not know that, miles away, her mother has died, died on the afternoon of December 31. Marie is even more alone in her world. You can hope for her that she does have some memory of her mother, of being well, of being loved, and you can take some mild sentimental comfort from the fact that she does not have to face her loss, this New Year's Eve. And maybe even from the fact that Marie's mother does not survive to mourn her little daughter. Take what sentimental comfort you can.

Alexander last Tuesday, finishing, finally, his rainbow, then painstakingly piecing together a white background to show the colors off well. Using every single white tile in the set, but running short. About to cry. Amelia suggested a frame of black tiles, a couple of circles around the perimeter. Alexander gluing down the last tile, while his mother watches from across the kitchen table, spread with newspapers. Overwhelmed by his beauty, by the delicacy of his head bent to his work, his hair on the back of his neck. Alexander looking up from his completed plate, his face lit up, as if he too realizes that this moment is worth something extra. Amelia looks carefully at his rainbow, nods her head, smiles at him. "Oh, I am so entirely proud of myself, I am so entirely proud!" Alexander says.

Marie is the saddest child in the hospital, the saddest child in this book, even though she is getting better. The truth is, Amelia might have said, the death of a child is not in itself the worst thing in the world. All lives end, some sooner than others. It's the grief of the adults, the ones who outlive when they should have been outlived, that makes the child's death tragic and gives it grandeur. Amelia responds to the pain of the children, but even more to the pain of the parents. But in fact the saddest thing of all is a child dying without that tragedy, that grandeur. And poor little Marie is alone, deprived even of her share of grieving. She is too young to say it for herself: What a terrible thing that I should die. And there is no one to say it for her.

Amelia spreads goose liver on a cracker but doesn't bite into it, puts it down on the coffee table. She gets up and finds the copy of *King John,* reads over Luke's note one more time, then puts it away, carefully, in her desk, then settles back down on the couch and begins to read the play. It's actually quite a simple story, and she reads with pleasure, waiting to come upon that scene she has already read, to find it again, properly in its place in the play.

The satisfying thing about *King John,* from Amelia's peculiar point of view, is that young Arthur, who eventually does indeed die, is not killed by a random microbe. He is the target of evil men, or at least men driven by ambition and expedience. It is King John who orders Arthur killed, to protect his own dubious claim to the throne. Very refreshing, to have a child deliberately murdered, for the profit to his murderers, and not struck down for being good, or beautiful, or well beloved. Amelia sits on the couch and cries, for Arthur or for other children or for herself, reads through to the end of the scene. What a picture, welcoming in the New Year: a plump woman with curly dark hair and a lush, beautiful party dress, sits on a couch, in an unnaturally neat room, a table in front of her spread with untasted delicacies, and cries over a book. Cries silently, tears sliding down onto the sides of her neck, sudden bits of wetness collecting in the hollows at her collarbones. Finally cannot see to read, gives up and closes her eyes, but holds the book open on her lap.

This is the picture Matt and Alexander would have seen if Matt had used his key and let them quietly into the house. But for whatever reason, to warn her they are coming, or to show her that all is not yet resolved, he chooses to ring the doorbell instead. So what he actually sees is Amelia, eyes open now and hastily wiped with tissues, standing startled in the doorway.

What does it really matter which microbe took over which child? What does it matter, the frequency and appearance of the diarrhea, the nature of the garbage clogging up the lungs? Darren died; he was a little boy held in his father's arms, and his body could not go on. He couldn't pull the oxygen he needed into his bloodstream, carry it around to his tissues, and use it to power his cells. He couldn't take what he needed from the air and turn it into thought and digestion and sensation, vision and movement and the purification of the blood.

Alexander wears his parka over his fuzzy purple pajamas. Matt is carrying him. He hands him to Amelia, who carries him carefully to the couch, unzips the jacket. Alexander is willing to be hugged, to wrap his own arms obligingly around her neck.

"I get to stay up till the New Year," he announces.

"Of course you do. We'll all stay up together." Her voice is choking, her tears are starting again, but Alexander has already wriggled free and is investigating the food on the coffee table.

"Do I like this?" He is pointing at the caviar, so tempting and red, so unlike food.

"I don't think you've ever had it."

"Sure he did," Matt says. "We had it last New Year's Eve, when Jeremy was here, and you loved it."

Now Amelia remembers: the four adults dipped potato chips in a mixture of caviar and sour cream. Neither little boy would touch the stuff.

"I liked it?"

"You ate it all," Amelia tells him. She is not looking at Matt. She spreads a little caviar on a cracker and hands it to Alexander, who nudges at it with the tip of his tongue, bravely takes on a couple of little red dots. His face is tensed, he is ready to reject, to spit if necessary. Amelia makes another cracker for Matt, a third for herself.

"Do you like it?" Matt is watching Alexander, whose tongue has advanced again to tease off a few more eggs.

"Well, it's not so bad, but it's not my favorite thing." He nibbles off a corner of the cracker.

Finally Matt and Amelia look directly at each other, proud of their son, who is eating his first caviar.

"Oh, God," Matt says, "he's going to grow up and eat all sorts of things, he's going to outgrow us."

"It's inevitable."

"If he likes caviar, shall we give him a taste of champagne?" Matt says.

"I have champagne. It's in the refrigerator."

Imagine them all getting better. All through the hospital, the children get better. Their breathing gets easier, they poke their heads out of the oxygen tents and take deep breaths of room air. They pull the IVs out of their hands, their feet, their chests, their heads. No one needs antibiotics; the evil bacteria are dead. No one needs intravenous nutrition; they are all hungry for milk, baby food, hamburgers. Imagine them strong enough to jump from their beds and swarm through the corridors. Imagine Marie, running for the playroom, a tiny potbelly pouching out above her dimpled thighs. Imagine Sara smearing her face with applesauce, getting some of every spoonful into her mouth, eager to feed herself, growing bigger with every mouthful. Nothing more mysterious about her than the standard-issue miracles, growth, personality, beauty. Imagine the corridors full of children, the big ones running, the toddlers toddling, the little ones crawling. No more fevers, no more wheezing, above all, no more pain.

Imagine even Darren, sturdy legs pumping, all the undiagnosed poisons gone from his lungs, the little air sacs inflating with air at every breath. Imagine him intact, properly defended, his body sealed off against the tiny menaces around it, protected by his own vigorous cells, his well-nourished child strength. And in every room, on every ward. Imagine them pouring out the front doors, the big ones now carrying the babies, reaching down to hold the hands of the toddlers, the whole pack disappearing down the street, leaving the hospital, with its humming lights and beeping monitors, leaving it behind.

The hospital is active but abandoned, like a factory newly automated, or perhaps like something more sinister. Like a ghost ship. No more chemotherapy, no more dialysis, no more ventilators. No more fighting to pull air in against a tight swollen throat. No more inflammation of the brain. No leukemia, pneumonia, croup, seizures. No fevers of unknown origin, no occult malignancies, no failure to thrive. The children are out of sight now, heading home.

The textbook quoted on pages 38 and 50 is *Principles and Practice of Infectious Diseases*, Gerald L. Mandell, R. Gordon Douglas, Jr., and John E. Bennett, editors (second edition, John Wiley & Sons, 1985).

ABOUT THE AUTHOR

Perri Klass is a pediatrician in Boston. She is the author of a novel, *Recombinations*, a collection of short stories, *I Am Having an Adventure*, and an account of medical training, *A Not Entirely Benign Procedure*. She was graduated from Harvard Medical School in 1986 and lives in Cambridge, Massachusetts, with Larry Wohl, a writer and history professor, and their two children.